Graham Piedros.

pg. 268 # ②
use info on 267

Investigation ③ pg. 269 1-2

pg 333-334
11-14

Katie V. 2006
Brockman

Maggie Clapperton
Rm 117
Feb 05

TEEEE

Mathematics of Personal Finance

11

**Addison-Wesley
Secondary
Mathematics
Authors**

Robert Alexander
Elizabeth Ainslie
Paul Atkinson
Maurice Barry
Cam Bennet
Barbara J. Canton
Ron Coleborn
Fred Crouse
Garry Davis
Jane Forbes
George Gadanidis
Liliane Gauthier
Florence Glanfield
Katie Pallos-Haden
Peter J. Harrison
Terry Kaminski
Brendan Kelly
Stephen Khan
Ron Lancaster
Duncan LeBlanc
Kevin Maguire
Rob McLeish
Jim Nakamoto
Nick Nielsen
Linda Rajotte
Brent Richards
David Sufrin
Paul Williams
Elizabeth Wood
Rick Wunderlich
Leanne Zorn

Paul Pogue
Mathematics Teacher
and Consultant
Barrie

Carol Besteck Hope
Head of Mathematics
Elmwood High School
Winnipeg

Paul Zolis
Head of Mathematics
Albert Campbell
Collegiate Institute
Toronto

Margaret Sinclair
Vice Principal
Dante Alighieri Academy
Toronto

Kevin Spry
Head of Mathematics
Centre Dufferin District
High School
Shelburne

Developmental Editor
Nirmala Nutakki

Senior Consulting Mathematics Editor
Lesley Haynes

Coordinating Editor
Mei Lin Cheung

Production Coordinator
Stephanie Cox

Editorial Contributors

Marg Bukta   Melissa Lee
Rosina Daillie   Gay McKellar
David Gargaro   Alison Rieger

Managing Editor
Enid Haley

Marketing Manager
Dawna Day Harris

Product Manager
Reid McAlpine

Publisher
Claire Burnett

Design/Production
Pronk&Associates

Art Direction
Pronk&Associates

Electronic Assembly/Technical Art
Pronk&Associates

Our Cover Story:
This text is based on a curriculum that will enable students to make intelligent financial decisions about situations that will affect them directly. Our cover photo symbolizes a path cutting through the many possible choices to successful personal finance.

The publisher has taken every care to meet or exceed industry specifications for the manufacturing of textbooks. The spine and the endpapers of this sewn book have been reinforced with special fabric for extra binding strength. The cover is a premium, polymer-reinforced material designed to provide long life and withstand rugged use. Mylar gloss lamination has been applied for further durability.

ISBN: 0-201-72652-1

This book contains recycled product and is acid free.

Printed and bound in Canada

1 2 3 4 5 G 05 04 03 02 01

Program Consultants

Vic D'Amico
Executive Director
NECTAR Foundation
Nepean

John Kitney
Head of Mathematics
Bayridge Secondary School
Kingston

Duncan LeBlanc
Sir Robert L. Borden Business and
  Technical Institute
Toronto

Gizele M. Price
Holy Name of Mary Secondary School
Mississauga

Jamie Pyper
Head of Mathematics
H.B. Beal Secondary School
London

Assessment Consultant

Lynda E. C. Colgan
Professor
Department of Education
Queen's University
Kingston

Reviewers

CONTENTS

3 Exponential Growth

4 Annuities

5 Annuities: The Cost of Credit

6 Mortgages

7 Planning for the Future

Utilities

ADDISON-WESLEY

Mathematics of Personal Finance 11

This book is specifically for the Ontario grade 11 course **Mathematics of Personal Finance**. It's about your personal path, your goals, and how you'll manage your finances. It covers new content that relates to your life now, and in your future. This means you get a fresh start in a mathematics course that emphasizes applications.

This book is built on a few key mathematical ideas and formulas:

> simple interest
> compound interest
> exponential growth
> annuities

After you work with these central ideas in early chapters of the book, the course opens up to involve you in many relevant applications, and in-depth investigations.

In this way, even though some concepts may be sophisticated, you'll have lots of opportunities to see each one applied in a variety of meaningful contexts. The more applications you investigate, the better your understanding of financial mathematics will become. By the end of the course, you will have learned about

> The advantages and disadvantages of borrowing
> The relative advantages of leasing versus buying
> Career trends
> Setting personal goals and budgeting for them
> The long-term advantages of saving, even a little, regularly
> How mortgages work

You will apply what you learn in this course throughout your life.

Explorations: An Organizing Influence for the Book

The Mathematics of Personal Finance course includes several specific expectations that require you to investigate particular applications. This is different from having us tell you how the application works. It's also different from investigations you may have done in grade 10, where you followed specific steps to arrive at a single mathematical concept. The investigations in this course are open-ended problems that are meant to reveal some of the general principles of working, saving, spending, and borrowing. For most of these problems, you need to have some basic tools before you start — this is at the root of the structure of ***Addison-Wesley Mathematics of Personal Finance 11: Ontario.***

> **Chapters 1 and 2** establish the basic concepts related to simple interest, linear growth, and compound interest. You learn the formulas for simple interest and compound interest, and apply them in context, using technology tools.

> **Explore/Research/Report: Travelling Abroad** involves you in planning a travel itinerary while you work with current foreign exchange rates, travel costs, and accommodation costs.

> **Chapters 3, 4, and 5** introduce the important concepts behind exponential growth and working with annuities in both saving and borrowing situations. You expand your toolkit of financial formulas, and continue to use technology tools to apply them in specific cases.

> **Explore/Research/Report: Being an Informed Consumer** invites you to compare a variety of selling options to help you make informed decisions.

> **Chapters 6 and 7** involve applications of the work you did in the first 5 chapters, while teaching you how to work with mortgages, how to determine the costs of owning and operating a vehicle, and how to plan a budget. These chapters also involve you in some in-depth case studies in which you will learn some of the basic principles behind the mathematics of finance.

> **Explore/Research/Report: Careers** involves you in self-assessment related to personal career goals, and provides guidelines for you to investigate current career trends.

Each **Explore/Research/Report** ties to curriculum expectations that specify student investigation. In each case, we've listed the relevant **Curriculum Expectations** on the first two pages of the Explore/Research/Report feature.

Here are other pieces that make up the structure of *Addison-Wesley Mathematics of Personal Finance 11: Ontario*.

- A **Utilities** appendix, with short tutorials to support your use of technology tools
- An **Answers** section, for you to check your work as you go
- A **Glossary** of terms, including specialized terms used in the financial world
- An **Index** to provide quick reference to specific topics

Chapter Organization

Each chapter in *Addison-Wesley Mathematics of Personal Finance 11: Ontario* follows the same structure.

Chapter Project
A chapter starts with a short introduction to a specific financial application, for example, Registered Retirement Savings Plans. You won't have all the concepts you need to work with this application until you have worked through the chapter. A numbered section near the end of the chapter provides more background for the Project, and specific exercises in which you investigate the financial application.

Curriculum Expectations
Below the introductory description of the Chapter Project, the first page of the chapter lists the **Curriculum Expectations** you'll cover in that chapter.

Necessary Skills
Before you proceed with new concepts, it's important to review relevant prerequisite skills. **Necessary Skills** gives a quick refresher in the prerequisite skills you need for the chapter. Your teacher will probably assign Necessary Skills before you work with the numbered sections in the chapter.

Occasionally, a "New" skill comes up in **Necessary Skills**. You didn't learn this skill in previous grades, usually because it wasn't in the curriculum. We teach it in **Necessary Skills** because it's relatively straightforward, and you have all the related concepts you need to develop an understanding quickly.

Numbered Sections

These develop the new content of the course. We've designed each numbered section to be clear and to the point. Exercises are organized into A, B, and C categories according to their level of difficulty.

✓ You'll see that some exercises have a check mark beside them; try these exercises to be sure you have covered all core curriculum requirements.

Each exercise set identifies one exercise for each of the four categories of the provincial **Achievement Chart**. These show you what to expect when you are assessed on any of the four categories. We have highlighted exactly four exercises as examples only. Each exercise set has several exercises that relate to one, or more, of the categories of achievement. Exercises that are labelled are not limited to one category only, but the focus helps to simplify assessment.

Some exercise sets are shorter than others; this is based on the time it takes to complete each exercise. For example, in Chapter 7, a single exercise may involve a case study. This in-depth application will take more time than a drill exercise, and so we've deliberately provided fewer of them to reflect the greater time requirement.

Review

Self-Checks are one-page reviews that occur mid-chapter. They let you check your knowledge and understanding of the content of preceding sections.

Each chapter review starts with a **Mathematics Toolkit** to summarize important chapter results. The Toolkit, together with the **Review Exercises**, helps you study the contents of a chapter.

Self-Test at the end of each chapter helps you prepare for a class test.

Cumulative Review after Chapter 7 will help you prepare for end-of-semester examinations.

Careers

As a student in a college-bound course, you may be among the first in your age group to head into a career after graduation. **Career Profiles** describes some current careers that may appeal to you, such as Small Business Owner or Hotel Manager. Each **Career Profile** includes **Where's the Math?** This section highlights the specific mathematical skills required in the featured career.

You'll also investigate possible careers in depth, when you complete **Explore/Research/Report: Careers.**

Technology

Scientific calculators, spreadsheets, and graphing calculators are tools that can help you solve applied problems. Technology tools are especially powerful for solving problems with large numbers or many calculations — like the financial applications you'll study in this course. This book establishes a few standard technology tools — the TI-30X IIS for scientific calculator work, the TI-83 for graphing calculator work — and provides explicit instruction in their use.

The Utilities appendix at the end of this book provides additional support for working with scientific calculators, graphing calculators, and spreadsheets.

This book also contains some projects and investigations where we suggest research on the Internet to obtain current data. You may start your search from the Addison-Wesley web site: http://www.pearsoned.ca/onmath11

Communication

Communication is a key part of all learning. **Discuss** questions in this book prompt you to think about solutions or the implications of new concepts. Exercises ask you to explain your reasoning, or describe your findings. Each numbered section contains an exercise highlighted with a "Communication" emphasis. Investigations and projects require you to write a report.

Assessment

Several features in this book relate to a balanced assessment approach.
- **Achievement Chart Categories** highlighted in each exercise set
- **Communication** opportunities in Examples and exercises
- **Self-Checks** to support your knowledge and understanding
- **Projects** with applied problems for you to investigate
- **Self-Tests** to support your preparation for class tests
- **Explore/Research/Report** for opportunities to work with open-ended problems

Linear Growth

Chapter Project

Where Do I Save My Money?

The project in Section 1.7 provides an opportunity to investigate and analyse different ways to save your money. These include savings accounts and guaranteed investment certificates (GICs). As you work through the chapter, pay attention to the investments you study and how the interest is paid.

Curriculum Expectations

By the end of this chapter, you will:

> Determine terms that follow three or more given terms in a sequence.

> Determine whether a sequence is arithmetic.

> Solve problems related to the formulas for the nth term and the sum of n terms of arithmetic sequences and series.

> Solve problems involving the calculation of any variable in the simple-interest formula ($I = Prt$), using scientific calculators.

> Demonstrate an understanding of the relationships between simple interest, arithmetic sequences, and linear growth.

> Determine, through investigation, the characteristics of various savings alternatives available from financial institutions.

> Collect relevant information related to the alternatives to be considered in making a decision.

> Summarize the advantages and disadvantages of the alternatives to a decision,... .

NEC**Necessary Skills**

1 Review: Percent

Percent means out of 100; for example, $25\% = \frac{25}{100}$.

Example 1

Write each percent as a decimal.

    a) 9%   **b)** 14.5%   **c)** 107%   **d)** $7\frac{1}{2}\%$

Solution

To write a percent as a decimal, divide by 100.

a) $9\% = \frac{9}{100}$

    $= 0.09$

Remember that to divide by 100, move the decimal point 2 places to the left. Add zeros as placeholders where necessary.

$9\% = 0.09$

b) $14.5\% = \frac{14.5}{100}$ Move the decimal point 2 places to the left.

    $= 0.145$

c) $107\% = \frac{107}{100}$

    $= 1.07$

d) $7\frac{1}{2}\%$

First, write the fraction as a decimal.
To write a fraction as a decimal, divide the numerator by the denominator.

$\frac{1}{2} = 1 \div 2$

    $= 0.5$

So, $7\frac{1}{2}\% = 7.5\%$

        $= \frac{7.5}{100}$

        $= 0.075$

Example 2 Write each decimal as a percent.

    a) 0.5   **b)** 0.08   **c)** 1.15

Solution

To write a decimal as a percent, multiply by 100%.

  a) $0.5 \times 100\% = 50\%$

    Remember that to multiply by 100, move the decimal point 2 places to the right. Add zeros as necessary.

    $0.5 \times 100 = 50$

  b) $0.08 \times 100\% = 8\%$ Move the decimal point 2 places to the right.

  c) $1.15 \times 100\% = 115\%$

Example 3 Find each percent.

    a) 5% of $365   **b)** 8.5% of $4560

Solution

To find a percent of a number, change the percent to a decimal, then multiply.

  a) 5% of $365

    Write 5% as a decimal.

    $5\% = 0.05$

    Multiply the decimal by the number.

    $5\% \text{ of } \$365 = 0.05 \times \$365$
                    $= \$18.25$

  b) $8.5\% \text{ of } \$4560 = 0.085 \times \$4560$
                         $= \$387.60$

Exercises

1. Write each percent as a decimal.
   a) 24%　　　b) 6%　　　c) 50%　　　d) 12%
   e) 95%　　　f) 1%　　　g) 25%　　　h) 100%

2. Write each percent as a decimal.
   a) 4.6%　　　b) 14.2%　　　c) 0.8%　　　d) 7.25%
   e) 16.75%　　f) 64.1%　　　g) 0.25%　　　h) 105%

3. Write each percent as a decimal.
   a) $6\frac{1}{4}\%$　　　b) $15\frac{1}{8}\%$　　　c) $\frac{1}{2}\%$　　　d) $2\frac{3}{4}\%$
   e) $24\frac{5}{8}\%$　　　f) $110\frac{1}{2}\%$　　g) $5\frac{3}{8}\%$　　　h) $104\frac{1}{4}\%$

4. Write each decimal as a percent.
   a) 0.85　　　b) 0.3　　　c) 0.07　　　d) 0.035
   e) 1.3　　　f) 0.125　　　g) 0.15　　　h) 8

5. Find the percent of each number. Give the answer to 2 decimal places.
   a) 7% of $28　　　　　　　b) 35% of $145
   c) 110% of $125　　　　　d) 1.5% of $296
   e) 12% of $764　　　　　f) 4% of $86
   g) 407% of $500　　　　　h) 6.25% of $436

2 Review: Solving Linear Equations

To solve an equation means to find the value of the variable that makes the equation true. That is, the left side of the equation is equal to the right side of the equation. You may:

- Add or subtract the same term from each side of the equation.
- Multiply or divide each side of the equation by the same non-zero number.

Example 1 Solve.

   a) $x + 7 = 12$ **b)** $x - 5 = -3$ **c)** $2x = -8$ **d)** $\frac{1}{3}x = 1$

Solution

   a) $x + 7 = 12$
             $x + 7 - 7 = 12 - 7$ Subtract 7 from each side.
                   $x = 5$

   b) $x - 5 = -3$
             $x - 5 + 5 = -3 + 5$ Add 5 to each side.
                   $x = 2$

   c) $2x = -8$

          $\frac{2x}{2} = \frac{-8}{2}$ Divide each side by 2.

            $x = -4$

   d) $\frac{1}{3}x = 1$

          $3\left(\frac{1}{3}x\right) = 3(1)$ Multiply each side by 3. Remember, $3\left(\frac{1}{3}\right) = \frac{3}{1} \times \frac{1}{3} = 1$

              $x = 3$

You may have been able to solve the one-step equations in *Example 1* mentally. Some equations require more than one step.

Example 2 Solve.

   a) $3x - 2 = 10$ **b)** $-2x + 7 = -2$

Solution

   a) $3x - 2 = 10$ Add 2 to each side.
            $3x = 12$ Divide each side by 3.
             $x = 4$

   b) $-2x + 7 = -2$ Subtract 7 from each side.
           $-2x = -9$ Divide each side by -2.
             $x = 4.5$

Exercises

1. Solve these mentally or by recording steps.

a) $x + 3 = 5$ **b)** $2x = 6$ **c)** $x - 5 = 3$

d) $\frac{1}{4}y = -2$ **e)** $m + 5 = -2$ **f)** $3n = -9$

g) $x + 5 = 13$ **h)** $\frac{x}{5} = 2$ **i)** $-2r = -10$

j) $m + 3 = -2$ **k)** $-\frac{1}{2}x = -3$ **l)** $3x = -15$

2. Solve.

a) $2x + 4 = 18$ **b)** $5b - 2 = 13$ **c)** $3y + 4 = -8$

d) $7a - 5 = 30$ **e)** $3m + 5 = 14$ **f)** $7p - 6 = 57$

g) $\frac{1}{4}x + 2 = 5$ **h)** $\frac{1}{2}m - 4 = 12$ **i)** $\frac{x}{5} - 3 = 4$

3. Solve.

a) $4x - 1 = 8$ **b)** $5n + 6 = 7$ **c)** $-2x - 4 = -15$

d) $-5 = 3 - 4x$ **e)** $\frac{2}{3}x - 5 = 3$ **f)** $0.5n + 1.6 = 2.4$

g) $2 = 8x - 3$ **h)** $3 = 7 + 5x$ **i)** $1.5x - 3.2 = -2.3$

3 New: Evaluating a Formula

To evaluate a formula, replace the variables with the numbers given.

Note: The keystrokes in this text are for the TI-30X IIS scientific calculator. If your calculator is different, check your manual.

Example 1

The area, A, of a circle with radius r is given by $A = \pi r^2$. Find the area of a circle with radius 4 cm. Write the area to the nearest whole number.

Solution

$A = \pi r^2$

Substitute $r = 4$. Use the $\boxed{\pi}$ key on a calculator.

$A = (\pi)(4)^2$ Key in: $\boxed{\pi}$ $\boxed{\times}$ 4 $\boxed{x^2}$ $\boxed{\text{ENTER}\atop=}$ to display 50.26548246

$\doteq 50.2655$

The area is approximately 50 cm^2.

Example 2

Given the formula $P = \frac{I}{rt}$, determine P when $I = 400$, $r = 0.045$, and $t = 8$. Give the answer to 2 decimal places.

Solution

$P = \dfrac{I}{rt}$

Substitute the given values into the formula. Use a calculator to evaluate.

$P = \dfrac{400}{(0.045)(8)}$　　Key in: 400 ÷ 0.045 ÷ 8 [ENTER]
　　　　　　　　　　　　　　to display 1111.111111

$\doteq 1111.11$

P is approximately 1111.11.

Exercises

1. Find the value of the indicated variable in each formula. Where necessary, give the answer to 2 decimal places.

   a) For $p = 2(l + w)$, find p when $l = 13.9$ and $w = 7.2$.

   b) For $A = \frac{1}{2}bh$, find A when $b = 5.9$ and $h = 3.4$.

   c) For $I = Prt$, find I when $P = 525$, $r = 0.0375$, and $t = 5.5$.

   d) For $P = 4s$, find P when $s = 64.75$.

   e) For $V = \pi r^2 h$, find V when $r = 5.1$ and $h = 9.4$.

   f) For $C = 2\pi r$, find C when $r = 17.5$.

   g) For $A = 2\pi rh$, find A when $r = 6.2$ and $h = 7.3$.

2. Find the value of the indicated variable in each formula. Where necessary, give the answer to 2 decimal places.

   a) For $S = \frac{n(n+1)}{2}$, find S when $n = 87$.

   b) For $A = \frac{h(a+b)}{2}$, find A when $a = 4.6$, $b = 5.7$, and $h = 6.4$.

   c) For $r = \frac{I}{Pt}$, find r when $I = 58.27$, $t = 5.4$, and $P = 500$.

   d) For $P = \frac{A}{(1+i)^n}$, find P when $A = 1500$, $i = 0.035$, and $n = 24$.

   e) For $V = \frac{1}{3}\pi r^2 h$, find V when $r = 4.1$ and $h = 8.3$.

   f) For $V = \frac{4}{3}\pi r^3$, find V when $r = 3.5$.

You may already have a job, or be planning to look for a job. In this section, you will see different ways to calculate your earnings from a job.

Jose works part time at home assembling toys. He earns $8.00 per toy. His earnings are calculated by multiplying the number of toys assembled by 8.

The table of values shows the earnings for different numbers of toys completed. The graph shows how the earnings grow.

Number of toys assembled	Earnings ($)
0	$0 \times 8 = 0$
2	$2 \times 8 = 16$
4	$4 \times 8 = 32$
6	$6 \times 8 = 48$
8	$8 \times 8 = 64$
10	$10 \times 8 = 80$
12	$12 \times 8 = 96$

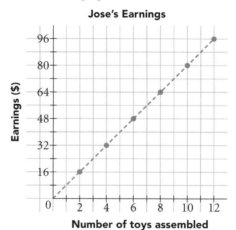

Jose is paid only for the toys assembled. The points are joined with a broken line to show the trend.

The table shows that Jose's earnings increase by a constant amount, $16, for every 2 toys he assembles. In the graph, the points lie on a straight line. Jose's earnings are an example of *linear growth*.

Number of toys assembled	Earnings ($)	
0	0	F.D
2	16	) 16
4	32	) 16
6	48	) 16
8	64	) 16
10	80	) 16
12	96	) 16

- linear
- slope

Example 1 Sylvie has a job in sales. She earns a monthly salary of $2500, plus a commission of 8% of her sales.

a) Make a table of values to represent Sylvie's monthly earnings on sales from $0 to $10 000, in steps of $2000.

b) Draw a graph to show Sylvie's earnings. Plot *Sales* horizontally and *Monthly earnings* vertically.

c) Are Sylvie's earnings an example of linear growth? Explain.

Solution

a) Remember that to find 8% of a number, multiply the number by 0.08.
To calculate the commission, multiply the sales by 0.08.
To calculate the monthly earnings, add the commission to the monthly salary, $2500.

Sales ($)	Commission ($)	Monthly earnings ($) = Salary + Commission
0	$0.08(0) = 0$	$2500 + 0 = 2500$
2 000	$0.08(2000) = 160$	$2500 + 160 = 2660$
4 000	$0.08(4000) = 320$	$2500 + 320 = 2820$
6 000	$0.08(6000) = 480$	$2500 + 480 = 2980$
8 000	$0.08(8000) = 640$	$2500 + 640 = 3140$
10 000	$0.08(10\ 000) = 800$	$2500 + 800 = 3300$

b) Choose a scale for the graph. Use 1 square to represent $1000 on the horizontal axis, and $250 on the vertical axis. Plot the points from the table. Use a ruler to join the points. The points are joined because all amounts of sales are possible.

c) The table shows that the monthly earnings increase by a constant amount. For every additional $2000 in sales, Sylvie earns an additional $160. The graph of the monthly earnings is a straight line. Sylvie's earnings are an example of linear growth.

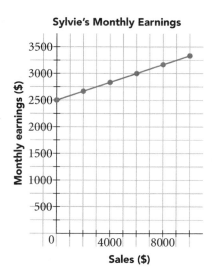

Sylvie's Monthly Earnings

1.1 Exercises

A

1. Calculate the earnings.

a) 4 h at $5/h

b) 10 h at $8/h

c) 12 h at $6/h

d) 15 h at $5.50/h

e) 20 h at $6.75/h

f) 25 h at $8.25/h

g) 30 h at $7.30/h

h) 17 h at $9.30/h

 2. Mei Lin earns $7.40 per hour. She works 20 h. How much does she earn?

3. Dennis earns $6.60 per hour. He works 13 h. How much does he earn?

4. Jan earns $5.95 per hour. She is paid for part hours worked. Jan works 10.5 h. How much does she earn?

 5. Fred earns $6.15 per hour. He is paid for part hours worked. Fred works 7.5 h. How much does he earn?

B

6. Josh works part time in a take-out restaurant. He earns $10.75 per hour. In one week, Josh works three 6-h shifts. How much money does he earn?

7. Marcie has a part-time job that pays $9 per hour. The chart below shows the hours Marcie worked during a week. Determine Marcie's pay.

	Mon.	Tues.	Wed.	Thurs.	Fri.	Sat.
Number of hours worked	3.5	5.75	4.5	3.5	5.25	4

8. **Knowledge/Understanding** Jeong works as a labourer on a construction site. She is paid $12.50 per hour.

   a) Jeong works 40 h in one week. How much does she earn?

   b) Make a table of values to show Jeong's earnings every 10 h for a 40-h week.

   c) Draw a graph to show Jeong's earnings.

   d) Are Jeong's earnings an example of linear growth? Explain.

9. A real estate agent earns a commission of 2.5%. She sells a house for $285 000. How much will the agent earn?

10. Greg is a salesman. He has a weekly salary of $350, plus a commission of 6% of his sales. One week, his sales were $10 000. How much did Greg earn that week?

11. Celine works in advertising. She is paid $950 per week plus a monthly bonus of 2% of the revenue generated by her department. Last month her department generated revenue of $86 000. Determine Celine's income for the month.

12. Jean has a job in sales. He has a weekly salary of $500, plus a commission of 3% of his sales.

   a) Make a table of values to show Jean's weekly earnings on sales from $0 to $20 000, in steps of $4000.

   b) Draw a graph to show Jean's earnings.

   c) Are Jean's earnings an example of linear growth? Explain.

13. Wally delivers papers seven days a week. He is paid by the number of papers delivered: $0.22 per paper during the week and $0.31 per paper on the weekends. Wally delivers 210 papers on weekdays, 320 papers on Saturday, and 250 papers on Sunday. Determine Wally's income for the week.

14. **Thinking/Inquiry/Problem Solving** Jeff is a seasonal worker. He works in sales for a lawn care company from April 1st to November 15th. Jeff is paid a salary and a bonus. His weekly salary is $600. His bonus is 5.4% of his sales for the season. The income from Jeff's sales one season was $240 000. Determine Jeff's total income for the season.

15. **Application** Nadine earns $15.75 per hour up to 40 h a week. She receives time-and-a-half for any hours worked over 40. One week, Nadine worked 55 h.

   a) Explain what "time-and-a-half" means. If you are not sure, ask a friend or your teacher.

   b) How much did Nadine earn?

   c) Draw a graph to show Nadine's earnings.

   d) Identify a characteristic of the graph and describe its significance.

16. **Communication** Elaine sells cars. She receives a commission on the gross profit the company makes on each vehicle she sells. Elaine earns a 30% commission on new vehicles and 25% on used vehicles. Last week Elaine sold 3 vehicles: a used truck with a gross profit of $1150, and two new cars with gross profits of $996 and $875, respectively. How much did Elaine earn that week? Present your solution to show all your thinking.

17. Jaina works as a waitress. She earns $8.75 per hour plus tips. Her average tip is 15% of the bill. One evening Jaina worked 5.5 h. She served 6 customers whose bills were $107.50, $87.90, $118.65, $96.30, $144.75, and $56.20. About how much did Jaina earn that evening?

C

18. Travis is a handyman. He charges $18 per hour plus a $40 flat fee for each job he does. Travis' work for a week is shown below. The chart contains the names of his customers. Determine Travis' gross income for the week.

	Mon.	Tues.	Wed.	Thurs.	Fri.
A.M.	Peelar 3.5 h	Morris 4 h	Morris 4 h	Lee 2.5 h	Downer 4 h
P.M.	Peelar 4 h	Morris 4 h	Lee 4.5 h	Smith 4 h	Downer 2 h

When you have an interview for a job, you may be required to take an aptitude test. Many tests use questions similar to these. They test a person's ability to recognize patterns.

Instruction: Fill each blank with the next item in the list.

1. b, c, d, f, g, h, ___

2. ◀, ▲, ▶ ___

3. 8, 15, 24, 35, ___

An ordered list of items is a *sequence*.

There is usually a pattern that relates the items in a sequence. This pattern can be used to predict other items in the sequence.

For example, consider the sequences in the aptitude test.

1. b, c, d, f, g, h, ___
   b, c, d, f, g, h are the first 6 consonants of the alphabet.
   So, the next item is j.

2. ◀, ▲, ▶, ___
   ◀, ▲, ▶ are a triangle being rotated 90° in each step.
   So, the next item is ▼ .

3. 8, 15, 24, 35, ___
   This sequence requires some calculation to complete.
   8, 15, 24, 35
       7 9 11
   The difference between consecutive numbers is 7, then 9, then 11.
   So, the next number is 13 more than 35, or 48.

   Another solution is that each number is 1 less than the sequence of square numbers: 9, 16, 25, 36, 49. So, the next number is $49 - 1$, or 48.

There is often more than one way to describe the pattern in a sequence. So, there may be different ways to find the next item in a sequence.

There may be different sequences that result after a certain number of items.

The items that make up a sequence are the *terms* of the sequence. We use the notation t_1 for the first term, t_2 for the second term, t_3 for the third term, and so on.

For example, these are the terms in the sequence 8, 15, 24, 35, ...

$$t_1 \quad t_2 \quad t_3 \quad t_4$$

Example 1

The first 4 terms of a sequence are 3, 6, 12, 24. Determine the next 3 terms of the sequence.

Solution

Look for a pattern in the terms.

$t_1 = 3$
$t_2 = 3 \times 2 = 6$
$t_3 = 6 \times 2 = 12$
$t_4 = 12 \times 2 = 24$

Each term is obtained by multiplying the previous term by 2. Use this pattern to determine the next 3 terms.

$t_5 = 24 \times 2 = 48$
$t_6 = 48 \times 2 = 96$
$t_7 = 96 \times 2 = 192$

The next 3 terms of the sequence are 48, 96, and 192.

Discuss

Describe the pattern in the sequence in a different way.

We have represented a sequence by listing its terms in order. A sequence can also be represented by its *general term*, t_n. The general term is a formula for any term in a sequence. We call "any term" the nth term. Notice that n is a natural number because it corresponds to a position in the sequence: $n = 1$, 2, 3, ..., and cannot be negative, zero, or a fraction.

Example 2

The general term of a sequence is $t_n = n + 3$. Write the first 4 terms of the sequence.

Solution

The general term, $t_n = n + 3$, is a formula for the nth term of the sequence.

To find the first term, substitute $n = 1$ in the general term.
$t_1 = 1 + 3 = 4$

To find the second term, substitute $n = 2$ in the general term.
$t_2 = 2 + 3 = 5$

Similarly, the next two terms are determined by substituting $n = 3$ and $n = 4$ in the general term.

$t_3 = 3 + 3 = 6$
$t_4 = 4 + 3 = 7$

The first 4 terms of the sequence are 4, 5, 6, 7.

Example 3 The general term of a sequence is $t_n = n^2 + n$. Determine the 5th and the 13th terms of the sequence.

Solution

For the 5th term, substitute $n = 5$ into the general term, $t_n = n^2 + n$.

$t_5 = (5)^2 + 5$
$\quad = 25 + 5$
$\quad = 30$

For the 13th term, substitute $n = 13$ into the general term.

$t_{13} = (13)^2 + 13$
$\quad\ = 169 + 13$
$\quad\ = 182$

The 5th term is 30 and the 13th term is 182.

1.2 Exercises

A

1. Write the next 3 terms of each sequence.

a) a, b, c, d, …
b) a, c, e, g, …
c) aa, ab, ac, ad, …
d) 1, 11, 111, 1111, …
e) 1, 12, 123, 1234, …
f) 111, 121, 131, 141, …
g) ←, ↖, ↑, ↗, …
h) ▲, △, ▶, ▷, …

2. Write the next 3 terms of each sequence.

a) 1, 2, 3, 4, …
b) 1, 3, 5, 7, …
c) 5, 10, 15, 20, …
d) 10, 20, 30, 40, …
e) 3, 6, 9, 12, …
f) 4, 8, 12, 16, …

g) 10, 9, 8, 7, … **h)** 3.5, 3, 2.5, 2, …

i) 40, 36, 32, 28, … **j)** 20, 18, 16, 14, …

k) 30, 27, 24, 21, … **l)** 39, 34, 29, 24, …

 3. Write the next 3 terms of each sequence.

a) 1, 2, 4, 8, … **b)** 1, 3, 9, 27, …

c) 5, 10, 20, 40, … **d)** 1, 10, 100, 1000, …

e) 2, 6, 18, 54, … **f)** 1, 5, 25, 125, …

g) 1, 4, 16, 64, … **h)** 64, 32, 16, 8, …

i) 81, 27, 9, 3, … **j)** 81, −27, 9, −3, …

4. Communication Write the next 3 terms of each sequence. Describe the pattern.

a) 2, 4, 6, 8, … **b)** 2, 4, 8, 16, …

c) 2, 3, 5, 8, … **d)** 1, 3, 7, 13, …

e) 3, 6, 12, 24, … **f)** 99, 88, 77, 66, …

g) $\frac{1}{2}, \frac{1}{3}, \frac{1}{4}, \frac{1}{5}, \ldots$ **h)** 0.1, 0.22, 0.333, 0.4444, …

B

5. Find the next 3 terms of each sequence. Describe the pattern.

a) 5, 7, 9, 11, … **b)** 1, 4, 9, 16, …

c) $\frac{1}{2}, \frac{2}{3}, \frac{3}{4}, \frac{4}{5}, \ldots$ **d)** $\frac{1}{2}, \frac{3}{4}, \frac{5}{6}, \frac{7}{8}, \ldots$

e) 1, 8, 27, 64, … **f)** 100, 99, 97, 94, …

g) $\frac{1}{2}, \frac{1}{4}, \frac{1}{8}, \frac{1}{16}, \ldots$ **h)** $\frac{3}{4}, \frac{8}{9}, \frac{15}{16}, \frac{24}{25}, \ldots$

 6. Find the next 3 terms of each sequence. Describe the pattern.

a) 4, 9, 14, 19, … **b)** 25, 21, 17, 13, …

c) 2, 20, 200, 2000, … **d)** 4, 20, 100, 500, …

e) −11, −8, −5, −2, … **f)** 1, −1, 1, −1, …

g) $\frac{1}{2}, \frac{3}{4}, \frac{5}{8}, \frac{7}{16}, \ldots$ **h)** 3, −6, 12, −24, …

 7. Thinking/Inquiry/Problem Solving Create 4 different sequences that begin with the digits 1 and 2. Describe the pattern for each sequence.

8. Knowledge/Understanding The formula for the *n*th term of a sequence is given. Write the first 4 terms of each sequence.

a) $t_n = n$ **b)** $t_n = n + 1$

c) $t_n = n^2$ **d)** $t_n = -3n$

e) $t_n = 2n + 1$ **f)** $t_n = n - 3$

g) $t_n = 12 - n$ **h)** $t_n = \frac{1}{n}$

9. Write the first 4 terms for the sequence with each given general term.

a) $t_n = n + 2$

b) $t_n = n^2 + 1$

c) $t_n = -5n$

d) $t_n = 3n - 1$

e) $t_n = n^3$

f) $t_n = 2n^2 - n$

g) $t_n = n^2 + n^3$

h) $t_n = n^2 - n - 1$

10. Write the first 5 terms for the sequence with each given general term.

a) $t_n = n(n - 1)$

b) $t_n = \dfrac{n}{n + 1}$

c) $t_n = 8 - n$

d) $t_n = \dfrac{n}{2}$

e) $t_n = n(n + 5)$

f) $t_n = \dfrac{n^2}{n + 1}$

g) $t_n = 3n + 2$

h) $t_n = \dfrac{n(n + 1)}{2}$

11. Application Make up a general term for a sequence. Write the first 4 terms of your sequence. Describe the pattern.

12. The formula for the general term of a sequence is given. Determine the 10th term.

a) $t_n = -2n$

b) $t_n = 5n - 7$

c) $t_n = 3n^2$

d) $t_n = 2 - 7n$

e) $t_n = n^3 + 1$

f) $t_n = \dfrac{2}{n}$

g) $t_n = (n - 1)^2$

h) $t_n = n^3 - n$

13. For each general term of a sequence, find the indicated terms.

a) $t_n = 2n - 3$, t_8 and t_{15}

b) $t_n = n^2 + 1$, t_7 and t_{20}

c) $t_n = -2n$, t_{18} and t_{100}

d) $t_n = -n + 2$, t_6 and t_{32}

e) $t_n = \dfrac{1}{2} - n$, t_5 and t_{20}

f) $t_n = n^2 - n$, t_{11} and t_{25}

g) $t_n = 0.4n + 0.5$, t_{12} and t_{50}

h) $t_n = 10^n$, t_7 and t_{12}

14. For each sequence given, determine a pattern that relates the terms. Then write the general term of the sequence.

a) 1, 4, 9, 16, …

b) 10, 100, 1000, 10 000, …

c) $\sqrt{1}$, $\sqrt{2}$, $\sqrt{3}$, $\sqrt{4}$, …

d) $\dfrac{1}{1}, \dfrac{1}{2}, \dfrac{1}{3}, \dfrac{1}{4}$, …

15. Each sequence below begins with 1, 2, 3. What is the next number? Describe each pattern.

a) 1, 2, 3, 1, 2, 3, _

b) 1, 2, 3, 2, 5, 2, _

c) 1, 2, 3, 5, 8, 13, _

d) 1, 2, 3, 6, 12, 24, _

16. Each sequence below begins with 2, 3, 5. What is the next number? Describe each pattern.

a) 2, 3, 5, 8, 12, 17, _

b) 2, 3, 5, 8, 13, 21, _

c) 2, 3, 5, 10, 20, 40, _

d) 2, 3, 5, 6, 8, 9, _

Keiko works part-time at a recycling plant. She is paid $4 per bin to sort recyclable materials.

For 1 bin sorted, she earns $4.
For 2 bins sorted, she earns $8.
For 3 bins sorted, she earns $12.
For 4 bins sorted, she earns $16, and so on.

Keiko's earnings can be written as the sequence:

   4, 8, 12, 16, …

In this sequence, each term is 4 more than its preceding term. This is an example of an *arithmetic sequence*. In an arithmetic sequence, the same number is added to each term to get the next term.

We can make a table of values, then draw a graph of the arithmetic sequence that represents Keiko's earnings.

Term, n	Term value, t_n	Difference
1	4	
		4
2	8	
		4
3	12	
		4
4	16	
		4
5	20	
		4
6	24	
		4
7	28	

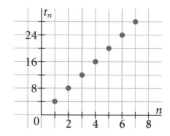

Discuss
Why are the points on the graph not joined? Why is there no dot at $(0, 0)$?

As n increases by 1, t_n increases by a constant amount, 4. The points on the graph lie on a straight line. These properties characterize linear growth.

In an arithmetic sequence, the same number is added to each term to get the next term. The number that is added is called the *common difference*. To find the common difference, subtract any term from the next term.

Here are two other arithmetic sequences.

Arithmetic sequence	Common difference
1, 3, 5, 7, ...	$3 - 1 = 2$
	$5 - 3 = 2$
	$7 - 5 = 2$
56, 51, 46, 41, ...	$51 - 56 = -5$
	$46 - 51 = -5$
	$41 - 46 = -5$

Example 1

Determine whether each sequence is arithmetic.

a) 15, 21, 27, 33, ...

b) 9, 10, 12, 15, ...

Solution

Check to see if there is a common difference.

a) $15, 21, 27, 33, \ldots$

$21 - 15 = 6$

$27 - 21 = 6$

$33 - 27 = 6$

There is a common difference of 6. The sequence is arithmetic.

b) $9, 10, 12, 15, \ldots$

$10 - 9 = 1$

$12 - 10 = 2$

$15 - 12 = 3$

There is no common difference. The sequence is not arithmetic.

Example 2

An arithmetic sequence has first term −2 and common difference 3. Write the first 5 terms of the sequence.

Solution

The common difference is 3. To list the sequence, add 3 to the first term to obtain the second term. Add 3 to the second term to obtain the third term, and so on.

$t_1 = -2$
$t_2 = -2 + 3 = 1$
$t_3 = 1 + 3 = 4$
$t_4 = 4 + 3 = 7$
$t_5 = 7 + 3 = 10$

The first 5 terms are −2, 1, 4, 7, 10.

In *Example 2*, we found the terms of the sequence by listing each term. However, it would be tedious to list each term to find the 12th or 41st term.

We can avoid listing each term by finding the general term of the sequence. The general term can then be used to determine any term in the sequence.

To find the general term of the sequence −2, 1, 4, 7, 10, …, look for a pattern in how each term is calculated.

Each term is 3 more than the preceding term.

n	t_n	Expanded version of t_n	Compact version of t_n
1	−2	−2	$-2 + 0(3)$
2	1	$-2 + 3$	$-2 + 1(3)$
3	4	$-2 + 3 + 3$	$-2 + 2(3)$
4	7	$-2 + 3 + 3 + 3$	$-2 + 3(3)$
5	10	$-2 + 3 + 3 + 3 + 3$	$-2 + 4(3)$

The number of 3s in each term is 1 less than the term number.

To find t_{12}, add eleven 3s to −2.
$t_{12} = -2 + 11(3)$
$\qquad = -2 + 33$
$\qquad = 31$

Similarly, to find t_{41}, add forty 3s to −2.
$t_{41} = -2 + 40(3)$
$\qquad = -2 + 120$
$\qquad = 118$

Remember that the general term, t_n, is the nth term of the sequence.
So, to find t_n, add $(n - 1)$ 3s to −2.
$t_n = -2 + (n - 1)(3)$

We can generalize this pattern to find the general term of any arithmetic sequence.

The general arithmetic sequence has first term a and common difference d.
Add d to each term after the first to get the next term.

$$t_1 = a \qquad\qquad = a + 0d$$
$$t_2 = a + d \qquad\qquad = a + 1d$$
$$t_3 = a + d + d \qquad\quad = a + 2d$$
$$t_4 = a + d + d + d \quad\; = a + 3d$$
$$t_5 = a + d + d + d + d = a + 4d$$

This pattern continues.

The number of differences in each term is 1 less than the term number.
Therefore, the nth term has $(n - 1)$ differences; that is, $t_n = a + (n - 1)d$.

TAKE NOTE

General Arithmetic Sequence

The general arithmetic sequence is $a, a + d, a + 2d, a + 3d, \ldots$.

The general term is $t_n = a + (n - 1)d$

  a is the first term.
  d is the common difference.
  n is the position of the term in the sequence.
  t_n is the value of the nth term.

Example 3

An arithmetic sequence has first term 5 and common difference -4.
a) Find t_n. **b)** Find t_{15}.

Solution

a) Use the formula $t_n = a + (n - 1)d$.
  Substitute $a = 5$ and $d = -4$.
  $$t_n = 5 + (n - 1)(-4)$$
  $$= 5 - 4n + 4$$
  $$= 9 - 4n$$
  The general term is $t_n = 9 - 4n$.

b) Use $t_n = 9 - 4n$.
  Substitute $n = 15$.
  $$t_{15} = 9 - 4(15)$$
  $$= 9 - 60$$
  $$= -51$$
  The 15th term is -51.

Example 4

An arithmetic sequence is 4, 7, 10, 13, … . One term in this sequence is 214. Which term is it?

Solution

Since $7 - 4 = 3$, the common difference is 3. The first term, a, is 4.
So, $d = 3$ and $a = 4$
Use the formula for the nth term: $t_n = a + (n - 1)d$

Substitute $t_n = 214$, $a = 4$, and $d = 3$.

$214 = 4 + (n - 1)(3)$
$214 = 4 + 3n - 3$
$214 = 3n + 1$ Subtract 1 from each side.
$213 = 3n$ Divide each side by 3.
  $n = 71$

214 is t_{71}, the 71st term of the sequence.

1.3 Exercises

A

1. State which sequences are arithmetic. For each sequence that is arithmetic, state the common difference.

a) 3, 5, 7, 9, …
b) 1, 2, 4, 8, …
c) 43, 40, 37, 34, …
d) 3.5, 4, 4.5, 5, …
e) 5, 15, 45, 135, …
f) 1, −1, 1, −1, …
g) −8, −2, 4, 10, …
h) 1.5, 4.5, 7.5, 10.5, …

2. **Knowledge/Understanding** State the common difference, then list the next 3 terms of each arithmetic sequence.

a) 12, 15, 18, 21, …
b) 45, 37, 29, 21, …

3. State the common difference, then list the next 3 terms of each arithmetic sequence.

a) 2, 4, 6, 8, …
b) 36, 32, 28, 24, …
c) 55, 44, 33, 22, …
d) 9, 16, 23, 30, …
e) 7, 2, −3, −8, …
f) −10, −4, 2, 8, …
g) 50, 45, 40, 35, …
h) 75, 50, 25, 0, …
i) 12, 24, 36, 48, …
j) 8, −1, −10, −19, …

B

4. Write the first 4 terms of each arithmetic sequence.

a) The first term is 4 and the common difference is 5.

b) The first term is −2 and the common difference is 8.

c) The first term is 38 and the common difference is −3.

d) The first term is 3.4 and the common difference is 2.5.

e) The first term is 2 and the common difference is 1.1.

f) The first term is −12 and the common difference is −5.

g) The first term is −8 and the common difference is 4.

h) The first term is 101 and the common difference is −25.

i) The first term is 5.6 and the common difference is 0.2.

5. For each arithmetic sequence in exercise 4, determine the general term, t_n.

6. Write the first 3 terms of the sequence defined by the given general term. Determine whether the sequence is arithmetic. If a sequence is arithmetic, state its common difference.

a) $t_n = 3n - 2$ **b)** $t_n = 6n$

c) $t_n = 5 - n$ **d)** $t_n = n^2 - 1$

e) $t_n = -2n + 7$ **f)** $t_n = \frac{1}{2}n$

g) $t_n = 2^n$ **h)** $t_n = 0.4n + 0.5$

7. Application Aziza's summer job lasts 8 weeks. She will earn $100 per week with a $5 raise each week, if she performs well. The first 4 terms of the sequence that represents Aziza's earnings are 100, 105, 110, 115, … .

a) Is the sequence arithmetic? Explain.

b) How much will Aziza earn in the 8th week?

8. Determine the missing terms in each arithmetic sequence. Write the first 5 terms of each sequence.

a) __, 16, 20, __, __ **b)** __, __, 7, 11, __

c) __, __, __, −5, −2 **d)** __, $\frac{1}{2}$, $\frac{1}{3}$, __, __

e) __, __, −3, 5, __ **f)** __, 1.7, 2.9, __, __

g) __, __, 25, 40, __ **h)** __, −7, 15, __, __

9. For each arithmetic sequence, determine t_n.

a) 4, 6, 8, 10, … **b)** 10, 9, 8, 7, …

c) 2.1, 2.6, 3.1, 3.6, … **d)** −17, −12, −7, −2, …

e) 30, 22, 14, 6, … **f)** −9, 1, 11, 21, …

g) 2.6, 5.4, 8.2, 11, … **h)** 1, 3, 5, 7, …

10. For each arithmetic sequence, determine the indicated term.

a) 5, 9, 13, 17, … t_{14}

b) 61, 71, 81, 91, … t_8

c) −8, −5, −2, 1, … t_{20}

d) 1, 4, 7, 10, … t_{100}

e) 7.3, 12.3, 17.3, 19.3, … t_{30}

f) 26, 27, 28, 29, … t_{15}

g) 30, 26, 22, 18, … t_{25}

h) −12, −6, 0, 6, … t_{11}

i) 1.5, 2.0, 2.5, 3.0, … t_9

j) 130, 115, 100, 85, … t_{33}

11. A cab company charges a flat fee of $2.50, plus a charge of $0.25 per 0.2 km or part thereof, for each journey. Determine the cab fare for a journey of 2 km.

12. A handywoman charges a fee of $40 for each home visit. Her labour charge is $25 per hour, or any part of an hour. Calculate her earnings for a visit to the Parkins' home that lasted 4 h to repair a roof leak.

13. An arithmetic sequence has a first term of 16 and a common difference of 7. Which term has the value 247?

14. Communication The first term of an arithmetic sequence is 23 and the common difference is −3. Which term has the value −292? Explain how you know.

15. Thinking/Inquiry/Problem Solving The first term of an arithmetic sequence is 3 and the third term is 15. Determine the common difference. Explain your solution.

C

16. Determine the number of terms in each sequence.

a) 3, 5, 7, 9, …, 383

b) 2, 5, 8, 11, …, 935

c) 87, 85, 83, 81, …, −11

d) 1, 1.5, 2, 2.5, …, 45.5

e) 16, 31, 46, 61, …, 1396

f) −9, −5, −1, 3, …, 171

g) 7.2, 8.5, 9.8, 11.1, …, 81.3

h) 0.375, 0.5, 0.625, 0.75, …, 3

i) 55, 54.1, 53.2, 52.3, …, 18.1

j) 125, 165, 205, 245, …, 2205

17. An arithmetic sequence has $t_5 = 19$ and $t_{12} = 40$. Determine the first term and the common difference.

Arithmetic Series

A series is the sum of the terms of a sequence. Here are two sequences and their corresponding series.

Sequence	**Series**
10, 15, 20, 25, …	10 + 15 + 20 + 25 + …
1, 4, 9, 16, …	1 + 4 + 9 + 16 + …

The sequence 10, 15, 20, 25, … is an arithmetic sequence.
So, 10 + 15 + 20 + 25 + … is an *arithmetic series*.
An arithmetic series is the sum of the terms of an arithmetic sequence.

The series 1 + 4 + 9 + 16 + … is not an arithmetic series since the corresponding sequence is not arithmetic.

The notation S_n is used to represent the sum of n terms of a series.
For example, S_2 is the sum of the first 2 terms of the series, S_4 is the sum of the first 4 terms, and so on.

For the series 10 + 15 + 20 + 25 + …
$S_2 = 10 + 15 = 25$
$S_4 = 10 + 15 + 20 + 25 = 70$

Example 1

Minh's summer job is for 8 weeks. He is paid $200 per week, with a weekly increase of $10.

a) How much does Minh earn for his last week?

b) What are Minh's total earnings for the summer?

Solution

a) Minh's earnings can be represented by the arithmetic sequence:
200, 210, 220, 230, … . In this sequence, a is 200 and d is 10.
The pay for the last week is t_8, the 8th term of the sequence.
Use the formula for the nth term. Substitute $n = 8$, $a = 200$, and $d = 10$.
$t_n = a + (n - 1)d$
$t_8 = 200 + (8 - 1)(10)$
$\quad = 200 + 7(10)$
$\quad = 200 + 70$
$\quad = 270$

Minh earns $270 for his last week.

b) The total earnings are S_8, the sum of the 8 terms of the arithmetic series.

$$S_8 = 200 + 210 + 220 + 230 + 240 + 250 + 260 + 270$$
$$= 1880$$

Minh's total earnings for the summer are $1880.

In *Example 1*, we calculated the sum of the series by adding all the terms. This method can be tedious for a series with many terms.

Here is another method for finding the sum of the series in *Example 1*. It leads to a formula for the sum of an arithmetic series.

Write the series: $\qquad S_8 = 200 + 210 + 220 + 230 + 240 + 250 + 260 + 270$

Write the

series backwards: $\qquad S_8 = 270 + 260 + 250 + 240 + 230 + 220 + 210 + 200$

Add the 2 equations: $2S_8 = 470 + 470 + 470 + 470 + 470 + 470 + 470 + 470$

$$2S_8 = 8 \times 470$$

Solve for S_8. $\qquad S_8 = \frac{(8)(470)}{2}$

$$S_8 = 1880$$

Look at the second last line, $S_8 = \frac{(8)(470)}{2}$.

- The number 8 is the number of terms in the series.
- The number 470 is $200 + 270$, the sum of the first and last terms in the series.
- The product of 8 and 470 is divided by 2, since we found twice the sum of the series.

This suggests that to find the sum of the general arithmetic series with n terms:
- Add the first and last terms, $a + t_n$.
- Multiply the sum by the number of terms, n.
- Divide by 2.

That is, $S_n = \frac{n(a + t_n)}{2}$, or $S_n = \frac{n}{2}(a + t_n)$

Since $t_n = a + (n - 1)d$

$$S_n = \frac{n[a + a + (n - 1)d]}{2} \text{ or } S_n = \frac{n}{2}[2a + (n - 1)d]$$

There are two versions of the formula for the sum of an arithmetic series. Use the first formula when the first and last terms are known. Otherwise, use the second formula.

TAKE NOTE

Sum of the General Arithmetic Series

The general arithmetic series with n terms is:
$$a + (a + d) + (a + 2d) + \ldots + [a + (n - 1)d]$$

The sum of the general arithmetic series with n terms is:
$$S_n = \frac{n}{2}(a + t_n)$$
or
$$S_n = \frac{n}{2}[2a + (n - 1)d]$$

n is the number of terms.
a is the first term.
t_n is the last term.
d is the common difference.

Example 2 The arithmetic series $2 + 4 + 6 + 8 + \ldots + 50$ has 25 terms. Find the sum of the series.

Solution

The first and last terms are known.

Use the formula $S_n = \frac{n}{2}(a + t_n)$.

Substitute $n = 25$, $a = 2$, and $t_n = 50$.

$$S_{25} = \frac{25}{2}(2 + 50)$$

$$= \frac{25}{2}(52) \qquad \text{Key in: } 25 \; \boxed{\div} \; 2 \; \boxed{\times} \; 52 \; \boxed{\text{ENTER} \atop =}$$

$$= 650$$

The sum of the series is 650.

Example 3 Consider the arithmetic series $2 + 5 + 8 + 11 + \ldots + 98$.

a) Find the number of terms in the series.

b) Find the sum of the series.

Solution

a) To find the number of terms, use $t_n = a + (n-1)d$.

Substitute $t_n = 98$, $a = 2$, and $d = 3$.

$98 = 2 + (n-1)(3)$

$98 = 2 + 3n - 3$

$98 = 3n - 1$

$99 = 3n$

$n = 33$

There are 33 terms in the series.

b) The first and last terms are known.

Use the formula $S_n = \frac{n}{2}(a + t_n)$.

Substitute $n = 33$, $a = 2$, and $t_n = 98$.

$S_{33} = \frac{33}{2}(2 + 98)$

$\quad = \frac{33}{2}(100)$

$\quad = 1650$

The sum of the series is 1650.

Example 4 For the arithmetic series $214 + 209 + 204 + 199 + \ldots$, find the sum of the first 43 terms.

Solution

The last term is the 43rd term. We do not know the 43rd term.

So, use the formula $S_n = \frac{n}{2}[2a + (n-1)d]$.

Substitute $n = 43$, $a = 214$, and $d = -5$.

$S_{43} = \frac{43}{2}[2(214) + (43-1)(-5)]$

$\quad = \frac{43}{2}[428 + (42)(-5)]$

$\quad = \frac{43}{2}(218)$

$\quad = 4687$

The sum of the first 43 terms is 4687.

Discuss

How would you use the formula $S_n = \frac{n}{2}(a + t_n)$ to find the sum?

A

1. Find the sum of each arithmetic series.

  a) $1 + 2 + 3 + 4 + 5$

  b) $2 + 4 + 6 + 8 + 10 + 12$

  c) $20 + 18 + 16 + 14 + 12$

  d) $10 + 13 + 16 + 19 + 22$

  e) $10 + 7 + 4 + 1 + (-2)$

  f) $21 + 11 + 1 + (-9) + (-19)$

2. Find the sum of the first 10 terms in each arithmetic series.

  a) $13 + 15 + 17 + 19 + \ldots$ *21,23,25,28,31,33*

  b) $23 + 26 + 29 + 32 + \ldots$ *35,38,41,44,4*

  c) $33 + 37 + 41 + 45 + \ldots$

  d) $43 + 41 + 39 + 37 + \ldots$

  e) $11 + 8 + 5 + 2 + \ldots$

  f) $3 + (-1) + (-5) + (-9) + \ldots$

3. Find the sum of the first 15 terms of each arithmetic series.

  a) $5 + 7 + 9 + 11 + \ldots$ *13,15,17,19,21,23,25,27,29,31,33*

  b) $12 + 15 + 18 + 21 + \ldots$

  c) $10 + 20 + 30 + 40 + \ldots$

  d) $200 + 185 + 170 + 155 + \ldots$

  e) $-21 - 18 - 15 - 12 - \ldots$

  f) $19 + 12 + 5 - 2 - \ldots$

  g) $2 + 4 + 6 + 8 + \ldots$

  h) $3 + 9 + 15 + 21 + \ldots$ *2250*

B

4. Knowledge/Understanding For an arithmetic series, the first term is 1 and the 10th term is 28. Find the sum of the 10 terms in the series.

5. For an arithmetic series, the first term is 7 and the 40th term is 241. Find the sum of the 40 terms in the series.

6. Find the sum of the 100 terms in the arithmetic series $1 + 2 + 3 + \ldots + 100$.

7. Find the sum of the 50 terms in the arithmetic series $2 + 4 + 6 + 8 + \ldots + 100$.

8. Given the arithmetic series $7 + 13 + 19 + 25 + \ldots$, find:

a) the 20th term **b)** the sum of the first 20 terms

9. For the arithmetic series $8 + 6 + 4 + 2 + \ldots$, find:

a) t_{25} **b)** S_{25}

10. For each arithmetic series, find the indicated sum.

a) $15 + 19 + 23 + 27 + \ldots$; S_{20}

b) $100 + 95 + 90 + 85 + \ldots$; S_{15}

c) $1.5 + 3 + 4.5 + 6 + \ldots$; S_{50}

d) $14 + 5 - 4 - 13 - \ldots$; S_9

e) $14 + 17 + 20 + 23 + \ldots$; S_{32}

f) $24 + 22 + 20 + 18 + \ldots$; S_{25}

g) $10 + 30 + 50 + 70 + \ldots$; S_{10}

h) $0.5 + 2.5 + 4.5 + 6.5 + \ldots$; S_{16}

11. Consider the arithmetic series $2 + 5 + 8 + 11 + \ldots + 92$.

a) Find the number of terms in the series.

b) Find the sum of the series.

12. Consider the arithmetic series $10 + 13 + 16 + 19 + \ldots + 79$.

a) Find the number of terms in the series.

b) Find the sum of the series.

13. Find the sum of the arithmetic series $2 + 4 + 6 + 8 + \ldots + 500$.

14. Communication Find the sum of the arithmetic series $28 + 25 + 22 + 19 + \ldots - 26$. Write to explain how you found the sum.

15. Application Find the sum of the first 1000 positive integers.

16. Find the sum of the first 30 odd positive integers.

17. Thinking/Inquiry/Problem Solving Find an expression for the sum of the first n positive integers. Use the expression to find the sum of the first 200 positive integers.

C

18. a) Find an expression for the sum of the first n odd positive integers.

b) Suppose the sum of the first n odd positive integers is 400. What is the value of n?

19. The sum of the first 15 terms of an arithmetic series is 1290. The sum of the first 16 terms is 1464.

a) Find t_{16}.

b) Find S_{20}.

1. Jill works at a gas station and earns $8.75 per hour. Jill works 5 h on Thursday, 6.5 h on Friday, and 8 h on Saturday. How much does Jill earn?

2. Find the next 3 terms of each sequence.

   a) 2, 5, 9, 14, …

   b) −8, 4, −2, 1, …

   c) 5, 10, 20, 40, …

   d) 1, 4, 9, 16, …

3. Write the first 4 terms of the sequence with each general term.

   a) $t_n = 3n - 1$

   b) $t_n = n^3 + 1$

   c) $t_n = -3n$

   d) $t_n = 3^n$

4. Describe how you would determine whether a given sequence is arithmetic.

5. Find which sequences are arithmetic. For each that is, state the common difference.

   a) 3, 7, 10, 13, …

   b) −3, 6, −12, 24, …

   c) 100, 98, 96, 94, …

   d) $\frac{1}{4}, \frac{1}{2}, \frac{3}{4}, 1, …$

6. Write the first four terms of an arithmetic sequence with first term −5 and common difference 7.

7. Find the missing terms in the arithmetic sequence:
   ___, 15, 21, ___, ___.

8. Find the number of terms in the arithmetic sequence 2, 5, 8, 11, …, 224.

9. For the arithmetic series 5 + 9 + 13 + 18 + …, find:

   a) an expression for t_n

   b) an expression for S_n

   c) S_{12}

10. For the arithmetic series 6 + 1 − 4 − 9 − …, find:

    a) the 27th term

    b) the sum of the first 27 terms

11. Find the sum of the first 100 terms of the series 0.5 + 2 + 3.5 + 5 + … .

12. Find the sum of the series 2 + 9 + 16 + 23 + … + 429.

13. Find the sum of the first 3000 positive integers.

You earn money to pay for lodging, food, and transportation. By saving some of the money you earn you can plan for large purchases, for retirement, or for education. Savings can help cover emergencies. Money saved for the short-term is usually deposited in a savings account at a bank, trust company, or credit union. Long-term savings include investments in bonds, guaranteed investment certificates (GICs), or term deposits.

When you deposit money in a bank account, you lend the money to the bank. The bank then pays you for the use of the money. Money earned or paid for the use of the money is called *interest*.

The time for which money is invested is the *term* of the investment. The simple interest is paid at *maturity*, the end of the term.

Banks offer many interest options. To understand how they all work, it is important to know how a simple savings scheme works.
Suppose $100 are deposited in an account that pays interest at the rate of 5% per year. For each year the money is in the account, it earns 5% of $100.

- 1-year savings   Interest $= \$100 \times 0.05$
  $= \$5$
- 2-year savings   Interest $= (\$100 \times 0.05) \times 2$
  $= \$10$
- 3-year savings   Interest $= (\$100 \times 0.05) \times 3$
  $= \$15$

The interest earned depends on three things:
- the money invested, called the *principal*, P
- the annual interest *rate*, r
- the *time*, t, for which the money is invested

The interest can be calculated using this formula.

Interest $=$ Principal $\times$ Rate $\times$ Time

Interest calculated this way is called *simple interest*. The formula for simple interest is written as $I = Prt$.

In the simple interest formula, when the interest rate is an annual rate, time is measured in years. When the time is given in months or days, it must be converted into a fraction of a year.

Simple Interest

$I = Prt$

> I is the interest earned in dollars.
> P is the principal invested in dollars.
> r is the annual interest rate, expressed as a decimal.
> t is the time in years.

Example 1

Elise invested \$3500 in a 6-month term deposit that paid $7\frac{3}{4}\%$ per year. How much interest was earned?

Solution

The interest rate is $7\frac{3}{4}\%$, or 7.75%. As a decimal, $r = 0.0775$

The time is 6 months. In years, $t = \frac{6}{12}$

Use the formula $I = Prt$. Substitute $P = 3500$, $r = 0.0775$, and $t = \frac{6}{12}$.

$I = Prt$
$I = 3500 \times 0.0775 \times \frac{6}{12}$ Key in: 3500 ⊗ 0.0775 ⊗ 6 ÷ 12 (ENTER)
$ = 135.625$

The interest earned is \$135.63.

Example 2

A savings account pays interest at 4.5% per year. The account has a balance of \$1285.67 on January 1. There are no deposits or withdrawals during the month. On January 31, the interest for that month is deposited into the account. What is the interest?

Solution

The time t is 31 days. In years, $t = \frac{31}{365}$

Use the formula $I = Prt$. Substitute $P = 1285.67$, $r = 0.045$, and $t = \frac{31}{365}$.

$I = Prt$
$I = 1285.67 \times 0.045 \times \frac{31}{365}$
$ \doteq 4.9137$

The interest earned is \$4.91.

Every fall, the federal government issues Canada Savings Bonds (CSBs). When you purchase a CSB, you lend money to the federal government. In return, you are paid interest until the bond *matures*. On the maturity date, you are repaid the original value of the bond.

You may redeem a CSB before it matures. At redemption, you will receive the original value of the bond plus accumulated interest. However, you will receive interest only if you have held the bond for at least 3 months.

Example 3

Felix bought a $500 regular interest CSB. A regular interest CSB pays simple interest annually. The interest rate for Felix's bond is 5% per year. He plans to keep the bond until it matures in 8 years.

a) Determine the interest at the end of the first year. Calculate the accumulated interest at the end of each year. Write the data in a table.

b) Graph the data in part a.

c) What type of growth does accumulated simple interest illustrate?

Solution

a) Use the formula $I = Prt$. Substitute $P = 500$, $r = 0.05$, and $t = 1$.

$I = Prt$

$I = (500)(0.05)(1)$

$ = 25$

The interest at the end of the first year is $25.

Use the formula $I = Prt$ to calculate the interest at the end of each of the next 7 years. The results are shown in the table.

Year	Accumulated interest ($)
1	$(500)(0.05)(1) = 25$
2	$(500)(0.05)(2) = 50$
3	$(500)(0.05)(3) = 75$
4	$(500)(0.05)(4) = 100$
5	$(500)(0.05)(5) = 125$
6	$(500)(0.05)(6) = 150$
7	$(500)(0.05)(7) = 175$
8	$(500)(0.05)(8) = 200$

b) Plot *Year* horizontally and *Accumulated interest* vertically.

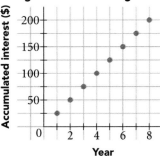

**Accumulated Interest on a
$500 Eight-Year CSB Earning 5% Interest**

c) In the table, the accumulated interest increases by a constant amount, $25, each year. The points on the graph lie on a straight line. Thus, accumulated simple interest illustrates linear growth.

Discuss

Why are the points on the graph not joined with a line?

Examples 1 to *3* illustrate interest earned on money saved. However, you pay interest when you use other people's money. For mortgages, car loans, bank loans, and outstanding credit balances, you pay interest rather than receive interest.

Example 4

A credit card company charges interest at $16\frac{3}{4}\%$ per year. Jim had an outstanding balance of $868.75 on his credit card for 35 days. How much interest did Jim pay?

Solution

Use the formula $I = Prt$.
The interest rate is $16\frac{3}{4}\%$, or 16.75%.
Substitute $P = 868.75$, $r = 0.1675$, and $t = \frac{35}{365}$.

$I = Prt$
$I = 868.75 \times 0.1675 \times \frac{35}{365}$
$\doteq 13.95$

Jim paid $13.95 interest.

1. Calculate the interest earned on each investment.

	Principal	Rate	Time (years)	Interest ($)
a)	$100	5%	3	
b)	$600	3%	1	
c)	$300	4%	2	
d)	$600	2%	4	
e)	$200	1%	2	

2. Calculate the interest earned on each investment.

	Principal	Rate	Time (years)	Interest ($)
a)	$250	4.5%	1	
b)	$175	2.5%	2.5	
c)	$1260	3.25%	2	
d)	$485	2.75%	1.5	
e)	$115	2.25%	0.5	

3. Knowledge/Understanding Calculate the interest earned on each investment.

	Principal	Rate	Time	Interest ($)
a)	$1100	3.4%	2.5 years	
b)	$640	$5\frac{1}{2}$ %	850 days	
c)	$4000	$6\frac{1}{4}$ %	15 months	
d)	$675	7.2%	420 days	
e)	$955	$4\frac{3}{4}$ %	15 weeks	
f)	$16 000	$6\frac{1}{8}$ %	18 months	
g)	$789	2.5%	720 days	
h)	$1 000 000	$5\frac{3}{8}$ %	5 months	

B

4. John invested $10 000 in treasury bills for 90 days. The interest rate was 4% per year. How much interest did John earn?

5. Carly put $800 in a deposit account for 10 months at 7% per year. How much interest did she earn?

6. Suzanne had an outstanding balance of $1865.23 on her credit card for 55 days. The annual interest rate is 18.9%. How much interest did Suzanne pay?

7. A credit card company charges interest at 24% per year on outstanding balances. How much interest would be charged on an outstanding balance of $1267.84 for 43 days?

8. Matte borrowed $500 from the credit union for 90 days. The interest rate is 10.9% per year. How much must Matte pay the credit union after 90 days?

9. Sun bought a $100 regular interest CSB that matures in 8 years. It earns interest at 6.5% per year.

   a) Draw a graph to show the accumulated interest until maturity.

   b) What type of growth does the graph represent?

10. **Communication** Will bought a 4-year GIC and an 8-year GIC. Each GIC had a value of $3000 and earned interest at 7.5% per year. Does doubling the term double the interest? Explain.

11. **Thinking/Inquiry/Problem Solving** Suppose the interest rate for an investment is doubled. Does the interest earned also double? Explain and include examples in your answer.

12. **Application** Tony has a credit account at a department store. He is charged interest at a rate of 1.9% per month on any outstanding balance. Tony's bill for November was $153.93. He only paid $100. During December, Tony made an additional $103.54 in purchases. How much will Tony owe when his December bill arrives?

C

13. Natalie bought a $1000, 10-year municipal bond. The bond paid interest at 4.8% per year for the first 4 years. Then, the interest rate was increased to 5.6% per year. Natalie kept the bond until maturity. How much interest did she earn?

14. Dena bought a $600 GIC. It earns interest at 5% per year for 3 years. Then the rate is increased to 8% per year for another 5 years. Draw a graph to show the accumulated interest for the term of the GIC.

The formula for simple interest, $I = Prt$, has four variables I, P, r, and t. When we know the values of three variables, we can calculate the fourth variable. We substitute the known values into the formula, then solve for the remaining variable.

Example 1

Denise received $1.52 interest on her savings account for April. She had not made any withdrawals or deposits during the month. At the beginning of April, the balance was $569.02. What rate of interest did the account pay?

Solution

Use the formula $I = Prt$.
There are 30 days in April, so $t = \frac{30}{365}$.

To calculate r, substitute the known values in the formula:
$I = 1.52$, $P = 569.02$, and $t = \frac{30}{365}$.

$$I = Prt$$

$1.52 = 569.02 \times r \times \frac{30}{365}$ Multiply each side by 365.

$1.52 \times 365 = 569.02 \times r \times 30$

$554.8 = 17\ 070.6r$ Divide each side by 17 070.6.

$\frac{554.8}{17\ 070.6} = r$

$r \doteq 0.0325$ To convert a decimal to a percent,

$\doteq 0.0325 \times 100\%$ multiply by 100%.

$\doteq 3.25\%$

The account paid 3.25% interest.

Example 2

A term deposit for 6 months at 6.7% per year paid $50.25 interest on maturity. Calculate the principal invested.

Solution

Use the formula $I = Prt$.
To calculate P, substitute the known values:
$I = 50.25$, $r = 0.067$, and $t = \frac{6}{12}$, or 0.5.

$$I = Prt$$
$$50.25 = P \times 0.067 \times 0.5$$
$$50.25 = 0.0335P \qquad \text{Divide each side by 0.0335.}$$
$$P = \frac{50.25}{0.0335}$$
$$= 1500$$

The principal invested was $1500.

Example 3

Cecille cashed a $1000 regular interest CSB that earns 5.8% per year. She received $348 interest. How long did Cecille hold the bond?

Solution

Use the formula $I = Prt$.
To calculate t, substitute the known values:
$I = 348$, $P = 1000$, and $r = 0.058$.

$$I = Prt$$
$$348 = 1000 \times 0.058 \times t$$
$$348 = 58t \qquad \text{Divide each side by 58.}$$
$$t = 6$$

Cecille held the bond for 6 years.

1.6 Exercises

A

1. Solve each equation. Where necessary, give the answer to 2 decimal places.

a) $96 = 24t$ b) $100 = 10r$ c) $15 = 30r$

d) $996.8 = 124.6t$ e) $50 = 0.04P$ f) $72 = 900r$

2. Calculate each principal.

	Principal	Rate	Time	Interest
a)		5%	2 years	$20
b)		4%	1.5 years	$90
c)		3.5%	2 years	$36.75
d)		2.75%	0.5 years	$41.25

3. Calculate each rate.

	Principal	Rate	Time	Interest
a)	$3000		2 years	$120
b)	$4560		1 year	$138.80
c)	$4000		3 years	$210
d)	$1250		1.5 years	$37.50

4. Calculate each time.

	Principal	Rate	Time	Interest
a)	$450	1.5%		$13.50
b)	$1150	3.25%		$74.75
c)	$3560	4%		$213.60
d)	$380	2.5%		$38.00

✓ **5.** Calculate each missing item in the chart.

	Principal	Rate	Time	Interest
a)	$150	4%		$18
b)		5%	6 years	$360
c)	$1000		8 years	$560
d)	$300	12%	4 years	
e)		7%	5 years	$280
f)	$600	8%		$144
g)	$1200		10 years	$720
h)	$700	3%		$252
i)		6%	7 years	$840
j)	$900		15 years	$675

6. Calculate each missing item in the chart.

	Principal	Rate	Time	Interest
a)	$375	7.25%		$95.16
b)		$4\frac{3}{4}$%	90 days	$16.98
c)	$945		10.5 years	$520.93
d)	$1375	$8\frac{1}{4}$%	18 months	
e)		6.4%	120 days	$105.73
f)	$665	10.8%		$466.83
g)	$8150		7.75 years	$5305.65
h)	$1995	3.45%		$34.41
i)		5.8%	180 days	$25.03
j)	$2950		1.5 years	$336.30

7. Communication In exercise 6, you calculated P, r, or t by substituting directly into the formula $I = Prt$. You could also have rearranged the formula $I = Prt$ in terms of P, r, or t before substituting.

a) Rearrange the formula $I = Prt$ to solve for P, r, and t, respectively.

b) Complete exercise 6a, b, and c again. Use the appropriate formula from part a.

c) Identify the advantages and disadvantages of the two methods for calculating P, r, or t. Which method would you prefer to use? Explain.

8. A three-month term deposit that pays 7% per year earned $140 interest on maturity. Determine the principal invested.

9. Knowledge/Understanding

a) A principal of $500 was invested for 3 years. The interest earned was $26.25. What was the annual interest rate?

b) A principal of $1500 was invested at 2.5% per year. The interest earned was $56.25. How long was the investment held?

c) A principal was invested at 1.75% per year for 2 years. The interest earned was $113.75. What was the principal?

10. Sid earned $3.21 interest on his savings account in January. His opening balance for the month was $945.63. Sid did not deposit or withdraw money during the month. The interest is calculated daily. What annual rate of interest does his account pay?

11. An investment earns 8.75% per year. What principal will earn interest of $75.75 in 14 months?

12. **Application** Kan Shu's telephone company charges interest at 1.5% per month on any unpaid balance. The company charged $10.24 for an unpaid balance. What was the unpaid balance?

13. At a 5% annual interest rate, a principal of $500 earns $30. How long was the principal invested?

14. Mailka cashed a $5000 regular interest CSB that pays annual interest at 5%. She received $1500 in interest. How long did she hold the bond?

15. Erik has $500 in a savings account. He earned $1.54 interest in 25 days. What annual rate of interest does his account pay?

16. **Thinking/Inquiry/Problem Solving** Emma's retirement account grew from $300 to $362.76 in 5 months. What annual rate of interest does her account pay?

17. An investment of $1200 earned $22.19 interest at 7.5% per year. How long was the investment held?

18. Cyril has a regular interest CSB that pays $250 interest each year. The annual interest rate is 4.5%. What principal did Cyril invest in the bond?

19. Over a period of 145 days, Pierre earned $39.85 interest on a term deposit that pays 5.75% per year. What was the principal?

C

20. Carmen had $254.73 in her savings account from June 1 to August 1. She earned $1.30 in interest during that time. The interest is calculated daily. What annual rate of interest does her account pay?

1. Calculate each missing item in the chart.

	Principal	Rate	Time	Interest
a)	$250	6%	2 years	
b)	$925	4%		$18.25
c)	$1387		3 months	$10.40
d)	$500	8%	8 weeks	
e)		5%	5 years	$249.50
f)	$1000	10%		$8.22
g)	$895		8 months	$23.84
h)		6%	450 days	$20.34

2. A $500 term deposit earns interest at 5% per year. How much interest is earned in 2 years?

3. Determine the total interest earned on a $1000 regular interest CSB at 5.6% annually with a term of 10 years.

4. Dave has a savings account that pays interest at $3\frac{1}{2}$% per year. His opening balance for May was $1374.67. He did not deposit or withdraw money during the month. The interest is calculated daily. How much interest did the account earn in May?

5. Joan cashed a regular interest CSB after 3 years and received $93 interest. The annual rate on the bond was 6.2%. What was the original value of the bond?

6. Medhi invested $10 000 in treasury bills for 90 days. He received $139.32 in interest. What rate of interest did the bills earn?

7. Sam invested $800 at 6.5% per year and received $25.64 interest on maturity. How many days did Sam hold his investment?

8. Suppose you are working with simple interest. If you double the length of time of an investment, do you double the interest earned? Justify your answer with a full explanation.

In this chapter, you learned about Canada Savings Bonds, GICs, term deposits, and bank accounts. In this section, you will investigate some of these options with emphasis on savings accounts.

Most banks, credit unions, and trust companies offer accounts for young people that provide many services free of charge. However, once you reach 18 or 19 years of age, you must select an account or accounts that suit your needs.

For most savings accounts, interest is calculated daily, on the daily closing balance, and paid monthly. The rate of interest may depend on the balance in the account. For example, one financial institution advertised these annual rates.

Interest Rate	Balance
0.2%	Between $0 and $4999.99
1.15%	Between $5000 and $24 999.99
3.29%	Between $25 000 and $49 999.99
4.5%	Over $50 000

When interest is structured in this manner, it is said to be *tiered*. *Examples 1* and *2* refer to the savings account above.

Example 1

Suppose Linda has $3750.87 in her savings account on January 1. During the month of January, she makes no deposits or withdrawals.

a) Use the rates above. How much interest would the account earn for the month?

b) What is the new balance?

Solution

a) Linda's balance is less than $5000, so the account earns interest at 0.2%. To find the interest, use the formula $I = Prt$.

$$I = 3750.87 \times 0.002 \times \frac{31}{365}$$
$$\doteq 0.64$$

The account earns $0.64 in interest for January.

b) New balance $= 3750.87 + 0.64$
$$= 3751.51$$

The new balance is $3751.51.

Example 2

On February 14, Linda deposited $1500 into her savings account. She made no other deposits or withdrawals in February. How much interest would be deposited in the account on February 28?

Solution

From February 1 to February 13, the account earns interest at 0.2% on the balance of $3751.51. With the deposit on February 14, the new balance is $5251.51. For the rest of the month, the account earns interest at 1.15%.

Since interest is paid on the daily closing balance, the account earns the higher rate for February 14 and for the remaining days in the month, a total of 15 days.

Use $I = Prt$.
Interest from February 1 to February 13:
$$I = 3751.51 \times 0.002 \times \frac{13}{365}$$
$$\doteq 0.27$$

Interest from February 14 to February 28:
$$I = 5251.51 \times 0.0115 \times \frac{15}{365}$$
$$\doteq 2.48$$

Total interest for February:
$$I = 0.27 + 2.48$$
$$\doteq 2.75$$

On February 28, $2.75 interest is deposited in the account.

1. Linda made the following deposits during the rest of the year.

March 19, $300	April 7, $220	May 28, $1670.85
June 14, $280	July 2, $150	July 27, $425
September 15, $170	October 3, $240	October 21, $680
November 10, $380	December 3, $160	

Assume the interest rates remain the same. Determine the interest the account earns each month. Determine the total interest earned for the year.

On the next page, there are some other options Linda could use to invest her money. Assume the money she uses for the investments is withdrawn from her savings account.

2. Option 1: Linda invests $2000 in a regular interest bond at 4.9% per year on January 1. Determine the total interest the bond earns for the year.

3. Option 2: Suppose Linda did not want to tie up all her money for a long time. Linda invested $2500 in 90-day treasury bills at 3.75% on January 1. When the bills matured, Linda withdrew enough money from her savings account so she could invest $3500 for another 90 days at the same rate. On July 1, Linda invested $5000 in a regular interest bond at 4.9% per year, which she cashed on December 31. Determine the total interest Linda will receive for the year.

4. Option 3: On January 1, Linda bought a $3000 GIC that paid 5.7% per year. She also bought three $500 regular interest bonds that paid 4.6%: the first on February 1, the second on March 1, and the third on April 1. Finally, on November 1, Linda bought a $2000 regular interest CSB that paid 4.9% per year. Determine the total interest Linda will earn for the year.

5. With a partner, use current rates to create a situation similar to Linda's in exercises 1 to 4. Make this available to other students in your class to complete for practice.

Investigation **1** **Savings and Chequing Accounts**

Visit a financial institution of your choice (or go to their website) and get information on the different accounts they provide. Write a report on the different options available for saving money. Include the conditions for which the different options should be used. The report should include answers to these questions.

- Which function does the account serve: chequing, savings, or both?
- Is there a monthly fee for the account?
- Can you write cheques on the account? If so, what is the charge per cheque?
- Do you have access by electronic means (ABMs, ATMs, telephone, Internet, and so on)? If so, what is the cost per transaction?
- Is there a monthly minimum balance that will result in the waiving of transaction fees? (This is usually called the no-charge level.)
- Is this an interest-bearing account?
- How is the interest calculated? When is it paid?
- Does the rate of interest paid depend on the balance in the account? If so, how many tiers are there?
- What are the current rates for the different tiers?

Tool and Die Maker

Tool and die makers are among the most highly skilled production workers in Ontario's manufacturing economy, which employs 19% of the province's workforce. Manufacturing alone accounts for 25% of Ontario's wealth. More jobs are now available in the province's manufacturing sector than in all other industries combined. Tool and die makers produce tools, dies, and special holding devices that enable machines to manufacture the various products people use daily — from clothing and furniture to heavy equipment and parts for automobiles and aircraft.

Toolmakers craft precision tools for cutting, shaping, and forming metal materials. They produce jigs, gauges, and fixtures that hold metal (while it is bored, stamped, or drilled).

Die makers construct metal forms or dies to shape metal in stamping and forging operations. They also make metal moulds for die-casting and for moulding plastics and ceramics. To do the job well, tool and die makers undergo rigorous training to acquire sound knowledge of machining properties, such as the hardness and heat tolerance of various metals and alloys. Of all machine workers, tool and die makers possess a broader knowledge of machining operations, mathematics, and blueprint reading. Technology is changing the ways tool and die makers perform their job — several CAD- and CAM-programs are used to develop parts and products.

The tool rooms where the work takes place are clean, cool, and quiet because of the increasing use of computer-operated machines. Safety measures, such as wearing safety glasses and masks, are in force to prevent injury from bits of flying metal, and to reduce exposure to hazardous lubricants.

Where's the Math?

The mathematics topics of algebra, geometry, trigonometry, and basic statistics are an integral component of the training in tool and die making. Because tools and dies must conform to strict specifications — precision to one-thousandth of an inch — the work necessitates extreme patience and attention to detail.

MATHEMATICS TOOLKIT

Sequences and Series Tools

> The general arithmetic sequence is
> $a, a + d, a + 2d, \ldots, a + (n - 1)d.$
>> a is the first term.
>> d is the common difference.
>> n is the number of terms.

> The general term is $t_n = a + (n - 1)d$.

> An arithmetic sequence illustrates linear growth, when the common difference is positive.

> The general arithmetic series is
> $a + (a + d) + (a + 2d) + \ldots + [a + (n - 1)d]$.

> The sum of the first n terms of an arithmetic series is
> $S_n = \frac{n}{2}[2a + (n - 1)d]$ or $S_n = \frac{n}{2}(a + t_n)$.

Financial Tools

> Simple interest, I dollars, can be determined using $I = Prt$.
>> P is the principal in dollars.
>> r is the annual interest rate, expressed as a decimal.
>> t is the time in years for which the principal is invested.

> Accumulated simple interest illustrates linear growth.

1.1 **1.** Martha works part time in a fast food outlet. She earns $7.85 per hour. Last week she worked 5 h on Thursday, 4.5 h on Friday, and 8 h on Saturday. Determine Martha's pay for the week.

2. Omar works as an electrician's helper. He earns $11.50 per hour.

a) How much does Omar earn in a week when he works 40 h?

b) Draw a graph to illustrate Omar's earnings.

c) Do Omar's earnings illustrate linear growth? Explain.

3. Kirsten works in sales and is paid a salary plus commission. She receives a weekly salary of \$400 plus a commission of 4.3% on her sales. During the last 4-week period, Kirsten's sales were \$43 784. What will Kirsten's total earnings be for the 4-week period?

1.2

4. The general term of a sequence is $t_n = n^2 + 3$. Find the first 4 terms of the sequence.

5. The first 4 terms of a sequence are $-1, 3, 9, 17$. Write the next 4 terms of the sequence.

6. Write the first 3 terms of the sequence with each general term.
   a) $t_n = 2n^2 - 1$ **b)** $t_n = \frac{n+1}{n^2}$ **c)** $t_n = 8n$ **d)** $t_n = 3n + 1$

7. The general term is given. Find the indicated terms for each sequence.
   a) $t_n = n - 3$, t_7 and t_{18} **b)** $t_n = n(n + 2)$, t_{11} and t_{35}
   c) $t_n = n^3 - 1$, t_{17} and t_6 **d)** $t_n = -3n$, t_8 and t_{200}

1.3

8. State which sequences are arithmetic. For each that is arithmetic, state the common difference.
   a) $1, 3, 5, 7, \ldots$ **b)** $2, 4, 8, 16, \ldots$ **c)** $75, 70, 65, 60, \ldots$
   d) $7.5, 4, 1.5, -2, \ldots$ **e)** $1, 5, 10, 17, \ldots$ **f)** $\frac{1}{2}, 2, \frac{7}{2}, 5, \ldots$

9. Find the missing terms in each arithmetic sequence.
   a) $\_\_, 13, 22, \_\_, \_\_$ **b)** $\_\_, \_\_, -7, -11, \_\_$
   c) $\_\_, \_\_, \_\_, 6, 1$ **d)** $\_\_, 0.75, 1.5, \_\_, \_\_$

10. For each arithmetic sequence, find t_n and t_{15}.
   a) $4, 7, 10, 13, \ldots$ **b)** $15, 14, 13, 12, \ldots$
   c) $2.1, 2.6, 3.1, 3.6, \ldots$ **d)** $-49, -42, -35, -28, \ldots$
   e) $\frac{1}{4}, 1, \frac{7}{4}, \frac{5}{2}, \ldots$ **f)** $70, 62, 54, 46, \ldots$

11. Find the number of terms in each sequence.
   a) $2, 5, 8, 11, \ldots, 488$ **b)** $4, 9, 14, 19, \ldots, 744$
   c) $-15, -9, -3, 3, \ldots, 555$ **d)** $\frac{3}{2}, 2, \frac{5}{2}, 3 \ldots, \frac{91}{2}$
   e) $12, 21, 30, 39, \ldots, 1002$ **f)** $9, 5, 1, -3, \ldots, -171$

1.4

12. Find the sum of the first 13 terms of each arithmetic series.
   a) $2 + 7 + 12 + 17 + \ldots$ **b)** $21 + 19 + 17 + 15 + \ldots$
   c) $1.6 + 3.2 + 4.8 + 6.4 + \ldots$ **d)** $50 + 40 + 30 + 20 + \ldots$
   e) $-12 - 16 - 20 - 24 - \ldots$ **f)** $12 + 10 + 8 + 6 + \ldots$

13. For the arithmetic series $3 + 11 + 19 + 27 + \ldots$, find:

    a) an expression for t_n

    b) an expression for S_n

    c) S_{22}

14. A plumber charges a basic fee of $50 for each call-out, plus a labour charge of $25 per hour. She earned $650 for one job. How many hours did she work?

15. Find the sum of the series $3 + 7 + 11 + 15 + \ldots + 999$.

16. Determine the sum of the first 250 positive integers.

17. Determine the sum of the first 400 even positive integers.

1.5   **18.** Olivia invested $5500 in 90-day treasury bills at 4.5% per year. How much interest will she receive after the 90 days?

19. Nadine has a term deposit of $5250 at 4.8% per year. She receives the interest from the deposit each month.

    a) Write a sequence to show the accumulated interest Nadine will receive for the first 5 months.

    b) What kind of sequence is it?

    c) Draw a graph to show the terms of the sequence.

    d) What type of growth does the graph display? Explain.

20. A principal of $10 000 is invested at 3.75% per year for 18 months. How much interest does the investment earn?

21. A credit card has an interest rate of 18.75% per year on balances that are not paid by the due date. How much interest would be charged on a balance of $356.60 that is 39 days overdue?

1.6   **22.** A term deposit of 9 months at 5.62% per year paid $75.87 interest on maturity. Calculate the principal invested.

23. Stefan cashed a $2000 regular interest CSB with an annual rate of 6.4%. He received $896 in interest during the time he held the bond. How long did he hold the bond?

24. Wade's savings account had a balance of $1265.74 during the month of January. At the end of the month, he received $1.88 interest. The interest is calculated daily. What rate of interest is Wade's account paying?

1. Janet works in sales. She is paid a monthly salary of $2000 plus a commission of 8% of her monthly sales. Last month Janet's sales were $17 580.

   a) Calculate Janet's earnings for the month.

   b) Draw a graph to illustrate Janet's monthly earnings for sales that range from $0 to $25 000.

2. Nigel earns $17.75 an hour up to 40 h per week. When Nigel works more than 40 h, he receives time-and-a-half for any extra hours worked. One week Nigel worked 49.5 h. How much did Nigel earn?

3. **Knowledge/Understanding** An arithmetic sequence has a first term −8 and a common difference of 3. Write the first 4 terms of the sequence.

4. For the series $3 + 9 + 15 + 21 + \ldots$, find:

   a) an expression for t_n b) an expression for S_n

   c) S_{20} d) t_{115}

5. Find the number of terms in the sequence $2, 6, 10, \ldots, 626$.

6. Find the sum of the series $-4 + (-1) + 2 + 5 + \ldots + 125$.

7. **Thinking/Inquiry/Problem Solving** The sum of the first n positive integers is 31 375. Determine the value of n.

8. Jonas earns $850 per week. Show how the sum of an arithmetic series may be used to determine his accumulated income for any number of weeks worked. Write to explain your answer. Include an example.

9. Bernice has a 90-day term deposit of $3500 that pays annual interest of 4.8%. How much interest will Bernice receive?

10. Cyril received $42.88 interest from a 180-day term deposit. The annual interest rate was 4.7%. Calculate the principal.

11. Lai invested $4150 for 18 months and received $326.81 interest at maturity. At what annual rate did Lai invest her money?

12. **Application** Mahmud invested $875 at 5.2% per year. When the investment matured, Mahmud received $897.44. Determine the term of Mahmud's investment.

13. **Communication** Suppose the term of an investment at simple interest is doubled. Does the interest received double? Explain.

Compound Interest

Chapter Project

Canada Savings Bonds

The project in Section 2.6 provides an opportunity to investigate and analyse investments in Canada Savings Bonds. They are issued each year, beginning on November 1. They provide Canadians an opportunity to invest with their government. Canada Savings Bonds are considered a safe investment.

Curriculum Expectations

By the end of this chapter, you will:

> Demonstrate the quick recall or calculation of simple powers of natural numbers, without using technology.

> Simplify algebraic expressions involving positive integral exponents, using the laws of exponents.

> Solve problems involving the calculation of the amount (A) and the principal (P) in the compound-interest formula $A = P(1 + i)^n$, using scientific calculators.

> Solve problems involving the calculation of the interest rate per period (i) and the number of periods (n) in the compound-interest formula $A = P(1 + i)^n$, using a spreadsheet.

> Determine the effect of compound interest on deposits made into savings accounts (for example, determine the doubling period of a single deposit, compare the effects of different compounding periods, and so on).

CANADA SAVINGS BOND
OBLIGATION D'ÉPARGNE DU CANADA

Émise le 1996/11/01

CANADA will pay to the registered owner

NOVEMBER 1, 2008

on redemption, subject to the NOTE on the reverse,

ONE THOUSAND DOLLARS

plus l'intérêt couru.

$**1000**$

LE GOUVERNEMENT DU CANADA paiera au propriétaire immatriculé,

le **1ER NOVEMBRE 2008**

conformément à la NOTE au verso, sur demande au gré du propriétaire, la somme de

MILLE DOLLARS

plus l'intérêt couru.

REDEMPTION VALUE / VALEUR DE RACHAT

OF THE BANK OF CANADA / DE LA BANQUE DU CANADA
FISCAL AGENT OF THE GOVERNMENT OF CANADA /
AGENT FINANCIER DU GOUVERNEMENT DU CANADA

DEPUTY MINISTER OF FINANCE
SOUS-MINISTRE DES FINANCES

-5-25P1821 220712   19514410446015

⑈00386⑈18⑈:   000000052207⑈2⑈

0099030M

SAVINGS BOND
ÉPARGNE DU CANADA

01

registered owner

reverse,

Échue le

INTÉRÊT COMPOSÉ

$**5000**$

LE GOUVERNEMENT DU CANADA paiera au propriétaire immatriculé,

le

conformément à la NOTE au verso, sur demande au gré du propriétaire, la somme de

1ER NOVEMBRE, 2007

CINQ MILLE DOLLARS

plus l'intérêt couru.

REDEMPTION VALUE / VALEUR DE RACHAT

19525200990309

0000000604418⑈

OF THE BANK OF CANADA / DE LA BANQUE DU CANADA
FISCAL AGENT OF THE GOVERNMENT OF CANADA /
AGENT FINANCIER DU GOUVERNEMENT DU CANADA

DEPUTY MINISTER OF FINANCE
SOUS-MINISTRE DES FINANCES

Émise le

NOVEMBER 1, 2007

on redemption, subject to the NOTE on the reverse,

FIVE HUNDRED DOLLARS

propriétaire immatriculé,

1ER NOVEMBRE, 2007

conformément à la NOTE au verso, sur demande au gré du propriétaire, la somme de

CINQ CENTS DOLLARS

plus l'intérêt couru.

REDEMPTION VALUE / VALEUR DE RACHAT

55

1 Review: Evaluating Powers

Note: Calculators are not to be used in this section.

Remember that 3^4 means $3 \times 3 \times 3 \times 3$.

$3^4 = 3 \times 3 \times 3 \times 3$
$\quad = 81$

Example 1

Evaluate.

a) 4^3 **b)** 2^5 **c)** 30^2

Solution

a) $4^3 = 4 \times 4 \times 4$
$\quad = 64$

b) $2^5 = 2 \times 2 \times 2 \times 2 \times 2$
$\quad = 32$

c) $30^2 = 30 \times 30$
$\quad = 900$

Exercises

1. Evaluate.

a) 4^2 **b)** 5^3 **c)** 6^2
d) 3^3 **e)** 8^2 **f)** 2^4
g) 9^2 **h)** 2^7 **i)** 7^2
j) 3^5 **k)** 2^6 **l)** 11^2
m) 2^3 **n)** 10^2 **o)** 2^{10}

2. Evaluate.

a) 10^5 **b)** 10^8 **c)** 10^4
d) 10^6 **e)** 10^9 **f)** 10^3
g) 10^7 **h)** 10^{10} **i)** 10^{12}

3. Evaluate.

a) 6^3 b) 4^4 c) 5^4

d) 4^3 e) 2^8 f) 20^2

g) 20^3 h) 30^2 i) 50^2

j) 80^2 k) 40^3 l) 20^5

4. Evaluate.

a) 25^2 b) 45^2 c) 35^2

d) 75^2 e) 65^2 f) 55^2

5. a) Look at your answers to exercise 4. There is a pattern that allows you to simply write down the answer. What is the pattern?

b) Use the pattern from part a to evaluate each power.

    i) 15^2 **ii)** 85^2 **iii)** 105^2

2 Review: Exponent Laws for Positive Integral Exponents

Note: Calculators are not to be used in this section.

In the expression 4^5,

    4 is the base
    5 is the exponent
    4^5 is the power

    4^5 is read as "4 to the 5th."

Products and quotients with the same base can be expressed as a single power of the base.

Multiplication Law

Since 4^2 means 4×4
and 4^5 means $4 \times 4 \times 4 \times 4 \times 4$,

$$\begin{aligned} \text{then } 4^2 \times 4^5 &= (4 \times 4) \times (4 \times 4 \times 4 \times 4 \times 4) \\ &= 4 \times 4 \times 4 \times 4 \times 4 \times 4 \times 4 \\ &= 4^7 \end{aligned}$$

Necessary Skills

Example 1

Write each product as a single power.

a) $2^3 \times 2^4$ **b)** $c^4 \times c^2 \times c$ **c)** $(1.06)^5(1.06)$

Solution

a) $2^3 \times 2^4 = 2^{3+4}$ Write the base, then add the exponents.

$= 2^7$

b) $c^4 \times c^2 \times c = c^{4+2+1}$ Remember that $c = c^1$.

$= c^7$

c) $(1.06)^5(1.06) = 1.06^{5+1}$

$= 1.06^6$

Division Law

$4^5 \div 4^2 = \dfrac{4^5}{4^2}$

$= \dfrac{4 \times 4 \times 4 \times 4 \times 4}{4 \times 4}$

$= \dfrac{4 \times 4}{4 \times 4} \times 4 \times 4 \times 4$ Remember that $\dfrac{4 \times 4}{4 \times 4} = 1$.

$= 4 \times 4 \times 4$

$= 4^3$

Example 2　Write each quotient as a single power.

    a) $(-2)^{11} \div (-2)^6$ **b)** $\dfrac{m^{30}}{m^{20}}$

Solution

    a) $(-2)^{11} \div (-2)^6 = (-2)^{11-6}$ Write the base, then subtract the exponents.
                                $= (-2)^5$

    b) $\dfrac{m^{30}}{m^{20}} = m^{30-20}$ Write the base, then subtract the exponents.
              $= m^{10}$

Power of a Power Law

Since $(4^2)^5$ means $4^2 \times 4^2 \times 4^2 \times 4^2 \times 4^2$,

then $(4^2)^5 = 4^2 \times 4^2 \times 4^2 \times 4^2 \times 4^2$
             $= 4^{2+2+2+2+2}$
             $= 4^{2 \times 5}$
             $= 4^{10}$

TAKE NOTE

Power of a Power Law

$(a^m)^n = a^{mn}$

To raise a power to a power, write the base then multiply the exponents.

Example 3　Write each power of a power as a single power.

    a) $(5^3)^2$ **b)** $(t^4)^5$

Solution

    a) $(5^3)^2 = 5^{3 \times 2}$ Write the base, then multiply the exponents.
              $= 5^6$

    b) $(t^4)^5 = t^{4 \times 5}$
              $= t^{20}$

Exercises

1. Write as a single power.

a) $2^2 \times 2^3$ **b)** $3^1 \times 3^4$ **c)** $(-2)^2 \times (-2)^4$

d) $4^5 \times 4^2$ **e)** $(1.02)^2 \times (1.02)^5$ **f)** $(-3)^3 \times (-3)^5$

g) $\left(\frac{1}{2}\right)^3 \times \left(\frac{1}{2}\right)^5$ **h)** $\left(-\frac{1}{3}\right)^4 \times \left(-\frac{1}{3}\right)^2$ **i)** $\left(\frac{2}{5}\right)^5 \times \left(\frac{2}{5}\right)^2$

2. Write as a single power.

a) $2^5 \div 2^3$ **b)** $\frac{3^4}{3^2}$ **c)** $(-2)^5 \div (-2)$

d) $4^5 \div 4^2$ **e)** $(-10)^6 \div (-10)^2$ **f)** $(-3)^8 \div (-3)^3$

g) $5^{10} \div 5^5$ **h)** $(-3)^7 \div (-3)^4$ **i)** $6^6 \div 6^2$

3. Write as a single power.

a) $c^5 \times c^3$ **b)** $a^2 \times a^3$ **c)** $e^6 \times e^5$

d) $d \times d^4$ **e)** $m^3 \times m^4$ **f)** $\left(\frac{a}{2}\right)^5 \times \left(\frac{a}{2}\right)^2$

4. Write as a single power.

a) $c^5 \div c^3$ **b)** $a^3 \div a^2$ **c)** $e^6 \div e^5$

d) $\frac{d^4}{d}$ **e)** $\frac{m^4}{m^3}$ **f)** $\frac{(-x)^8}{(-x)^3}$

5. Write as a single power.

a) $12^{10} \times 12^5$ **b)** $\frac{20^{10}}{20^7}$ **c)** $(-7)^8 \times (-7)^6$

d) $(-8)^8 \div (-8)^6$ **e)** $(1.09)^{22} \times (1.09)^4$ **f)** $16^5 \div 16^4$

6. Write as a single power.

a) $x^{30} \times x^{40}$ **b)** $\frac{x^{15}}{x^{13}}$ **c)** $(-a)^8 \times (-a)^3$

d) $\frac{(-a)^{18}}{(-a)^{15}}$ **e)** $m^2 \times m^6$ **f)** $\frac{r^{16}}{r^{14}}$

7. Write as a single power.

a) $(2^2)^3$ **b)** $(3^2)^{12}$ **c)** $(10^4)^2$

d) $(10^2)^4$ **e)** $[(-2)^4]^3$ **f)** $[(-5)^2]^6$

8. Write as a single power.

a) $(x^3)^2$ **b)** $(a^4)^5$ **c)** $[(-x)^3]^2$

d) $[(-a)^4]^5$ **e)** $(m^3)^3$ **f)** $[(-n)^2]^2$

2.1 Compound Interest

In Chapter 1, you learned about regular interest Canada Savings Bonds. They earn simple interest that is paid annually until maturity or at redemption. Each year, the interest is paid by cheque or is deposited directly into the owner's bank account.

A second type of bond, compound interest Canada Savings Bonds, may also be purchased. Compound interest savings bonds also earn interest annually, but this interest is reinvested. In the second year, interest is earned not only on the principal, but also on the first year's interest. This reinvestment continues until the bond matures or is redeemed.

When interest is earned on interest, we say the interest *compounds*; thus the term *compound interest*.

The tables below show the calculations to find the interest earned on a $1000, 5% Canada Savings Bond (CSB) with a 7-year term. Assume the bonds are kept until maturity.

In the first table, the bond earns simple interest; that is, $50 each year.

$1000, 5% CSB with a 7-Year Term Earning Simple Interest			
Year	Principal for year ($)	Interest earned ($)	Accumulated interest ($)
1	1000	$1000 \times 0.05 = 50$	50
2	1000	$1000 \times 0.05 = 50$	100
3	1000	$1000 \times 0.05 = 50$	150
4	1000	$1000 \times 0.05 = 50$	200
5	1000	$1000 \times 0.05 = 50$	250
6	1000	$1000 \times 0.05 = 50$	300
7	1000	$1000 \times 0.05 = 50$	350

For the CSB that earns simple interest, the interest is calculated on the original principal. Therefore, the interest earned is the same every year, $50.

In the second table, the bond earns compound interest; that is, $50 the first year, $52.50 the second year, and so on.

$1000, 5% CSB with a 7-Year Term Earning Compound Interest			
Year	Principal for year ($)	Interest earned ($)	Accumulated interest ($)
1	1000.00	$1000.00 \times 0.05 = 50.00$	50.00
2	$1000.00 + 50.00 = 1050.00$	$1050.00 \times 0.05 = 52.50$	102.50
3	$1050.00 + 52.50 = 1102.50$	$1102.50 \times 0.05 = 55.13$	157.63
4	$1102.50 + 55.13 = 1157.63$	$1157.63 \times 0.05 = 57.88$	215.51
5	$1157.63 + 57.88 = 1215.51$	$1215.51 \times 0.05 = 60.78$	276.29
6	$1215.51 + 60.78 = 1276.29$	$1276.29 \times 0.05 = 63.81$	340.10
7	$1276.29 + 63.81 = 1340.10$	$1340.10 \times 0.05 = 67.01$	407.11

For the CSB that earns compound interest, the interest earned becomes part of the principal. Therefore, the interest earned grows every year.

The compound interest CSB adds an extra $407.11 − $350 = $57.11 in interest earnings over the 7 years.

The difference between the interest earned under simple interest and under compound interest can also be compared graphically.

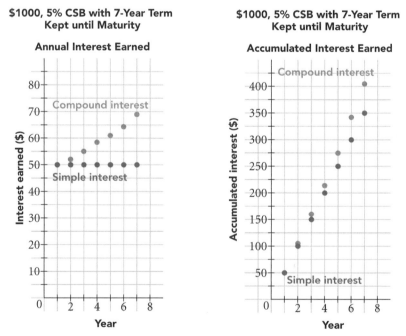

$1000, 5% CSB with 7-Year Term Kept until Maturity

Annual Interest Earned

$1000, 5% CSB with 7-Year Term Kept until Maturity

Accumulated Interest Earned

In the first year, the interest earned under simple interest and under compound interest is the same. After the first year, the compound interest earned is greater than the simple interest earned.

The difference between the simple interest earned and the compound interest earned increases as the length of the investment increases. Money grows more rapidly when interest is compounded.

Example 1

Amanda purchased a $500 guaranteed investment certificate (GIC). The certificate matures in 5 years. It earns interest at 4.5% compounded annually. How much interest will the GIC have earned at maturity?

Solution

Use a table to organize the calculations.
When interest is compounded annually, the second-year principal includes the first-year interest. The third-year principal includes the second-year interest, and so on.

Year	Principal for year ($)	Interest earned ($)
1	500.00	$500.00 \times 0.045 = 22.50$
2	$500.00 + 22.50 = 522.50$	$522.50 \times 0.045 = 23.51$
3	$522.50 + 23.51 = 546.01$	$546.01 \times 0.045 = 24.57$
4	$546.01 + 24.57 = 570.58$	$570.58 \times 0.045 = 25.68$
5	$570.58 + 25.68 = 596.26$	$596.26 \times 0.045 = 26.83$

Total interest = $22.50 + $23.51 + $24.57 + $25.68 + $26.83
= $123.09

At maturity, the GIC will have earned $123.09.

2.1 Exercises

1. Each investment matures in 1 year. Calculate the interest.

a) $100 invested at 5% **b)** $100 invested at 2%

c) $100 invested at 1.5% **d)** $1000 invested at 2.5%

2. Each investment matures in 1 year. Calculate the interest.

a) $150 invested at 4% **b)** $275 invested at 1%

c) $352 invested at 2.5% **d)** $489 invested at 1.25%

e) $654 invested at 1.75% **f)** $3251 invested at 2.25%

3. Each investment matures in 2 years. The interest is compounded annually. Calculate the interest at maturity.

a) $200 invested at 4%
b) $200 invested at 2%
c) $200 invested at 2.5%
d) $2000 invested at 3.5%

4. Explain the difference between simple interest and compound interest.

B

5. Each investment matures in 2 years. The interest is compounded annually. Calculate the interest at maturity.

a) $275 invested at 4%
b) $621 invested at 2.5%
c) $832 invested at 5%
d) $2348 invested at 3.5%

6. Knowledge/Understanding Calculate the interest earned on each investment. The interest compounds annually.

a) $300 invested at 5% for 2 years
b) $1500 invested at 4% for 3 years
c) $800 invested at 3% for 4 years
d) $2000 invested at 6% for 4 years

7. Suppose each investment in exercise 6 pays simple interest.

a) Calculate the interest earned on each investment.

b) How much extra interest is earned under compound interest?

8. Calculate the interest earned on each investment. The interest compounds annually.

a) $750 invested at $4\frac{1}{2}$% for 5 years

b) $2500 invested at $5\frac{3}{4}$% for 4 years

c) $1225 invested at $3\frac{1}{4}$% for 6 years

d) $1775 invested at 3.9% for 3 years

9. Communication Bill bought a $1500 GIC. The certificate matures in 5 years. It earns interest at 3.5% compounded annually. Explain how to calculate the interest Bill will receive when the certificate matures.

10. Application Draw a graph to illustrate the interest earned each year on an investment of $2000 at 5% compounded annually for 4 years. Does the graph show linear growth? Explain.

11. Draw a graph to show the accumulated interest earned on an investment of $2500 at 6% compounded annually for 5 years. Does the graph show linear growth? Explain.

12. Thinking/Inquiry/Problem Solving A $2000 GIC can be purchased two ways: at 5.5% compounded annually for 5 years; or, at 6% simple interest for 5 years. Find which GIC earns more interest. How much more interest does it earn?

The Amount of an Investment

When a compound interest investment matures, both the original principal and the interest due are paid to the investor. This sum is called the amount due, or simply the *amount* of the investment.

Amount = Principal + Interest

Suppose $200 is invested in a GIC that earns 6% a year for a 5-year term. The amount at the end of any year is the principal for that year increased by 6%. To determine the amount, consider the principal and interest as percents. The principal represents 100%. It increases by 6% to 106% of its original value.

Amount = Principal + Interest
   = 100% of principal + 6% of principal
   = 106% of principal

The amount at the end of any year is 106% of the principal for that year.

After 1 year, the amount of the GIC is $200 plus 6% of $200.
   Amount = 106% of $200
      = 1.06 × $200
      = $212

After 2 years, the amount of the GIC is $212 plus 6% of $212.
   Amount = 106% of $212
      = 1.06 × $212
      = $224.72

After 3 years, the amount of the GIC is $224.72 plus 6% of $224.72.
   Amount = 106% of $224.72
      = 1.06 × $224.72
      = $238.20

After 4 years, the amount of the GIC is $238.20 plus 6% of $238.20.
   Amount = 106% of $238.20
      = 1.06 × $238.20
      = $252.50

After 5 years, the amount of the GIC is $252.50 plus 6% of $252.50.
   Amount = 106% of $252.50
      = 1.06 × $252.50
      = $267.65

Therefore, the amount on the maturity date is $267.65.

We could have obtained this result in another way.

Each year, the amount at the end of the year is 106% of, or 1.06 times the principal for that year. We can write these amounts in a table and look for a pattern. We use the exponent law for multiplication.

Year	Principal for year ($)	Amount at end of year ($)	Amount at end of year simplified ($)
1	200	200(1.06)	$200(1.06)^1$
2	200(1.06)	200(1.06)(1.06)	$200(1.06)^2$
3	$200(1.06)^2$	$200(1.06)^2(1.06)$	$200(1.06)^3$
4	$200(1.06)^3$	$200(1.06)^3(1.06)$	$200(1.06)^4$
5	$200(1.06)^4$	$200(1.06)^4(1.06)$	$200(1.06)^5$

At the end of each year, the amount can be written using an exponent. The amount at the end of the 5th year is $\$200(1.06)^5$.

$$
\begin{aligned}
\text{Amount at maturity} &= \$200(1.06)^5 \\
&= \$267.65
\end{aligned}
$$

The number 1.06 in the calculation above is the compounding multiplier. It is obtained by adding 1 and 0.06.

In general, the compounding multiplier is $1 + i$, where i is the annual interest rate expressed as a decimal. To obtain the amount, multiply the principal by the compounding multiplier each time the interest compounds.

The table below shows how the amount, A, for a principal, P, at an annual interest rate, i, can be found.

Year	Principal for year	Amount at end of year	Amount at end of year (simplified)
1	P	$P(1 + i)$	$P(1 + i)^1$
2	$P(1 + i)^1$	$P(1 + i)(1 + i)$	$P(1 + i)^2$
3	$P(1 + i)^2$	$P(1 + i)^2(1 + i)$	$P(1 + i)^3$
4	$P(1 + i)^3$	$P(1 + i)^3(1 + i)$	$P(1 + i)^4$
$\vdots$	$\vdots$	$\vdots$	$\vdots$
n	$P(1 + i)^{n-1}$	$P(1 + i)^{n-1}(1 + i)$	$P(1 + i)^n$

In general, after n years, $A = P(1 + i)^n$

Amount of an Investment under Annual Compounding

$A = P(1 + i)^n$

A is the amount in dollars.

P is the principal in dollars.

i is the annual interest rate, expressed as a decimal.

n is the time in years.

Example 1

Sophie invests $800 in a GIC that pays 4% compounded annually for 5 years. Determine the amount when the investment matures.

Solution

Use the formula $A = P(1 + i)^n$.

Substitute $P = 800$, $i = 0.04$, and $n = 5$.

$A = 800(1 + 0.04)^5$

   $= 800(1.04)^5$ Key in: 800 ⓧ 1.04 ⌃ 5 (ENTER =)

   $\doteq 973.32$

The amount is $973.32 when the investment matures.

Example 2

A principal of $100 is invested at 8% compounded annually for 6 years.

a) Graph the amount of the investment at the end of each year.

b) Is the growth of the investment linear? Explain.

Solution

a) Make a table of values. Use the formula $A = P(1 + i)^n$ to calculate the amount for each year. Use the table of values to draw the graph.

Year	Amount ($)
0	100
1	$100(1 + 0.08) = 108$
2	$100(1 + 0.08)^2 = 116.64$
3	$100(1 + 0.08)^3 \doteq 125.97$
4	$100(1 + 0.08)^4 \doteq 136.05$
5	$100(1 + 0.08)^5 \doteq 146.93$
6	$100(1 + 0.08)^6 \doteq 158.69$

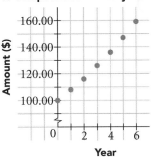

Amount of an Investment of $100 at 8% Compounded Annually for 6 Years

b) Calculate the differences in
the amounts.

Since the differences are not
constant, the growth is not linear.

Also, since the points on the graph
do not lie on a straight line, the
growth is not linear.

Discuss

How can you use your calculator
efficiently to calculate the amounts?

Amount ($)	Difference ($)
100.00	
	8.00
108.00	
	8.64
116.64	
	9.33
125.97	
	10.08
136.05	
	10.88
146.93	
	11.76
158.69	

Example 3

Julio invested $1250 at $5\frac{3}{4}$% compounded annually for 8 years. How much
interest does his investment earn?

Solution

Use the formula $A = P(1 + i)^n$ to find the amount.
Substitute $P = 1250$, $i = 0.0575$, and $n = 8$.
$A = 1250(1 + 0.0575)^8$
$ = 1250(1.0575)^8$
$ \doteq 1955.03$
Use Amount = Principal + Interest. Rearrange this formula.
Interest = Amount − Principal
$ = 1955.03 − 1250$
$ = 705.03$

The investment earned $705.03 interest.

2.2 **Exercises**

1. In each expression, identify the principal, interest rate, and time.
Evaluate each expression.

a) $\$450(1.05)^4$ **b)** $\$5000(1.075)^8$ **c)** $\$875(1 + 0.0375)^5$

d) $\$1535(1 + 0.0825)^7$ **e)** $\$915(1 + 0.066)^6$ **f)** $\$1200(1 + 0.052)^2$

2. Determine each amount. The interest is compounded annually.

   a) $600 at 5% for 7 years   **b)** $1500 at 3% for 6 years

   c) $100 at 7% for 4 years   **d)** $2000 at 6% for 8 years

   e) $800 at 4% for 5 years   **f)** $10 000 at 2% for 15 years

   g) $900 at 12% for 3 years   **h)** $1800 at 15% for 9 years

B

3. Determine the interest earned. The interest is compounded annually.

   a) $500 at 3% for 5 years   **b)** $1800 at 5% for 2 years

   c) $800 at 4% for 6 years   **d)** $1000 at 5% for 4 years

   e) $600 at 3% for 2 years   **f)** $2300 at 6% for 8 years

   g) $1750 at 5% for 12 years   **h)** $700 at 2% for 10 years

4. Determine each amount. The interest is compounded annually.

   a) $750 at $4\frac{3}{4}$% for 3 years

   b) $9250 at 5.6% for 12 years

   c) $2300 at 3.5% for 8 years

   d) $15 000 at $8\frac{3}{8}$% for 10 years

   e) $850 at 4.2% for 9 years

   f) $243 at $6\frac{1}{2}$% for 19 years

   g) $100 000 at $5\frac{1}{4}$% for 4 years

   h) $7280 at 7.65% for 6 years

   i) $5000 at 12% for 20 years

   j) $1600 at 18% for 7 years

5. Determine the interest earned. The interest is compounded annually.

   a) $375 at 3.5% for 4 years

   b) $298 at $3\frac{3}{4}$% for 5 years

   c) $1372 at 2.25% for 3 years

   d) $554 at $4\frac{3}{4}$% for 6 years

   e) $256 at $3\frac{1}{4}$% for 2 years

   f) $1032 at 5.25% for 3 years

   g) $431 at 1.9% for 7 years

   h) $2333 at 3.3% for 3 years

6. A principal of $1000 is invested in a compound interest CSB at $4\frac{1}{4}$% compounded annually. Calculate the amount of the bond after each time.

   a) 2 years   **b)** 4 years   **c)** 7 years

7. Calculate the interest earned on each bond in exercise 6.

8. A compound interest CSB earns $4\frac{1}{4}$% compounded annually for 7 years. Calculate the amount of each bond at maturity.

   a) a $500 bond   b) a $1000 bond   c) a $1500 bond

9. Calculate the interest earned on each bond in exercise 8.

10. **Knowledge/Understanding** Kareem purchased a $2500 compound interest CSB with an annual rate of $4\frac{1}{4}$% and a 7-year term.

   a) What is the amount of the investment at maturity?

   b) How much interest was earned?

11. In the advertisement, the interest earned by each GIC is compounded annually. Calculate the amount of each GIC at maturity.

   a) a $500, 1-year GIC

   b) a $2000, 2-year GIC

   c) a $4000, 3-year GIC

   d) a $3200, 4-year GIC

   e) a $10 000, 5-year GIC

GIC Rates	
1 year	4.75%
2 years	5.5%
3 years	5.75%
4 years	6.25%
5 years	6.5%
ABC Bank	

12. A principal of $500 is invested at 6% compounded annually for 5 years.

   a) Draw a graph to show the amount of the investment at the end of each year.

   b) Is the growth of the investment linear? Explain.

13. A principal of $3450 is invested at $3\frac{3}{4}$% compounded annually for 6 years.

   a) Draw a graph to show the amount of the investment at the end of each year.

   b) Is the growth of the investment linear? Explain.

14. A $2000 GIC that pays 5% compounded annually for a 3-year term is purchased. At maturity, the amount is reinvested at 5.5% compounded annually for a 5-year term. Calculate the amount when the second investment matures.

15. **Application** A person donated $3 000 000 to a city to help build a new library. The city plans to begin construction of the library in 5 years. The money is invested at 6.2% compounded annually. How much will the city have available when construction begins?

16. Alexie invested $500 at 6% compounded annually for 7 years. Meja invested $500 at 7% compounded annually for 6 years.

   a) Which investment earned more money?

   b) How much more?

17. Communication Marie invested \$375 in a GIC at $4\frac{1}{4}$% compounded annually for 18 years. Marie keeps the investment until maturity. Does she double her money? Explain.

18. Thinking/Inquiry/Problem Solving Josh invested \$1500 at $5\frac{1}{2}$% compounded annually for 3 years. Amelia invested \$1500 at $5\frac{1}{2}$% compounded annually for 6 years. Does the interest double when the time is doubled? Explain.

Career Profile

Banking Customer Service Representative (CSR)

Canada's financial services industry is changing. The banking sector of this industry has become aggressively competitive. The large banks compete to offer customers different ways to meet their financial services needs. In this rapidly changing competitive market, what is the job of a Banking Customer Service Representative?

Customer service representatives represent the bank and the bank's image to the customers. A banking CSR assists customers by answering questions about various accounts and loans, and provides general information on registered retirement savings plans and mutual funds. CSRs process deposits, withdrawals, transfers, and payment transactions. They must have a sound general knowledge of all the types of financial products and services the bank offers.

As traditional banking services are replaced by technology, communication skills are essential. A CSR should provide quality service, be precise, cordial, and helpful with customers at all times. He or she should be willing to spend time to discuss the products and services that best meet the customers' requirements. The bank wants clients to feel welcomed and to know that their business is valuable. "If you love dealing with the public, possess good communication skills, and are at ease with numbers, then a career as a CSR in a financial institution may be for you," comments a senior CSR at one of Canada's major banks.

A CSR works, on average, 7.5 hours a day. With banks offering flexible hours of operation, weekend and evening shifts may be expected.

Where's the Math?

Although most calculations in a bank are done using computers, a CSR must be able to track down any errors that occur, and to analyse the numbers to locate the mistake. A CSR is also expected to do interest rate calculations on loans, deposits, GICs, and bonds. More experienced CSRs may provide customers with detailed information on equity investments, such as stocks and mutual funds.

In Section 2.2, the interest was compounded annually. We say that the compounding period is 1 year.

In practice, compounding periods are frequently less than 1 year. For example, the interest on mortgages in Canada is compounded semi-annually. The interest on some savings accounts is compounded monthly. Other savings accounts have interest that is compounded daily, but the interest earned is deposited into the account monthly.

The most commonly used compounding periods are listed below.

Compounding frequency	Number of compounding periods per year
Annually	1
Semi-annually	2
Quarterly	4
Monthly	12
Daily	365

For compounding periods less than 1 year, we adapt the compound interest formula $A = P(1 + i)^n$.

TAKE NOTE

Amount of an Investment for Compounding Periods Less than One Year

$A = P(1 + i)^n$
   A is the amount in dollars.
   P is the principal in dollars.
   i is the interest rate per compounding period, expressed as a decimal.
   n is the number of compounding periods.

Suppose an investment earns 6% per year for 4 years.

When the interest is compounded semi-annually, it is compounded twice a year.
6% is the annual rate. The semi-annual rate is one-half of 6% = 3%.
In 4 years, there are 4×2, or 8 compounding periods.
Thus, $i = 0.03$ and $n = 8$

When the interest is compounded monthly, it is compounded 12 times a year. The monthly rate is $\frac{1}{12}$ of 6% = 0.5%.
In 4 years, there are 4×12, or 48 compounding periods.
Thus, $i = 0.005$ and $n = 48$

Example 1

A principal of $400 is invested at 5% compounded semi-annually for 6 years.

   a) Determine i, the semi-annual rate, as a decimal.

   b) Determine n, the number of compounding periods.

   c) Determine A, the amount of the investment.

Solution

   a) The annual rate is 5%, or 0.05.

      The semi-annual rate is $\frac{1}{2}$ the annual rate.

$$i = \frac{0.05}{2}$$
$$= 0.025$$

      The semi-annual rate is 0.025.

   b) Interest is compounded twice a year for 6 years.

$$n = 6 \times 2$$
$$= 12$$

      The number of compounding periods is 12.

   c) Use the formula $A = P(1 + i)^n$.

      Substitute $P = 400$, $i = 0.025$, and $n = 12$.

$$A = 400(1 + 0.025)^{12}$$
$$= 400(1.025)^{12} \qquad \text{Key in: } 400 \boxed{\times} 1.025 \boxed{\wedge} 12 \boxed{\text{ENTER} =}$$
$$\doteq 537.96$$

      The amount is $537.96.

Example 2

Henry invested $850 at 6% compounded monthly for 5 years. What is the amount of the investment at maturity?

Solution

The annual rate is 6%, or 0.06.
The monthly rate is $\frac{1}{12}$ the annual rate.

$$i = \frac{0.06}{12} = 0.005$$

Interest is compounded 12 times a year for 5 years.
$n = 5 \times 12 = 60$

Use the formula $A = P(1 + i)^n$.
Substitute $P = 850$, $i = 0.005$, and $n = 60$.
$A = 850(1 + 0.005)^{60}$
$\doteq 1146.52$
At maturity, the amount is $1146.52.

Example 3

A $500 GIC pays $3\frac{3}{4}$% compounded quarterly. How much interest will the GIC earn in 4.5 years?

Solution

Interest compounded quarterly is compounded 4 times in a year.

The annual rate is $3\frac{3}{4}$%, or 0.0375.

The quarterly rate is $\frac{1}{4}$ the annual rate.

$i = \frac{0.0375}{4} = 0.009\ 375$

Interest is compounded 4 times a year for 4.5 years.
$n = 4.5 \times 4 = 18$

Use the formula $A = P(1 + i)^n$.
Substitute $P = 500$, $i = 0.009\ 375$, and $n = 18$.
$A = 500(1 + 0.009\ 375)^{18}$
$\doteq 591.45$

Interest = Amount − Principal
$= 591.45 - 500$
$= 91.45$
The GIC will earn $91.45 interest in 4.5 years.

In *Example 3*, the calculation of i resulted in a decimal too tedious to write. To avoid this, leave i as a fraction and evaluate the expression using the fraction. Remember the keystrokes are for the TI-30X IIS calculator.

$A = 500(1 + \frac{0.0375}{4})^{18}$ Key in: 500 (1 + 0.0375 ÷ 4)
$\doteq 591.45$ ∧ 18 ENTER =

See *Utility 2* to find out how to use the memory in a calculator.

Example 4

Draw a graph to illustrate the growth of $100 invested at 10% compounded monthly for 7 years.

a) Has the investment doubled by the end of 7 years? Explain.

b) Is the growth of the investment linear? Explain.

Solution

To make a table of values, calculate the amount at the end of each year. Plot the points and join them with a smooth curve.

Year	Amount ($)
0	100
1	$100(1 + \frac{0.1}{12})^{12} \doteq 110.47$
2	$100(1 + \frac{0.1}{12})^{24} \doteq 122.04$
3	$100(1 + \frac{0.1}{12})^{36} \doteq 134.82$
4	$100(1 + \frac{0.1}{12})^{48} \doteq 148.94$
5	$100(1 + \frac{0.1}{12})^{60} \doteq 164.53$
6	$100(1 + \frac{0.1}{12})^{72} \doteq 181.76$
7	$100(1 + \frac{0.1}{12})^{84} \doteq 200.79$

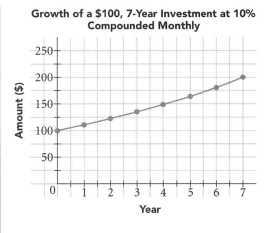

Growth of a $100, 7-Year Investment at 10% Compounded Monthly

a) The initial investment is $100. After 7 years, the amount is $200.79. The investment has doubled by the end of the 7 years.

b) Calculate the differences in the amounts.

Since the differences are not constant, the growth is not linear.

Also, since the points on the graph do not lie on a straight line, the growth is not linear.

Amount ($)	Difference ($)
100.00	
	10.47
110.47	
	11.57
122.04	
	12.78
134.82	
	14.12
148.94	
	15.59
164.53	
	17.23
181.76	
	19.03
200.79	

A

1. An investment earns 8% per year. Find i when the interest is compounded:

   a) annually   b) semi-annually   c) quarterly   d) monthly

2. An investment matures in 6 years. Find n when the interest is compounded:

   a) annually   b) semi-annually   c) quarterly   d) monthly

3. In each expression, identify the principal, interest rate per compounding period, and number of compounding periods. Evaluate each expression.

   a) $\$200(1 + 0.045)^{10}$ b) $\$750(1 + 0.175)^{15}$ c) $\$225(1 + 0.087)^8$

   d) $\$1475(1 + \frac{0.055}{12})^{36}$ e) $\$3000(1 + \frac{0.0525}{365})^{1825}$ f) $\$483(1 + \frac{0.15}{12})^{72}$

B

4. Determine the amount of each investment.

   a) $600 at 5% compounded annually for 8 years

   b) $2000 at 4% compounded semi-annually for 5 years

   c) $1500 at 8% compounded quarterly for 3 years

   d) $900 at 6% compounded monthly for 7 years

   e) $1200 at 7% compounded semi-annually for 6 years

   f) $1000 at 3% compounded monthly for 12 years

5. Determine the amount of each investment.

   a) $775 at 4.5% compounded semi-annually for 6 years

   b) $1750 at $6\frac{1}{8}$% compounded quarterly for 4 years

   c) $2500 at 3.25% compounded monthly for 10 years

   d) $12 000 at $7\frac{3}{4}$% compounded monthly for 7.5 years

   e) $375 at 6.6% compounded quarterly for 4 years

   f) $1325 at $4\frac{1}{4}$% compounded semi-annually for 5.5 years

   g) $100 at 8% compounded monthly for 8 years

   h) $1150 at 5.75% compounded quarterly for 6.5 years

6. Determine the interest earned on each investment.

   a) $600 at 5% compounded semi-annually for 14 years

   b) $3000 at $3\frac{3}{4}$% compounded monthly for 8 years

   c) $250 at 8.5% compounded quarterly for 6 years

   d) $1100 at 4.75% compounded monthly for 7.5 years

e) $1650 at $2\frac{1}{2}$% compounded semi-annually for 10.5 years

f) $25 000 at 3.25% compounded quarterly for 15 years

g) $425 at 4.6% compounded annually for 16 years

h) $767 at 5.2% compounded monthly for 12 years

7. Claire invested $1500 at 5% compounded semi-annually for 10 years. What is the amount of the investment at maturity?

8. Chun invested $800 at 4% compounded quarterly for 5 years. What is the amount of the investment at maturity?

9. Knowledge/Understanding Iona invested $2500 at 3.5% compounded semi-annually for 3 years. What is the amount of the investment at maturity?

10. Communication Draw a graph to illustrate the growth of $500 invested at 8% compounded quarterly for 10 years.

a) Has the investment doubled by the end of 10 years? Explain.

b) Is the growth of the investment linear? Explain.

11. Elise has $875.83 in her savings account. The account pays 4.5% compounded monthly. Elise does not make any deposits or withdrawals over the next 6 months. How much interest does the account earn?

12. Application When Ali was born, his grandfather deposited $5000 in a bank account for his college education. The account earns 6.5% compounded monthly. How much will the investment be worth in 18 years?

13. One $1000 investment pays 4% compounded monthly for 5 years. A second $1000 investment pays 8% compounded monthly for 5 years.

a) Determine the amount of each investment after 5 years.

b) How much interest does each investment earn?

c) Suppose the interest rate is doubled. Does the interest earned also double? Explain.

14. Draw a graph to illustrate the growth of $750 invested at 7% compounded monthly for 20 years.

a) Has the investment tripled by the end of 20 years? Explain.

b) Is the growth of the investment linear? Explain.

15. Mark plans to invest $500 in a GIC for 2 years. He has a choice of 2 plans:
Plan A: 6.75% compounded annually
Plan B: 6.60% compounded quarterly
In which plan should Mark invest? Explain.

16. **Thinking/Inquiry/Problem Solving** Usually, interest is compounded annually, semi-annually, quarterly, monthly, or daily. With the use of computers, compounding can be done more often: every hour, or every minute, or even every second.

a) Copy and complete this table. Show the different amounts that $1000 invested at 10% would grow to in 1 year.

Compounding frequency	Number of compounding periods per year	Calculations	Amount ($)
Annually	1	$1000(1 + 0.1)$	
Semi-annually	2	$1000\left(1 + \frac{0.1}{2}\right)^2$	
Quarterly			
Monthly			
Weekly			
Daily			
Hourly			
Every minute			
Every second			

b) How do the amounts change when interest is compounded more often? Is there a maximum amount that can be earned in one year?

c) Suggest reasons why banks rarely offer interest compounded hourly or by the minute or second.

 17. Pat has $800 to invest. He may invest at 5% compounded monthly for 6 years or at 5.1% compounded semi-annually for 6 years. Which investment should he make? Explain.

18. A principal of $500 is invested at 7.5% compounded monthly for 7 years.

a) Calculate the accumulated interest at the end of each year.

b) Draw a graph to show the accumulated interest.

c) Use the graph to determine when the accumulated interest is $250.

19. Determine how long it takes money to double in each situation.

a) 7% compounded semi-annually

b) $5\frac{1}{4}$% compounded quarterly

c) $8\frac{1}{2}$% compounded monthly

1. Evaluate. Do not use a calculator.

   a) 2^2 **b)** 2^3 **c)** 2^4 **d)** 2^5 **e)** 2^6 **f)** 2^7

2. Evaluate. Do not use a calculator.

   a) 7^2 **b)** 3^3 **c)** 3^4 **d)** 4^2 **e)** 10^3 **f)** 5^4

3. Write as a single power.

   a) $25^4 \times 25^5$ **b)** $\frac{x^{13}}{x^{10}}$

   c) $(5^4)^3$ **d)** $(1.04)^2 \times (1.04)^3$

4. Determine the amount of each investment.

   a) \$500 at 5% compounded annually for 5 years

   b) \$475 at 4% compounded monthly for 4 years

   c) \$10 000 at $6\frac{1}{2}$% compounded semi-annually for 3 years

   d) \$725 at 3.6% compounded quarterly for 8 years

   e) \$1500 at 7% compounded daily for 2 years

5. Determine the interest earned at maturity.

   a) \$200 at 6% compounded daily for 5 years

   b) \$350 at 4.5% compounded monthly for 7 years

   c) \$475 at $3\frac{1}{2}$% compounded annually for 4 years

   d) \$115 at $1\frac{1}{2}$% compounded semi-annually for 3 years

   e) \$2500 at $2\frac{3}{4}$% compounded quarterly for 6 years

6. Phil invested \$600 at 4% compounded monthly for 6.5 years. How much interest did the investment earn?

7. State which investment you would choose and explain why.
   Investment 1: \$600 invested at 4% compounded annually for 10 years
   Investment 2: \$600 invested at 4% compounded monthly for 10 years

8. What effect does doubling the interest rate have on the amount earned under compound interest?

9. Kari bought a \$500 GIC that earns 4.5% compounded semi-annually. How much will Kari receive when she cashes her certificate at the end of 3 years?

Mrs. Lam has some money to invest. She would like to give her grandson, Jason, $10 000 on his 15th birthday. Jason is celebrating his 9th birthday today. How much must Mrs. Lam invest today at 6% compounded monthly?

In this situation, the amount is known and the principal is not.

We can use the formula $A = P(1 + i)^n$ and some algebra skills to solve the problem.

We identify known values. Since Jason is now 9, the length of the investment is $(15 - 9)$ years, or 6 years.

n is $6 \times 12 = 72$; i is $\frac{0.06}{12} = 0.005$.

Substitute $A = 10\ 000$, $n = 72$, and $i = 0.005$ into the formula. Then solve for P.

$$10\ 000 = P(1 + 0.005)^{72} \quad \text{Divide each side by } (1 + 0.005)^{72}.$$
$$\frac{10\ 000}{(1 + 0.005)^{72}} = P$$
$$P = \frac{10\ 000}{1.005^{72}} \qquad \text{Key in: } 10000\ \boxed{\div}\ 1.005\ \boxed{\wedge}\ 72\ \boxed{\text{ENTER}}$$
$$\doteq 6983.02$$

Mrs. Lam must invest $6983.02 today to have $10 000 in 6 years.

The principal that must be invested today to obtain a given amount in the future is called the *present value* of an investment.

Example 1

An investment earns $5\frac{3}{4}\%$ compounded semi-annually. Determine the present value of $900, 5 years from now.

Solution

Think: In 5 years' time, I want $900. How much do I invest today?
Use the formula $A = P(1 + i)^n$.
n is $5 \times 2 = 10$.
Substitute $A = 900$, $n = 10$, and $i = \frac{0.0575}{2}$.

$900 = P(1 + \frac{0.0575}{2})^{10}$ Divide each side by $(1 + \frac{0.0575}{2})^{10}$.

$P = \dfrac{900}{\left(1 + \frac{0.0575}{2}\right)^{10}}$ Key in: 900 ⊕ (1 ⊕ 0.0575 ⊕ 2

) ^ 10 ENTER

$\doteq 677.87$

The present value is $677.87.

Discuss

How could you check that the present value is correct?

Example 2

Tricia has $1500 in her bank account. She wants to buy a CD player and invest the remainder at $6\frac{1}{2}\%$ compounded monthly for 4 years. At the end of the 4 years, Tricia wants $1500 in her bank account. Approximately how much can Tricia spend on the CD player?

Solution

First, calculate the present value of $1500. This is the principal Tricia must invest today to get $1500 in 4 years.
Use the formula $A = P(1 + i)^n$.
n is $4 \times 12 = 48$.
Substitute $A = 1500$, $n = 48$, and $i = \frac{0.065}{12}$.

$1500 = P(1 + \frac{0.065}{12})^{48}$

$P = \dfrac{1500}{\left(1 + \frac{0.065}{12}\right)^{48}}$

$\doteq 1157.39$

Tricia needs to invest $1157.39 today to have $1500 in 4 years.
She can spend $1500 - $1157.39 = $342.61.

Tricia has about $340 to spend on a CD player.

A

1. Solve for P.

  a) $100 = P(1.05)^2$ **b)** $250 = P(1.075)^6$

  c) $500 = P(1 + 0.06)^{15}$ **d)** $875 = P(1 + 0.0375)^{18}$

  e) $1000 = P(1 + \frac{0.045}{12})^{60}$ **f)** $1687 = P(1 + \frac{0.073}{365})^{1095}$

2. Calculate the present value of each amount.

  a) $100 in 5 years at 4% compounded annually

  b) $100 in 2 years at 6% compounded annually

  c) $100 in 4 years at 3% compounded annually

3. Calculate the present value of each amount.

  a) $200 in 3 years at 5% compounded semi-annually

  b) $200 in 4 years at 4% compounded semi-annually

  c) $200 in 2 years at 6% compounded semi-annually

 4. Calculate the present value of each amount.

  a) $1000 in 4 years at 5.5% compounded annually

  b) $1000 in 4 years at 5.5% compounded semi-annually

  c) $1000 in 4 years at 5.5% compounded quarterly

B

 5. Knowledge/Understanding Calculate the present value of each amount.

  a) $750 in 6 years at 5% compounded annually

  b) $2000 in 7 years at 8% compounded semi-annually

  c) $950 in 5 years at 6% compounded monthly

  d) $500 in 8 years at 4% compounded quarterly

6. Calculate the principal that must be invested now, to provide:

  a) $3000 in 6 years when the rate is $6\frac{1}{2}$% compounded monthly

  b) $875 in 5 years when the rate is $5\frac{3}{4}$% compounded semi-annually

  c) $485 in 3 years when the rate is $4\frac{1}{2}$% compounded quarterly

  d) $1125 in 8 years when the rate is 10% compounded monthly

7. Calculate the present value of each amount.

  a) $1420 in 6.5 years at $3\frac{3}{4}$% compounded quarterly

  b) $585 in 2 years at 8% compounded daily

  c) $15 000 in 12 years at 6.25% compounded monthly

  d) $1850 in 4.5 years at 4.13% compounded semi-annually

8. A parent plans to invest money to amount to $10 000 in 4 years when her daughter starts college. The interest is compounded annually. What is the present value of $10 000 at each interest rate?

   a) 4%   **b)** 5%   **c)** 6%   **d)** 7%

9. What principal invested today at $4\frac{1}{4}$% compounded semi-annually will amount to $3000 in 7 years?

10. Marc's savings account pays interest at 3% compounded monthly. Marc has not made any deposits or withdrawals in the last 3 months. His bank statement today shows a balance of $678.59. How much was in the account 3 months ago?

11. **Application** Donovan won $10 000 in a lottery. He decides to spend some of the money and save the rest. Donovan wants the money he saves to amount to the original winnings in 7 years. He can invest the money at 5.5% compounded monthly. How much money must Donovan save?

12. **Thinking/Inquiry/Problem Solving** Gillian has a savings account that pays interest at 3.5% compounded monthly. She has not made any deposits or withdrawals in the past 6 months. There is $2385.47 in the account today. How much interest has the account earned in the 6 months?

13. **Communication** Paula wants to have $5000 in 4 years' time. She has two options for investments:
    • A savings account with an interest rate of 3.5% compounded monthly
    • A GIC with an interest rate of 3.4% compounded semi-annually
    Which investment should Paula choose? Write to explain your decision.

14. Bill borrowed some money from a trust company and will repay the loan in 2 years. The interest rate is 10.5% compounded monthly. Bill must repay $1170.92 in 2 years. How much did Bill borrow?

15. Adrian received $5000 on his 21st birthday. This is the amount of an investment his parents made on the day he was born. The interest rate was $4\frac{3}{4}$% compounded semi-annually. Calculate the principal of the investment.

16. Linda won $25 000 in a lottery. She will spend some of her winnings and save the rest. The money Linda saves must amount to $40 000 in 20 years. Linda can invest the money at 5.25% compounded monthly. About how much should Linda spend?

17. A loan at 14% compounded semi-annually must be repaid with one single payment of $1800.88 in 3 years. What was the principal borrowed?

You have solved for A and P in the compound-interest formula $A = P(1 + i)^n$. In this section, you will solve for i and n. Since you cannot solve for i and n directly, you will use a spreadsheet.

Using a Spreadsheet

The advertisement states that money invested will be doubled in 12 years. What rate of interest compounded annually is the investment paying?

Consider an investment of $1. It will double to $2 in 12 years. Use the formula $A = P(1 + i)^n$. Substitute $A = 2$, $P = 1$, and $n = 12$.

$$A = P(1 + i)^n$$
$$2 = 1(1 + i)^{12}$$
$$2 = (1 + i)^{12}$$

Look at the spreadsheet on page 85. It shows the amount of a principal of $1 that earns compound interest for different interest rates and time periods. The interest rate, i, increases in steps of 0.005.

Look at the first entry in the spreadsheet: when $i = 0.005$, $A = 1.01$
In the compound-interest formula, i is the interest rate per compounding period. In this example, the interest compounds annually.
Thus, $i = 0.005$ corresponds to an annual interest rate of 0.5%.
When $i = 0.5\%$, $A = 1.01$
So, the amount is $1.01 when a principal of $1 is compounded annually at 0.5% for 1 year.

Similarly, in the 8th column:
When $i = 0.04$, $A = 1.04$
Therefore, the amount is $1.04 when a principal of $1 is compounded annually at 4% for 1 year.

We want the value of i that corresponds to $A = 2$, after 12 years. Look along the row for $n = 12$ until you find a value of A that is close to 2.
The closest value is $A = 2.01$ when $i = 0.06$.

The amount is $2.01 when a principal of $1 is compounded annually at 6% for 12 years.

Money invested at 6% compounded annually will double in approximately 12 years.

Spreadsheet
Amount of a Principal of $1

Number of periods, n	Interest rate per period, i													
	0.005	0.01	0.015	0.02	0.025	0.03	0.035	0.04	0.045	0.05	0.055	0.06	0.065	0.07
1	1.01	1.01	1.02	1.02	1.03	1.03	1.04	1.04	1.05	1.05	1.06	1.06	1.07	1.07
2	1.01	1.02	1.03	1.04	1.05	1.06	1.07	1.08	1.09	1.10	1.11	1.12	1.13	1.14
3	1.02	1.03	1.05	1.06	1.08	1.09	1.11	1.12	1.14	1.16	1.17	1.19	1.21	1.23
4	1.02	1.04	1.06	1.08	1.10	1.13	1.15	1.17	1.19	1.22	1.24	1.26	1.29	1.31
5	1.03	1.05	1.08	1.10	1.13	1.16	1.19	1.22	1.25	1.28	1.31	1.34	1.37	1.40
6	1.03	1.06	1.09	1.13	1.16	1.19	1.23	1.27	1.30	1.34	1.38	1.42	1.46	1.50
7	1.04	1.07	1.11	1.15	1.19	1.23	1.27	1.32	1.36	1.41	1.45	1.50	1.55	1.61
8	1.04	1.08	1.13	1.17	1.22	1.27	1.32	1.37	1.42	1.48	1.53	1.59	1.65	1.72
9	1.05	1.09	1.14	1.20	1.25	1.30	1.36	1.42	1.49	1.55	1.62	1.69	1.76	1.84
10	1.05	1.10	1.16	1.22	1.28	1.34	1.41	1.48	1.55	1.63	1.71	1.79	1.88	1.97
11	1.06	1.12	1.18	1.24	1.31	1.38	1.46	1.54	1.62	1.71	1.80	1.90	2.00	2.10
12	1.06	1.13	1.20	1.27	1.34	1.43	1.51	1.60	1.70	1.80	1.90	2.01	2.13	2.25
13	1.07	1.14	1.21	1.29	1.38	1.47	1.56	1.67	1.77	1.89	2.01	2.13	2.27	2.41
14	1.07	1.15	1.23	1.32	1.41	1.51	1.62	1.73	1.85	1.98	2.12	2.26	2.41	2.58
15	1.08	1.16	1.25	1.35	1.45	1.56	1.68	1.80	1.94	2.08	2.23	2.40	2.57	2.76
16	1.08	1.17	1.27	1.37	1.48	1.60	1.73	1.87	2.02	2.18	2.36	2.54	2.74	2.95
17	1.09	1.18	1.29	1.40	1.52	1.65	1.79	1.95	2.11	2.29	2.48	2.69	2.92	3.16
18	1.09	1.20	1.31	1.43	1.56	1.70	1.86	2.03	2.21	2.41	2.62	2.85	3.11	3.38
19	1.10	1.21	1.33	1.46	1.60	1.75	1.92	2.11	2.31	2.53	2.77	3.03	3.31	3.62
20	1.10	1.22	1.35	1.49	1.64	1.81	1.99	2.19	2.41	2.65	2.92	3.21	3.52	3.87
21	1.11	1.23	1.37	1.52	1.68	1.86	2.06	2.28	2.52	2.79	3.08	3.40	3.75	4.14
22	1.12	1.24	1.39	1.55	1.72	1.92	2.13	2.37	2.63	2.93	3.25	3.60	4.00	4.43
23	1.12	1.26	1.41	1.58	1.76	1.97	2.21	2.46	2.75	3.07	3.43	3.82	4.26	4.74
24	1.13	1.27	1.43	1.61	1.81	2.03	2.28	2.56	2.88	3.23	3.61	4.05	4.53	5.07
25	1.13	1.28	1.45	1.64	1.85	2.09	2.36	2.67	3.01	3.39	3.81	4.29	4.83	5.43
26	1.14	1.30	1.47	1.67	1.90	2.16	2.45	2.77	3.14	3.56	4.02	4.55	5.14	5.81
27	1.14	1.31	1.49	1.71	1.95	2.22	2.53	2.88	3.28	3.73	4.24	4.82	5.48	6.21
28	1.15	1.32	1.52	1.74	2.00	2.29	2.62	3.00	3.43	3.92	4.48	5.11	5.83	6.65
29	1.16	1.33	1.54	1.78	2.05	2.36	2.71	3.12	3.58	4.12	4.72	5.42	6.21	7.11
30	1.16	1.35	1.56	1.81	2.10	2.43	2.81	3.24	3.75	4.32	4.98	5.74	6.61	7.61
31	1.17	1.36	1.59	1.85	2.15	2.50	2.91	3.37	3.91	4.54	5.26	6.09	7.04	8.15
32	1.17	1.37	1.61	1.88	2.20	2.58	3.01	3.51	4.09	4.76	5.55	6.45	7.50	8.72
33	1.18	1.39	1.63	1.92	2.26	2.65	3.11	3.65	4.27	5.00	5.85	6.84	7.99	9.33
34	1.18	1.40	1.66	1.96	2.32	2.73	3.22	3.79	4.47	5.25	6.17	7.25	8.51	9.98
35	1.19	1.42	1.68	2.00	2.37	2.81	3.33	3.95	4.67	5.52	6.51	7.69	9.06	10.68
36	1.20	1.43	1.71	2.04	2.43	2.90	3.45	4.10	4.88	5.79	6.87	8.15	9.65	11.42
37	1.20	1.45	1.73	2.08	2.49	2.99	3.57	4.27	5.10	6.08	7.25	8.64	10.28	12.22
38	1.21	1.46	1.76	2.12	2.56	3.07	3.70	4.44	5.33	6.39	7.65	9.15	10.95	13.08
39	1.21	1.47	1.79	2.16	2.62	3.17	3.83	4.62	5.57	6.70	8.07	9.70	11.66	13.99
40	1.22	1.49	1.81	2.21	2.69	3.26	3.96	4.80	5.82	7.04	8.51	10.29	12.42	14.97
41	1.23	1.50	1.84	2.25	2.75	3.36	4.10	4.99	6.08	7.39	8.98	10.90	13.22	16.02
42	1.23	1.52	1.87	2.30	2.82	3.46	4.24	5.19	6.35	7.76	9.48	11.56	14.08	17.14
43	1.24	1.53	1.90	2.34	2.89	3.56	4.39	5.40	6.64	8.15	10.00	12.25	15.00	18.34
44	1.25	1.55	1.93	2.39	2.96	3.67	4.54	5.62	6.94	8.56	10.55	12.99	15.97	19.63
45	1.25	1.56	1.95	2.44	3.04	3.78	4.70	5.84	7.25	8.99	11.13	13.76	17.01	21.00
46	1.26	1.58	1.98	2.49	3.11	3.90	4.87	6.07	7.57	9.43	11.74	14.59	18.12	22.47
47	1.26	1.60	2.01	2.54	3.19	4.01	5.04	6.32	7.92	9.91	12.38	15.47	19.29	24.05
48	1.27	1.61	2.04	2.59	3.27	4.13	5.21	6.57	8.27	10.40	13.07	16.39	20.55	25.73

Discuss

On page 84, why was an investment of $1 considered? Why not $100 or another principal? Explain.

Example 1

A savings account pays 6% compounded semi-annually. How long will it take for the principal to triple?

Solution

For the principal to triple, $1 amounts to $3.
Use the formula $A = P(1 + i)^n$.

i is $\frac{0.06}{2} = 0.03$.

Substitute $A = 3$, $P = 1$, and $i = 0.03$.

$3 = 1(1 + 0.03)^n$
$3 = 1.03^n$

Use the spreadsheet on page 85.
Part of this spreadsheet is shown.

We want the value of n that corresponds to $A = 3$ and $i = 0.03$.
Look down the column for $i = 0.03$. The closest entry greater than or equal to 3 is $A = 3.07$ when $n = 38$.

Number of periods, n	0.005	0.01	0.015	0.02	0.025	0.03	0.035	0.04	0.045	0.05
1	1.01	1.01	1.02	1.02	1.03	1.03	1.04	1.04	1.05	1.05
2	1.01	1.02	1.03	1.04	1.05	1.06	1.07	1.08	1.09	1.10
3	1.02	1.03	1.05	1.06	1.08	1.09	1.11	1.12	1.14	1.16
4	1.02	1.04	1.06	1.08	1.10	1.13	1.15	1.17	1.19	1.22
•	•	•	•	•	•	•	•	•	•	•
•	•	•	•	•	•	•	•	•	•	•
•	•	•	•	•	•	•	•	•	•	•
36	1.20	1.43	1.71	2.04	2.43	2.90	3.45	4.10	4.88	5.79
37	1.20	1.45	1.73	2.08	2.49	2.99	3.57	4.27	5.10	6.08
38	1.21	1.46	1.76	2.12	2.56	3.07	3.70	4.44	5.33	6.39
39	1.21	1.47	1.79	2.16	2.62	3.17	3.83	4.62	5.57	6.70
40	1.22	1.49	1.81	2.21	2.69	3.26	3.96	4.80	5.82	7.04

It will take approximately 38 compounding periods, or 19 years, for money to triple at 6% compounded semi-annually.

Discuss

Why did we look for a value of A greater than or equal to 3?

Using a Spreadsheet Template

The spreadsheet on page 85 goes up to $i = 0.07$ and $n = 48$.

To solve problems that have interest rates greater than 7% or more than 48 compounding periods, you can use a spreadsheet template. This is the computer file into which you substitute values of n or i.

Ask your teacher for the spreadsheet template. When you open the file, it should look like this:

Solving for i and n in the Compound Interest Formula				
This spreadsheet calculates the amount for a principal of $1 under compound interest for different interest rates or time periods.				
Instructions: Input the values of i (as a decimal) and n in the blue cells. Use ? if the value is unknown.				
i				
n				
	A			

Suppose you want to find out how long it takes for money to double at 2% compounded semi-annually.

We know that $i = \frac{0.02}{2} = 0.01$

We need to find the value of n, the number of compounding periods.
Enter 0.01 in the blue cell for i.
Enter ? in the blue cell for n.
The spreadsheet generates values of A, as n increases in steps of 1 period.

Solving for i and n in the Compound Interest Formula				
This spreadsheet calculates the amount for a principal of $1 under compound interest for different interest rates or time periods.				
Instructions: Input the values of i (as a decimal) and n in the blue cells. Use ? if the value is unknown.				
i	0.01			
n	?			
n	A			
•	•			
•	•			
•	•			
69	1.9869			
70	2.0068			
71	2.0268			

Look down the column headed A for the value closest to 2, but greater than 2.
It is 2.0068, when $n = 70$.
Money invested at 2% compounded semi-annually will double in
70 periods $= \frac{70}{2}$ years $= 35$ years.

Example 2

When John was born, his grandparents deposited $5000 in an account that pays interest compounded quarterly. No further deposits or withdrawals were made. On John's 25th birthday, the amount in the account was $22 160.23. What annual rate of interest did the account pay?

Solution

Use the formula $A = P(1 + i)^n$.

n is $25 \times 4 = 100$.

Substitute $A = 22\ 160.23$, $P = 5000$, and $n = 100$.

$$A = P(1 + i)^n$$

$22\ 160.23 = 5000(1 + i)^{100}$ Divide each side by 5000.

$$\frac{22\ 160.23}{5000} = (1 + i)^{100}$$

$$(1 + i)^{100} \doteq 4.4320$$

Use the spreadsheet template.

Enter 100 in the blue cell that corresponds to n.
Enter ? in the blue cell that corresponds to i.

Solving for i and n in the Compound Interest Formula						
This spreadsheet calculates the amount for a principal of $1 under compound interest for different interest rates or time periods.						
Instructions: Input the values of i (as a decimal) and n in the blue cells. Use ? if the value is unknown.						
i	?					
n	100					
i	**A**					
0.005	1.6467					
0.01	2.7048					
0.015	4.4320					
0.02	7.2446					
0.025	11.8137					

Look down the row for A until you find $A = 4.4320$.
When $A = 4.4320$, $i = 0.015$

The interest rate per quarter is 0.015, or 1.5%.
Thus, the annual interest rate is $1.5\% \times 4 = 6\%$.

The account paid 6% compounded quarterly.

Using Guess and Check

If you do not have a spreadsheet, you can use guess and check to calculate i or n.

Example 3

How long does it take money to triple at 8% compounded quarterly?

Solution

For money to triple, $1 amounts to $3.
Use the formula $A = P(1 + i)^n$.

i is $\frac{0.08}{4} = 0.02$.

Substitute $A = 3$, $P = 1$, and $i = 0.02$.

$3 = 1(1 + 0.02)^n$
$3 = 1.02^n$

Use guess and check to find n, where n is the number of quarters of a year.

1st guess:	$n = 20$, then $1.02^{20} \doteq 1.49$ — too small
2nd guess:	$n = 50$, then $1.02^{50} \doteq 2.69$ — still too small
3rd guess:	$n = 60$, then $1.02^{60} \doteq 3.28$ — too large, but close
4th guess:	$n = 55$, then $1.02^{55} \doteq 2.97$ — too small
5th guess:	$n = 56$, then $1.02^{56} \doteq 3.03$ — too large, but close enough

It takes 56 quarters of a year for money to triple.

This is $\frac{56}{4}$ years = 14 years.

At 8% compounded quarterly, money triples in 14 years.

Example 4

A principal of $850 amounts to $1298.27 in 6 years. The interest was compounded monthly. What is the annual interest rate?

Solution

Use the formula $A = P(1 + i)^n$.
n is $6 \times 12 = 72$.

Substitute $A = 1298.27$, $P = 850$, and $n = 72$.

$1298.27 = 850(1 + i)^{72}$

$\frac{1298.27}{850} = (1 + i)^{72}$

$(1 + i)^{72} \doteq 1.5274$

Since the interest is compounded monthly, the rate will be small; that is, the annual rate has been divided by 12. Use guess and check.

1st guess: $i = 0.005$, then $1.005^{72} \doteq 1.4320$ — too small
2nd guess: $i = 0.006$, then $1.006^{72} \doteq 1.5383$ — too large, but close
3rd guess: $i = 0.0059$, then $1.0059^{72} \doteq 1.5274$ — this is correct.

The monthly rate is 0.0059 as a decimal.
This is $0.0059 \times 100\% = 0.59\%$.
The annual rate is $0.59\% \times 12 = 7.08\%$.

The annual interest rate is 7.08%.

2.5 Exercises

Use the spreadsheet on page 85 or the spreadsheet template.

1. Determine each value of i or n.

a) $1.63 = (1 + i)^{10}$ **b)** $1.72 = (1 + i)^{8}$ **c)** $2.10 = (1 + 0.07)^{n}$

d) $1.90 = (1 + 0.06)^{n}$ **e)** $2.08 = (1 + i)^{15}$ **f)** $2.02 = (1 + 0.045)^{n}$

2. Assume a principal of $1 invested at an annual interest rate of 5%. When will the amount be each value?

a) $1.41 **b)** $2.53 **c)** $4.12 **d)** $6.08

✓ **3.** Assume a principal of $1 invested for 22 years. Which annual interest rate will earn each amount?

a) $1.39 **b)** $1.92 **c)** $2.93 **d)** $4.43

4. Assume a principal of $1 invested at 3% compounded annually. When will the amount be each value?

a) $1.56 **b)** $1.97 **c)** $2.50 **d)** $3.90

✓ **5.** Assume a principal of $1 invested at 9% compounded semi-annually. When will the amount be each value?

a) $1.70 **b)** $2.52 **c)** $3.75 **d)** $7.25

B

6. Determine each value of i or n.

a) $1711.08 = 900(1 + 0.055)^{n}$ **b)** $1378.88 = 750(1 + i)^{9}$

c) $1376.20 = 500(1 + i)^{14}$ **d)** $1003.12 = 675(1 + 0.045)^{n}$

e) $282.86 = 150(1 + 0.05)^{n}$ **f)** $1070.10 = 600(1 + i)^{8}$

7. How long will it take for money to double at each interest rate compounded annually?

    a) 4%   **b)** 5%   **c)** 6%   **d)** 7%

8. How long will it take for money to double at each interest rate compounded semi-annually?

    a) 4%   **b)** 5%   **c)** 6%   **d)** 8%

9. How long will it take for money to triple at each interest rate compounded quarterly?

    a) 6%   **b)** 8%   **c)** 10%   **d)** 12%

10. **Knowledge/Understanding** A principal of $100 amounts to $125.97 in 3 years. Determine the interest rate compounded annually.

11. A savings account pays 8% compounded annually. In how many years will $2000 amount to $2938.66?

12. **Communication** A savings account pays 6% compounded quarterly. In how many years will $500 amount to $580.25? Write to explain how you calculated the time.

13. A principal of $500 amounted to $620 in 11 years. Determine the annual interest rate compounded quarterly.

14. A principal of $600 grew to $624 in 7 years. Determine the annual interest rate compounded monthly.

15. **Application** How long will it take money to triple at 6.5% compounded semi-annually?

16. Noah redeemed a $1000 GIC and received $1350. The GIC paid interest at 6% compounded monthly. For how long was the money invested?

17. Sarah has $250 to invest. She wants it to amount to $387.50 in 10 years. At what rate, compounded annually, must Sarah invest her money?

18. Nikki invested $400 for 4 years compounded semi-annually. She received $496 at maturity. At what annual rate did Nikki invest her money?

19. **Thinking/Inquiry/Problem Solving**
The 50¢ Bluenose is one of Canada's most famous postage stamps. In 1929, it could be bought at the post office for 50¢. In 2000, a superb copy was sold at an auction for $529. What annual interest rate corresponds to an investment of 50¢ in 1929 that grows to $529 in 2000?

Stamp reproduced courtesy of Canada Post Corporation

1. Determine the present value of $1000, 10 years from now, at each interest rate.

   a) 5% compounded annually   b) 5.5% compounded semi-annually

   c) 6% compounded quarterly   d) 6.5% compounded monthly

2. Determine the present value of $1000, at 4% compounded annually, after each time.

   a) 6 years from now   b) 8 years from now

   c) 5 years from now   d) 7 years from now

3. Determine the present value of each investment, 6 years from now, at 3% compounded semi-annually.

   a) $1000   b) $2500   c) $3600   d) $5900

4. Determine the principal that must be invested now, to provide:

   a) $900 in 6 years when the rate is 8% compounded semi-annually

   b) $1460 in 5.5 years when the rate is $5\frac{3}{4}$% compounded monthly

   c) $10 000 in 20 years when the rate is 7.2% compounded monthly

5. Determine each value of i, to 4 decimal places where necessary.

   a) $563.41 = 500(1 + i)^{12}$ b) $8592.77 = 2500(1 + i)^{50}$

   c) $278.07 = 125(1 + i)^{25}$ d) $1989.97 = 750(1 + i)^{20}$

   e) $1869.27 = 1500(1 + i)^{5}$ f) $556.68 = 350(1 + i)^{10}$

6. Determine each value of n, to the nearest whole number.

   a) $983.17 = 600(1.025)^{n}$ b) $283.24 = 250(1.0025)^{n}$

   c) $1433.44 = 1350(1.001)^{n}$ d) $757.29 = 550(1.0325)^{n}$

   e) $2690.98 = 2150(1.005)^{n}$ f) $1773.31 = 840(1.0075)^{n}$

7. A principal of $750 amounts to $915.14 after 5 years. The interest rate is compounded quarterly. What is the annual interest rate?

8. A principal of $1200 amounts to $1947.42 at 9% compounded annually. How long does it take?

9. Lyn's grandparents invested a sum of money for her for 9 years. The investment earned an average of 7.5% compounded semi-annually. Lyn received $2500 when the investment matured. How much did Lyn's grandparents invest?

10. Is the interest earned on a compound interest investment after 30 years triple that earned after 10 years? Explain.

Press Release: September 29, 2000.

2000-2001 New Canada Savings Bonds Campaign Launched

Secretary of State Jim Peterson today announced terms and conditions for the New Canada Savings Bonds, including Canada Premium Bonds (CPBs) and Canada Savings Bonds (CSBs), which go on sale October 2, 2000.

The Secretary of State highlighted key plans and activities for this year's campaign, including direct telephone sales, new electronic processing options for the new Payroll Savings Program and an expanded focus on youth and their parents.

Mr. Peterson noted that the Government of Canada will continue with the six-month sales pilot offering two bonds at the same time: new CPBs and the original CSBs. This year, Canadians will be able to purchase CPBs and CSBs between October 2, 2000, and April 1, 2001, either where they bank or invest or by phone.

There are 4 different choices of Canada Savings Bonds.

Type	Redeemable
Regular interest Canada Premium Bond (CPB) with simple interest paid each year	Only on the anniversary of the issue date and for 30 days thereafter
Compound interest Canada Premium Bond (CPB) with interest compounded annually and paid on maturity or when the bond is cashed	Only on the anniversary of the issue date and for 30 days thereafter
Regular interest Canada Savings Bond (CSB) with simple interest paid each year	Any time
Compound interest Canada Savings Bond (CSB) with interest compounded annually and paid on maturity or when the bond is cashed	Any time

Because there are restrictions on the CPBs, they earn interest at a higher rate.

Note: Rates for all CSBs and CPBs can change. The rates set at the time of sale are guaranteed minimums for the time indicated; they may change after this time. We will assume that the rates remain constant until maturity.

Complete these exercises to investigate CSBs.

1. The rate for CSBs is 4.85% and for CPBs is 5.5%. Suppose $1000 are invested in each of the four types of bonds available and will be redeemed at maturity in 10 years.

   a) Determine the total interest earned for each investment.

   b) Determine the difference in the total interest earned for the regular interest CSBs and the regular interest CPBs.

   c) Determine the difference in the total interest earned for the compound interest CSBs and the compound interest CPBs.

   d) Explain why the differences in parts b and c are not the same.

   e) Draw a graph to compare the accumulated interest earned after each year for the two types of regular interest Bonds.

   f) Draw a graph to compare the accumulated interest earned after each year for the two types of compound interest Bonds.

When you have completed exercises 2 to 5, you should be able to decide under what conditions you think the different types of bonds should be purchased. In these exercises, use the interest rates in exercise 1.

2. Anthony has recently retired. He has $20 000 to invest in government bonds. The bonds will not be cashed during the year.

   a) What bonds should Anthony choose?

   b) How much yearly income will Anthony receive from his bonds?

3. Susan starts a long-term savings plan. Government bonds are part of that plan. She has a steady, secure job and plans to invest $3000 annually.

   a) What bonds should Susan choose?

   b) How much will the bonds Susan buys in her first year be worth at maturity 10 years later?

4. Lita has been working in her current job for 18 months. She has $1000 to invest in government bonds. Lita does not yet have job security and will probably want to buy a car when her job is secure. When a bond is redeemed part way through a year, simple interest is calculated on the bond.

   a) What bonds should Lita choose?

   b) How much interest will Lita receive if she redeems her bond in 10 months? In 27 months?

5. Glenn recently inherited some money. He decided to invest $30 000 in government bonds. He wants a yearly income to be used for travel. Glenn also wants to have money for a large purchase if needed.

   a) What bonds should Glenn choose?

   b) How much will Glenn have available each year for travel?

6. The Canada Premium Bond Series 15, when issued, had guaranteed minimum rates for 3 years. Year one paid 5.5%, year two 5.7%, and year three 5.9%. Rates for further years were announced at future dates. Determine the interest earned for the first 3 years on each bond.

a) a $5000 regular interest CPB   **b)** a $2000 compound interest CPB

7. Series 45 CSBs were issued on November 1, 1990. The chart below shows the interest rates paid until maturity on these bonds. Each rate begins on the date of issue and lasts for 1 year. For example, 10.75% was the rate from November 1, 1990, until October 31, 1991. Then, on November 1, 1991, the rate changed to 7.5%. The rates were for both regular interest and compound interest bonds.

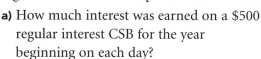

a) How much interest was earned on a $500 regular interest CSB for the year beginning on each day?

  i) November 1, 1991

  ii) November 1, 1997

  iii) November 1, 1999

b) Determine the interest earned on a $1000 regular interest CSB purchased on November 1, 1990, and held for 2 years.

c) Determine the interest earned on a $5000 compound interest CSB purchased on November 1, 1990, and held to maturity.

d) Draw a graph to illustrate the interest rates paid on CSBs from 1990 to 2000. Describe the graph.

Year	Annual rate
1990	10.75%
1991	7.50%
1992	6.00%
1993	5.13%
1994	6.38%
1995	6.75%
1996	7.50%
1997	2.56%
1998	4.25%
1999	5.25%
2000	5.50%

8. Exercises 1 to 5 assumed that the interest rates on the bonds do not change. In fact, the interest rates do change according to market conditions. Why do you think the government follows interest rate changes in the financial market?

Note: Research to obtain current information needed to complete exercises 9 and 10.

If you use the Internet, you can start your search from our web site.

www.pearsoned.ca/onmath11

9. Select a series of CPBs. Repeat exercise 7 using the rates for that series.

10. a) The Canada Savings Bonds web site has a frequently asked questions (FAQ) section. It provides answers to questions about government bonds. Some of these questions have been covered in this section. Visit the web site, then answer these questions.

  i) When will the rates be available?

  ii) How much can I buy?

  iii) When can I redeem my bonds?

  iv) Who is eligible to own bonds?

b) Investigate the section on "Saving for a Purchase." Write a short report on your findings.

Small Business Owner

"The independence of being your own boss is the biggest positive of owning your own business," says Marshall Miller, owner of Hook, Line and Sinker, a fishing supply store. "It's very rewarding to have the responsibility for your own success, but that responsibility is also the biggest drawback of owning your own shop: there is no one else to blame when things go wrong."

If you are looking for a career in which you set your own goals, work your own hours, and have a direct connection to your success, then owning a small business might be for you. A small business offers a product or service and employs fewer than 200 people. There are many different types of small business, such as a restaurant, a retail store, a home-based business, a franchise, or an Internet e-business. You can expect to work very long hours, maybe twelve-hour days, seven days a week in the first year. You will need some money to cover start-up costs. Initial planning is crucial to success.

"The first thing I would tell young people who want to start a business is to do their homework," declares Miller. "That means extensive market research so they know who and where their customers are, and a comprehensive business plan to make sure the business is viable."

Owning a small business can be a stressful occupation. Seeing the business succeed as a result of hard work is exciting and can be financially rewarding. Miller says, "I love running my store. I wouldn't want to do anything else."

Where's the Math?

Small business owners should have some computer skills. Software can do much of the bookkeeping and calculation, but the owner must be able to interpret and apply the financial data. Understanding the cash flow position is critical. Controlling costs and determining prices needs an understanding of percents.

MATHEMATICS TOOLKIT

Algebra Tools

Exponent Laws

Multiplication law: $a^m \times a^n = a^{m+n}$
Division law: $a^m \div a^n = a^{m-n}$
Power of a power law: $(a^m)^n = a^{mn}$

Financial Tools

Compound Interest

> Amount of an investment = Principal + Interest
>   or $A = P + I$
> A is the amount in dollars.
> P is the principal in dollars.
> I is the interest earned in dollars.

> Amount of an investment: $A = P(1 + i)^n$
> A is the amount in dollars.
> P is the principal in dollars.
> i is the interest rate per compounding period, expressed as a decimal.
> n is the number of compounding periods.

> Present value of an investment: $P = \dfrac{A}{(1 + i)^n}$
> $P, A, i,$ and n are defined as above.

> To calculate i or n, use the formula $A = P(1 + i)^n$, then a spreadsheet.

NS

1. Evaluate.

a) 2^3 b) 3^3 c) 4^3 d) 5^3 e) 10^3

f) 20^3 g) 30^3 h) 40^3 i) 50^3 j) 60^3

2. Evaluate.

a) 5^2 b) 2^5 c) 6^2 d) 4^2 e) 3^4

f) 10^2 g) 15^2 h) 12^2 i) 20^2 j) 25^2

3. Write as a single power.

a) $3^2 \times 3^5$ **b)** $3^5 \div 3^2$ **c)** $a^4 \times a^2$

d) $c^6 \div c$ **e)** $b^3 \times b^8$ **f)** $4^4 \div 4^4$

4. Write as a single power.

a) $\left(3^2\right)^4$ **b)** $\left(4^2\right)^5$ **c)** $\left(a^3\right)^3$ **d)** $\left(10^3\right)^6$

2.1   **5.** Each investment matures in 1 year. Calculate the interest.

a) $100 invested at 3%

b) $2500 invested at 7%

c) $2000 invested at 4.5%

d) $3000 invested at 5.5%

6. Each investment matures in 2 years. The interest is compounded annually. Calculate the interest at maturity.

a) $482 invested at 2%

b) $947 invested at 6%

c) $5000 invested at 7%

d) $10 000 invested at 8.5%

7. Calculate the interest earned on each investment. The interest compounds annually.

a) $3000 invested at 3.5% for 4 years

b) $10 000 invested at 4.7% for 3 years

c) $875 invested at $5\frac{1}{2}$% for 7 years

d) $540 invested at $4\frac{1}{4}$% for 6 years

2.2   **8.** Evaluate.

a) $700(1.045)^6$ **b)** $976(1 + 0.072)^8$ **c)** $1500(1 + 0.035)^3$

d) $525(1 + \frac{0.065}{2})^4$ **e)** $450(1.035)^{12}$ **f)** $2000(1 + \frac{0.0575}{12})^{72}$

9. Determine the amount of each investment. The compounding period is annual.

a) $800 at 6% for 5 years

b) $1420 at 4% for 9 years

c) $1000 at 7% for 7 years

d) $200 at 3% for 15 years

2.3   **10.** Determine the amount of each investment.

a) $840 at 6% compounded annually for 6 years

b) $2150 at 7% compounded semi-annually for 8 years

c) $150 at 4% compounded quarterly for 5 years

d) $275 at 6% compounded monthly for 8 years

e) $10 000 at 5.5% compounded quarterly for 5 years

f) $2200 at 3.25% compounded monthly for 12 years

g) $300 at 8.1% compounded daily for 4 years

11. Determine the amount of each investment.

  a) $1375 at $5\frac{1}{2}$% compounded annually for 9 years

  b) $150 at $7\frac{1}{2}$% compounded semi-annually for 6.5 years

  c) $85 at $4\frac{3}{4}$% compounded quarterly for 5.5 years

  d) $1250 at $6\frac{1}{4}$% compounded monthly for 9.5 years

  e) $30 000 at $3\frac{1}{8}$% compounded quarterly for 15.25 years

  f) $3300 at $6\frac{3}{8}$% compounded monthly for 8.5 years

  g) $600 at $4\frac{3}{4}$% compounded daily for 1000 days

12. Determine the interest earned on each investment.

  a) $200 at 4.5% compounded monthly for 6.5 years

  b) $875 at 5% compounded semi-annually for 8 years

  c) $550 at $4\frac{3}{4}$% compounded daily for 3 years

  d) $950 at 6.3% compounded quarterly for 8.5 years

  e) $1175 at 3.7% compounded monthly for 25 years

  f) $1500 at $5\frac{1}{2}$% compounded daily for 6 years

  g) $300 at 8% compounded semi-annually for 9.5 years

  h) $450 at 3.75% compounded monthly for 20 years

2.4 **13.** Solve for P.

  a) $200 = P(1.06)^7$ **b)** $4500 = P(1 + 0.0325)^5$ **c)** $368 = P(1 + \frac{0.0625}{2})^{20}$

14. Determine the present value of each amount.

  a) $900 in 5 years, at 4% compounded annually

  b) $1450 in 7 years, at 5.2% compounded semi-annually

  c) $600 in 8 years, at 4.5% compounded monthly

  d) $2385 in 3 years, at 3.75% compounded quarterly

  e) $299 in 4 years, at 8.75% compounded daily

  f) $75 in 1.5 years, at 10% compounded monthly

15. Determine the principal that must be invested now, to provide:

  a) $750 in 4 years when the rate is 8% compounded semi-annually

  b) $925 in 5.5 years when the rate is $6\frac{3}{4}$% compounded monthly

  c) $1690 in 7.25 years when the rate is $5\frac{1}{2}$% compounded quarterly

d) $2465 in 5 years when the rate is $3\frac{1}{4}$% compounded daily

e) $387 in 2.25 years when the rate is 4.6% compounded monthly

f) $10 800 in 25 years when the rate is 5.8% compounded semi-annually

2.5 **16.** Determine the value of i or n.

a) $2.6533 = (1 + i)^{20}$

b) $1.4233 = (1 + 0.04)^n$

c) $814.62 = 560(1 + i)^7$

d) $223.64 = 96(1 + 0.058)^n$

e) $124.12 = 75(1 + i)^8$

f) $1031.87 = 765(1 + 0.005)^n$

17. Draw a graph to compare the annual interest earned on an investment of $500 at 6% simple interest for 6 years to that of the same investment at 6% compound interest for 6 years.

18. How long will it take for $650 to grow to $870.38 at 4.5% compounded monthly?

19. Linda invested $1500 at 5.25% compounded semi-annually for 8 years. At the end of the fourth year, the interest rate was raised to 6%. How much interest did Linda earn on her investment?

20. Devin's savings account pays 6.5% compounded monthly. He has just finished a summer job and received a bonus of $500. He decides to spend some of the money and save the rest. Having studied compound interest, he sets a goal of $750 in 8 years. Approximately how much can Devin spend now?

21. At what rate compounded monthly will $300 grow to $519.32 in 10 years?

22. Which investment would you choose: $650 at 5% compounded annually for 7 years or $650 at 4.9% compounded monthly for 7 years? Explain.

23. The more often the interest on an investment is compounded the better the investment. Is this statement true? Explain.

24. How long will it take for money to double at 8% compounded semi-annually?

25. Sunil won $1 000 000 in a lottery. He invested it at 6.25% compounded daily. How much does the money earn in a 30-day month?

1. Simplify.

   a) $a^3 \times a^2$ b) $m^{10} \div m^4$ c) $\dfrac{c^6}{c^3}$ d) $(m^3)^4$

2. Solve for P.

   a) $827.50 = P(1.065)^8$ b) $1816.62 = P(1 + \frac{0.075}{12})^{60}$

3. Determine the amount of each investment.

   a) $1500 invested at 7% compounded annually for 10 years

   b) $875 invested at $8\frac{1}{2}$% compounded quarterly for 5 years

   c) $1525 invested at 9% compounded monthly for 7.5 years

4. **Knowledge/Understanding** Determine the interest earned on each investment.

   a) $500 invested at 8% compounded annually for 7 years

   b) $6000 invested at 6.7% compounded monthly for 6.5 years

5. Determine the present value of each amount.

   a) $1918.40 in 8 years at 6.5% compounded semi-annually

   b) $1627.75 in 10 years at 8.9% compounded quarterly

6. Determine the principal that must be invested now to provide:

   a) $973.91 in 5 years when the rate is 7% compounded monthly

   b) $1973.72 in 8 years when the rate is 8.5% compounded daily

7. Determine the value of each variable.

   a) $2.0699 = (1 + i)^{12}$ b) $2.577 = (1 + 0.054)^n$

8. How long will it take for money to double at 9% compounded annually?

9. **Communication** Suppose the interest rate is doubled. Does the interest double if the investment is earning compound interest? Write a short paragraph to support your answer.

10. **Application** Ellen invested $500 at 8% compounded monthly for 3 years. Due to changes in the financial market, the rate was increased to 10% at the end of the first year, then decreased to 9% at the end of the second year. Determine the amount of Ellen's investment at the end of the third year.

11. **Thinking/Inquiry/Problem Solving** Which is the better investment: 5% compounded monthly or 5.25% compounded annually? Explain your answer using examples.

Travelling Abroad

**Suggested Group
Size: 3**

Materials:

World atlas or
maps

Internet access

Travel guides

Background

Many people travel to other countries for
vacation. Assume you are planning a trip
abroad. You will work with foreign currency and
exchange rates. One major factor when you choose
where to go is the value of the currency in foreign
countries compared to Canadian currency. This is
called an *exchange rate.*

Consider these aspects of travelling abroad.

- Is Canadian money easily exchanged in a
  particular country? Should you exchange money
  in Canada before you begin your trip? How can
  you decide whether to exchange money for
  foreign currency in Canada or abroad?
- Are there better places to exchange your money
  than others? That is, do some places charge a
  greater fee to exchange money?
- Are credit cards and traveller's cheques widely
  accepted, or do you need cash?

Here are the exchange rates for different countries in
November of a particular year. The table shows the
cost in Canadian dollars to buy 1 unit of each
country's currency.

Czech Republic koruna (CSK)	0.04181
British pound (GBP)	2.4058
Norwegian kroner (NOK)	0.1858
Polish zloty (PLZ)	0.3402
Swiss franc (CHF)	0.9543
Euro (EUR)	1.5352
United States dollar (USD)	1.4646

Different rates apply to sell currency.

Curriculum Expectations

By the end of Explore, Research, Report, you will:

> Compare the value of the Canadian dollar with the value of foreign currencies over a period of time, and identify possible effects on purchasing and travel decisions.

> Compare alternatives by rating and ranking information and by applying mathematical calculations and analysis, as appropriate, using technology.

> Explain the process used in making a decision and justify the conclusions reached.

Suppose you buy 3000 Norwegian kroner (NOK).
To find the cost in Canadian dollars:

$1 \text{ NOK} = \$0.1858 \text{ CAD}$

So, $3000 \text{ NOK} = 3000 \times \$0.1858 \text{ CAD}$

$\qquad = \$557.40 \text{ CAD}$

3000 Norwegian kroner cost $557.40 CAD.

Suppose you are in Poland. You have $85.00 CAD. To find how many Polish zlotys you can buy, use proportional reasoning.
Let x represent the amount in Polish zlotys.

$$\frac{x}{1} = \frac{85.00}{0.3402}$$

$$x = \frac{85.00}{0.3402}$$

$$\doteq 249.85$$

Polish zlotys	Canadian dollars
x	85.00
1	0.3402

$85 CAD is worth approximately 249.85 PLZ.

Explore

1. Here are some hotel rates. Copy the table. Use the November exchange rates on page 103. Calculate the cost of each room in Canadian dollars. The first 3 columns have been completed. Complete the 4th column for all cities except Prague. (You will complete the 5th and 6th columns later.)

Location	Hotel	Price per night	Price in Canadian dollars ($)	Price for 3 nights ($ CAD) (Nov)	Price for 3 nights ($ CAD) (May)
London, England	Bryanston Court	110 GBP			
Oslo, Norway	Europa	680 NOK			
Paris, France	Radisson	850 EUR			
Warsaw, Poland	Polonia	120 PLZ			
Prague, Czech Republic					
Zurich, Switzerland	Carlton	250 CHF			
		Total cost			

2. Here are the rates for 3 hotels in Prague, Czech Republic.

Hotel	Price per night	Price in Canadian dollars ($)
Qent	1000 CSK	
Jalta Praha	171 USD	
Obora	55 EUR	

Convert each rate to Canadian dollars. Which is the cheapest hotel? Write this information in the row for Prague in the table in exercise 1.

3. Refer to the table in exercise 1. Calculate the cost for 3 nights in each hotel in November, in Canadian dollars. Then calculate the total spent in Canadian dollars. Complete the 5th column.

Exchange rates change every day. Here are the rates for November and for the following May.

	November exchange rate	May exchange rate
Czech Republic koruna (CSK)	0.04181	0.03650
British pound (GBP)	2.4058	2.3057
Norwegian kroner (NOK)	0.1858	0.1642
Polish zloty (PLZ)	0.3402	0.3303
Swiss franc (CHF)	0.9543	0.8603
Euro (EUR)	1.5352	1.3319
United States dollar (USD)	1.4646	1.4961

4. a) Refer to the table in exercise 1. Use the May exchange rates. Calculate the cost for 3 nights in each hotel in May, in Canadian dollars. Complete the 6th column.

   b) Explain how the May rates might affect your plans made in November.

5. Suppose you visit the cities in the tables below, in order. When you leave a country, you convert your money to the currency of the next country you visit. Copy and complete the table. Convert each amount to Canadian dollars. Then convert the Canadian dollars to the currency of the next country on the list. At the end, convert the Swiss francs to Canadian dollars.

	Money left over to convert	Convert to Canadian dollars	Convert to:
London, England	25 GBP		NOK
Oslo, Norway	550 NOK		EUR
Paris, France	42 EUR		PLZ
Warsaw, Poland	100 PLZ		CSK
Prague, Czech Republic	1200 CSK		CHF
Zurich, Switzerland	20 CHF		CAD

Travelling Abroad

6. There are different exchange rates for buying and selling currency. Here are the rates in Canadian dollars in November.

	Buy	Sell
Czech Republic koruna (CSK)	0.04181	0.03814
British pound (GBP)	2.4058	2.3482
Norwegian kroner (NOK)	0.1858	0.1716
Polish zloty (PLZ)	0.3402	0.3183
Swiss franc (CHF)	0.9543	0.9252
Euro (EUR)	1.5352	1.4256
United States dollar (USD)	1.4646	1.4137

a) Why do you think the buy and sell rates are different?

b) What effects do the buy and sell rates have when you exchange more money than you will spend?

Research

To use the Internet, you can start your search from our web site: www.pearsoned.ca/onmath11

7. Work with a group to plan a trip to at least 4 different countries. Here are some ideas.

South America	The Orient	Mediterranean	Down Under
Chile	China	Egypt	Fiji
Brazil	Korea	Israel	Tahiti
Guyana	Japan	Greece	Indonesia
Columbia	Hong Kong	Italy	Australia
Venezuela	Philippines	Turkey	New Zealand

8. From the Internet or another source, obtain a price for a hotel in each city you will visit. Copy and complete the first 3 columns of this table.

Location	Hotel	Price per night	Price in Canadian dollars 6 months ago	Price in Canadian dollars today

9. Compare the value of the Canadian dollar with the value of the currency for each country you chose for the past 6 months. Use an Internet site that provides exchange rates for different dates. Ask your teacher for the web address.

a) Copy and complete this table.

Country and Currency				
Exchange rate:				
6 months ago				
5 months ago				
4 months ago				
3 months ago				
2 months ago				
1 month ago				
Currently				

b) Graph *Exchange rate* against *Time* for each country.

c) Examine the table and graphs. Describe any trends or patterns.

d) Refer to the table in exercise 8. Complete the 4th and 5th columns for each of your chosen countries and hotels.

e) Assume you will be leaving on your trip in two months. Use the answer to part c to predict the exchange rate for each country at that time.

f) Use the answer to part e. Plan your itinerary. How long will you stay in each country? Are there any countries you will not visit because of their exchange rates? You may want to delete some countries and add different countries.

g) When you have determined your itinerary, copy and complete this table for hotel costs.

Location	Hotel	Price per night	Price in Canadian dollars (current rates)	Number of nights	Total price for entire stay
		Total cost			

Travelling Abroad

Your completed project should include:
- your answers to exercises 1 to 9
- a brief outline of the trip planned
- a report from each group member that details her or his responsibilities, as outlined below

Recommendations should be supported by calculations or information.

Here are the details of each person's responsibilities:

The Itinerary Planner

Your task is to determine the best order in which to visit the countries.

Determine the best route to take, to reduce both travel time and costs. You will fly from your Canadian city to the first destination. You may travel by bus or train thereafter. Research costs. Will it be cheaper to buy a return ticket to and from one city, or to fly directly home from your last location?

Sketch a map of the countries you will be visiting, and draw the route you will take. Provide an estimated transportation cost. Explain the methods of travel you recommend, and why.

The Lodgings and Meals Planner

Your task is to determine the best priced lodging available in each city, and make recommendations about meals.

Research typical prices for meals in the cities you plan to visit. Use travel guides, magazines, or the Internet. Perhaps investigate youth hostels.

Decide how many restaurant meals per day the group should have. Prepare a budget for daily meals: will the group eat in restaurants, cook their own meals, or eat snacks? Allow for some variety and at least one special meal. Explain how the exchange rates may have affected your decisions.

The Budget Planner

Your task is to determine the total budget for the trip.

Examine the cost of both lodgings and food for each country, obtained from another group member. Assume your trip will be 21 days, including 2 days to travel from and to Canada. Make recommendations for the number of days to stay in each country. Estimate the amount of money required for food and lodgings for each country. Prepare a report, outlining the total budget for these items. Your report should include the estimated costs in both the country's currency as well as the Canadian equivalent. Finally, your task is to estimate the cost of the entire trip per student, including transportation.

Career Profile

Hotel Manager

In 1999, Canada's tourism industry employed over half a million people. As tourism continues to grow in importance, the hotel industry has to keep pace and provide the highest quality accommodation and service. For vacationing families and business travellers alike, hotels provide a "home away from home." It is the hotel manager's job to ensure that the guests are happy and satisfied during their stay.

A hotel manager runs the hotel on a day-to-day basis, ensuring its overall profitability. The manager of a large hotel oversees the staff of various departments (housekeeping, food and beverage, front office, convention services), draws up budgets, and creates and enforces policies. To generate revenue from special events, such as weddings, the hotel manager may promote the hotel locally. To be successful, a hotel manager must have excellent communication skills and always be polite, courteous, and sensitive to diverse cultures and traditions. Computers are used for billing, reservations, room assignments, ordering food and supplies, and in the preparation of reports, so the manager must be computer literate.

Hotel managers work long and varied hours, sometimes in stressful situations. A successful manager is one who can coordinate a broad array of functions, and deal with crisis situations (for example, irate guests), and computer failures. Graduates of a hotel or restaurant management course have excellent job opportunities.

Where's the Math?

Hotel managers must have excellent math skills to ensure the profitability of the operation. Mental math and skill in computation help when working with accounts. Basic knowledge of business math is an essential skill.

3 Exponential Growth

Chapter Project

Canada's National Debt

Our national debt has been growing since 1970.
By completing the project in Section 3.7, you can develop
a sense of the rate at which the national debt has
been increasing.

Curriculum Expectations

By the end of this chapter, you will:

> Describe the significance of exponential
growth or decay within the context of
applications represented by various
mathematical models.

> Compare the effects of exponential
growth within a context with the effects
of linear or quadratic growth within the
same context.

> Pose and solve problems related to models
of exponential functions drawn from a
variety of applications, and communicate
the solutions with clarity and justification.

> Sketch the graphs of simple exponential
functions, given their equations, without
using technology.

> Compare the rates of change of different
types of functions.

> Identify, through investigations, using
graphing calculators or graphing software,
the key properties of exponential
functions with equations of the form
$y = a^x$ $(a > 0, \ a \neq 1)$ and their graphs.

> Evaluate simple numerical expressions
involving rational exponents, without
using technology.

> Evaluate numerical expressions involving
negative and decimal exponents, using
scientific calculators.

> Simplify algebraic expressions involving
integral exponents, using the laws of
exponents.

> Demonstrate an understanding of the
relationship between compound interest,
… and exponential growth.

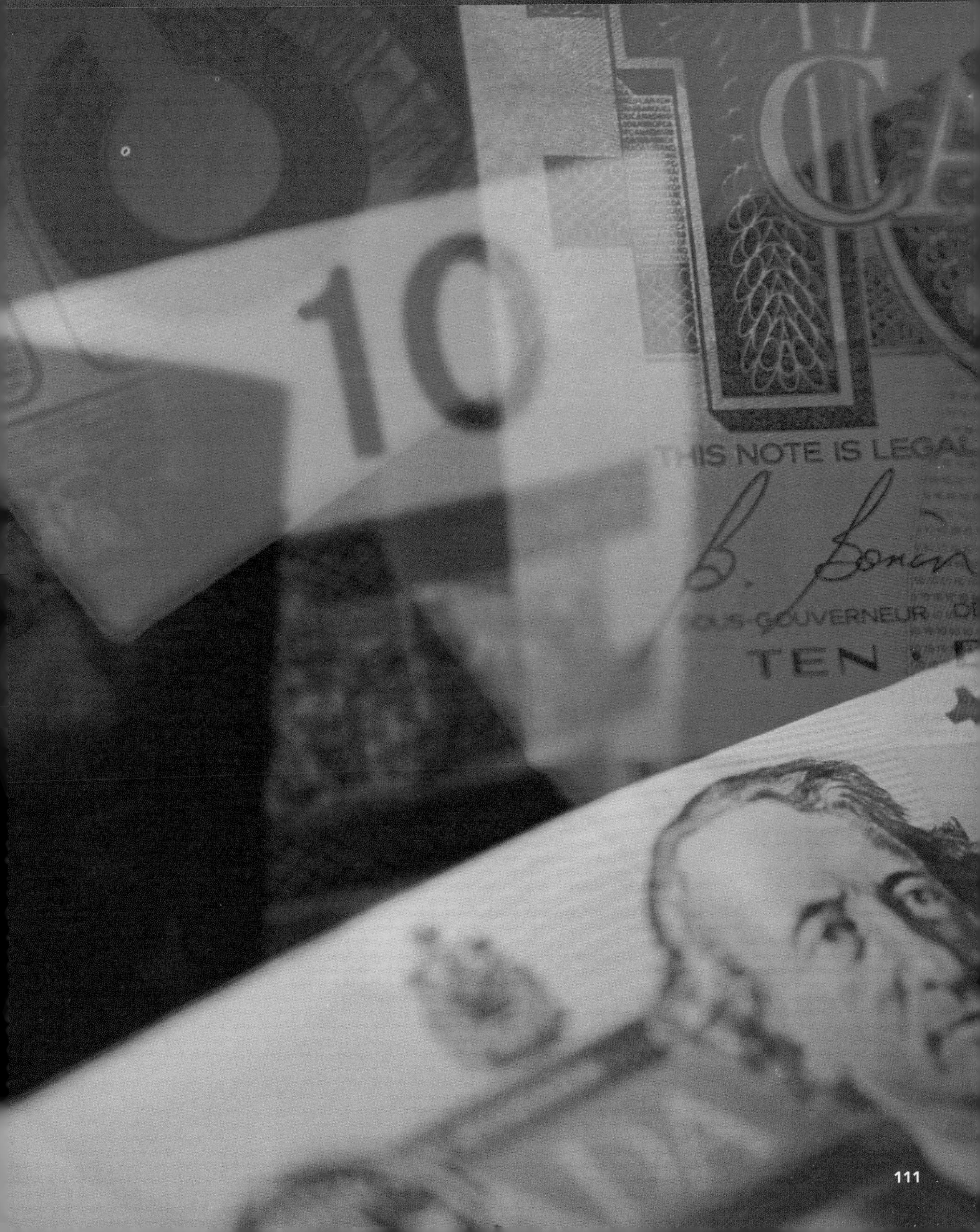
10
THIS NOTE IS LEGAL
TEN

Necessary Skills

1 Review: Number Systems

In grade 9, you learned about sets of numbers.

The Natural Numbers

These are the counting numbers: 1, 2, 3, …

The Whole Numbers

These are the natural numbers combined with zero: 0, 1, 2, 3, …

The Integers

Introduce negative numbers into the whole numbers: …, −2, −1, 0, 1, 2, …

The Rational Numbers

A rational number is a number that can be written as a fraction, where the numerator and denominator are integers, and the denominator is not 0. The set of rational numbers is denoted by Q.

Some examples are $\frac{3}{4}$, $-\frac{9}{4}$, 1, 0, −2, 1.56.

Any integer is also rational because it can be written with a denominator of 1; for example, $-2 = \frac{-2}{1}$.

The Irrational Numbers

An irrational number is a number that cannot be written as a fraction. In decimal form, an irrational number neither terminates, nor repeats. The set of irrational numbers is denoted by $\overline{Q}$.

Some examples are π, $\sqrt{2}$, 2.718 281 ….

The Real Numbers

The real numbers are the rational and irrational numbers; that is, all the numbers that can be expressed in decimal form. The set of real numbers is denoted by R.

This diagram illustrates how the sets of numbers are related.

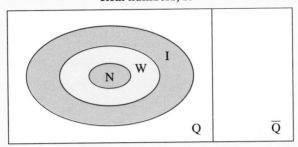

Real numbers, R

1. List three examples for each type of number.

a) Whole number   **b)** Rational number   **c)** Integer

d) Natural number   **e)** Irrational number   **f)** Real number

2. Classify each number as natural, integer, rational or irrational. (Some numbers may belong to more than one set.)

a) 54   **b)** -9 **c)** $-2\frac{2}{3}$ **d)** $\sqrt{3}$

e) 0   **f)** 4.99   **g)** $\sqrt{25}$ **h)** 1.111 111 …

3. Draw a diagram similar to that above. Insert these numbers correctly in the diagram:

8, -2.89, $\frac{3}{4}$, $\sqrt{5}$, 2π, -1, 0, $2.\overline{3}$

2 Review: Zero and Negative Exponents

Complete this section without a calculator.

Recall that any non-zero number raised to the exponent 0 equals 1.
For example, $2^0 = (-3)^0 = 10^0 = 1$

Recall that a non-zero number raised to a negative exponent equals the reciprocal of that number raised to the positive exponent.

For example, $2^{-3} = \frac{1}{2^3}$

Similarly, $\frac{1}{2^{-3}} = 2^3$

When the non-zero number is a fraction, such as $\left(\frac{3}{5}\right)^{-4}$,
then $\left(\frac{3}{5}\right)^{-4} = \dfrac{1}{\left(\frac{3}{5}\right)^4}$

$$= 1 \times \left(\frac{5}{3}\right)^4$$

$$= \left(\frac{5}{3}\right)^4$$

That is, $\left(\frac{3}{5}\right)^{-4} = \left(\frac{5}{3}\right)^4$

TAKE NOTE

Zero and Negative Exponents

$a^0 = 1, \ a \neq 0$

$a^{-m} = \frac{1}{a^m}; \ \frac{1}{a^{-m}} = a^m, \ a \neq 0$

Example 1

Evaluate.

a) 15^0 **b)** 5^{-1} **c)** $\frac{1}{4^{-2}}$ **d)** $\left(\frac{2}{3}\right)^{-2}$

Solution

a) $15^0 = 1$

b) $5^{-1} = \frac{1}{5^1}$

$\qquad\quad = \frac{1}{5}$

c) $\frac{1}{4^{-2}} = 4^2$

$\qquad\quad = 16$

d) $\left(\frac{2}{3}\right)^{-2} = \left(\frac{3}{2}\right)^2$ The reciprocal of $\frac{2}{3}$ is $\frac{3}{2}$. Raise $\frac{3}{2}$ to the power 2.

$\qquad\qquad = \frac{3}{2} \times \frac{3}{2}$

$\qquad\qquad = \frac{9}{4}$

1. Evaluate.

a) 3^{-1} b) 10^0 c) $\left(\frac{1}{2}\right)^0$

d) 8^{-2} e) 9^{-1} f) 1^0

g) 6^{-1} h) 5^{-2} i) 10^{-1}

j) 7^{-2} k) 4^{-1} l) 2^{-2}

2. Evaluate.

a) 10^{-2} b) 4^{-2} c) 2^{-3}

d) $\frac{1}{10^{-2}}$ e) $\frac{1}{4^{-2}}$ f) $\frac{1}{2^{-3}}$

g) 6^{-2} h) 2^{-5} i) 3^{-4}

j) $\frac{1}{8^{-2}}$ k) $\frac{1}{4^{-3}}$ l) $\frac{1}{10^{-1}}$

3. Evaluate.

a) $\left(\frac{1}{2}\right)^{-1}$ b) $\left(\frac{1}{3}\right)^{-1}$ c) $\left(\frac{2}{3}\right)^{-1}$

d) $\left(\frac{3}{4}\right)^{-3}$ e) $\left(\frac{5}{9}\right)^{-2}$ f) $\left(\frac{3}{2}\right)^{-3}$

g) $\left(\frac{1}{2}\right)^{-5}$ h) $\left(\frac{2}{3}\right)^{-4}$ i) $\left(\frac{7}{8}\right)^{-2}$

4. Evaluate. Remember the order of operations. Evaluate exponents before adding or subtracting.

a) $3^0 + 2^0$ b) $3^{-1} + 2^{-1}$ c) $10^2 - 9^0$

d) $3^0 + 4^{-1}$ e) $3^{-1} + 4^0$ f) $7^0 - 5^0$

g) $5^{-1} + 4^2$ h) $2^{-1} + 3^{-1}$ i) $2^{-2} + 3^{-2}$

5. Evaluate.

a) $2^0 \times 3^{-1}$ b) $2^0 \times 3$ c) $2^{-1} \times 3^0$

d) $2^{-1} \times 3$ e) $3^{-1} \times 2^2$ f) $3^{-2} \times 2^{-1}$

g) $\frac{2^0}{3^{-1}}$ h) $\frac{2^0}{3}$ i) $\frac{3^0}{2^{-1}}$

3 New: Evaluating Expressions with Negative Exponents

Use a scientific calculator to complete this section.

Example 1

Evaluate. Round to 2 decimal places where necessary.

a) 4^{-2} b) 3^{-2} c) 15^{-1}

Solution

a) $4^{-2} = 0.0625$ Key in: 4 $\boxed{\wedge}$ $\boxed{(-)}$ 2 $\boxed{\text{ENTER} =}$

b) $3^{-2} = 0.11111\ldots$
$\quad \doteq 0.11$

c) $15^{-1} = 0.06666\ldots$
$\quad \doteq 0.07$

Discuss

In part a, why did we not round 0.0625 to 2 decimal places?

Example 2

Evaluate. Round to 3 decimal places where necessary.

a) $4.6(5)^{-2}$ b) $2.4^{-3} \times 3.2^{-2}$ c) $2.5^{-2} + 6.4^{-3}$

Solution

a) $4.6(5)^{-2} = 0.184$ Key in: 4.6 $\boxed{\times}$ 5 $\boxed{\wedge}$ $\boxed{(-)}$ 2 $\boxed{\text{ENTER} =}$

b) $2.4^{-3} \times 3.2^{-2} \doteq 0.007\ 064\ 254$ Key in: 2.4 $\boxed{\wedge}$ $\boxed{(-)}$ 3 $\boxed{\times}$ 3.2 $\boxed{\wedge}$
$\quad \doteq 0.007$ $\boxed{(-)}$ 2 $\boxed{\text{ENTER} =}$

c) $2.5^{-2} + 6.4^{-3} \doteq 0.163\ 814\ 697$ Key in: 2.5 $\boxed{\wedge}$ $\boxed{(-)}$ 2 $\boxed{+}$ 6.4 $\boxed{\wedge}$
$\quad \doteq 0.164$ $\boxed{(-)}$ 3 $\boxed{\text{ENTER} =}$

1. Evaluate. Round to 3 decimal places where necessary.
   a) 7^{-1}
   b) 9^{-3}
   c) 12^{-2}
   d) 3^{-4}
   e) 8^{-2}
   f) 5^{-3}
   g) 27^{-1}
   h) 19^{-2}
   i) 6^{-3}

2. Evaluate. Round to 3 decimal places where necessary.
   a) $2(3)^2$
   b) $2.1(3.2)^{-2}$
   c) $4.7(3.21)^{-3}$
   d) $10.2(1.05)^2$
   e) $10.2(1.05)^{-2}$
   f) $1000(1.005)^{-3}$

3. Evaluate. Round to 3 decimal places.
   a) $3.2^{-1} \times 2.4^{-2}$
   b) $7.8^2 \times 2.9^{-3}$
   c) $0.2^{-2} \times 1.3^3$
   d) $3.2^{-1} \div 2.4^{-2}$
   e) $7.8^2 \div 2.9^{-3}$
   f) $0.2^{-2} \div 1.3^3$

4. Evaluate. Round to 3 decimal places where necessary.
   a) $3^{-2} + 2^3$
   b) $4.7^{-2} + 2.8^{-3}$
   c) $0.9^2 + 10.2^{-1}$
   d) $3^2 - 2^{-3}$
   e) $4.7^{-2} - 2.8^3$
   f) $0.9^2 - 10.2^{-1}$

5. Evaluate. Round to 3 decimal places where necessary.
   a) $2^5 \times 3^{-3}$
   b) $5^{-2} + 4^2$
   c) $7^{-2} - 2^{-3}$
   d) $3^{-4} \div 8^{-3}$
   e) $8^{-2} + 2^{-3}$
   f) $5^{-3} \times 8.79$
   g) $35^{-2} \div 16^{-5}$
   h) $27^{-2} - \left(\frac{1}{2}\right)^{-5}$
   i) $\left(\frac{2}{5}\right)^{-3} - \left(\frac{3}{4}\right)^{-2}$

4 New: Exponent Laws for Integer Exponents

In grade 9, you developed laws for some operations on exponents. Here are two more Exponent Laws you can use to simplify expressions.

Power of a Product Law

Since $(ab)^4$ means $(ab) \times (ab) \times (ab) \times (ab)$,
then $(ab)^4 = (ab) \times (ab) \times (ab) \times (ab)$
$$= a \times b \times a \times b \times a \times b \times a \times b$$
$$= a \times a \times a \times a \times b \times b \times b \times b$$
$$= a^4 b^4$$
Each factor is raised to the power 4: $(ab)^4 = a^4 b^4$

Example 1 Write as a product.

a) $(3z)^2$

b) $(2rs^2)^5$

Solution

a) $(3z)^2 = 3^2z^2$ Raise each factor to the power 2.

      $= 9z^2$

b) $(2rs^2)^5 = 2^5r^5(s^2)^5$ Raise each factor to the power 5.

       $= 32r^5s^{10}$ Use the power of a power law to simplify $(s^2)^5$.

Power of a Quotient Law

Since $\left(\frac{a}{b}\right)^4$ means $\left(\frac{a}{b}\right) \times \left(\frac{a}{b}\right) \times \left(\frac{a}{b}\right) \times \left(\frac{a}{b}\right)$,

then $\left(\frac{a}{b}\right)^4 = \left(\frac{a}{b}\right) \times \left(\frac{a}{b}\right) \times \left(\frac{a}{b}\right) \times \left(\frac{a}{b}\right)$

           $= \frac{a \times a \times a \times a}{b \times b \times b \times b}$

           $= \frac{a^4}{b^4}$

Both the numerator and denominator are raised to the power 4: $\left(\frac{a}{b}\right)^4 = \frac{a^4}{b^4}$

Example 2 Write as a quotient.

a) $\left(\frac{2}{3}\right)^3$

b) $\left(\frac{-2}{b^4}\right)^5$

Solution

a) $\left(\frac{2}{3}\right)^3 = \frac{2^3}{3^3}$ Raise the numerator and denominator to the power 3.

      $= \frac{8}{27}$

b) $\left(\frac{-2}{b^4}\right)^5 = \frac{(-2)^5}{(b^4)^5}$ Raise the numerator and denominator to the power 5.

       $= \frac{-32}{b^{20}}$ Use the power of a power law to simplify $(b^4)^5$.

Power of a Product Law	Power of a Quotient Law
$(ab)^m = a^m b^m$	$\left(\dfrac{a}{b}\right)^m = \dfrac{a^m}{b^m},\ b \neq 0$
To raise a product to the power m, raise each factor to the power m.	To raise a quotient to the power m, raise the numerator and denominator to the power m.

Here is a summary of the exponent laws.

Exponent Laws	
Multiplication Law	$a^m \times a^n = a^{m+n}$
Division Law	$a^m \div a^n = a^{m-n},\ a \neq 0$
Power of a Power Law	$(a^m)^n = a^{mn}$
Power of a Product Law	$(ab)^m = a^m b^m$
Power of a Quotient Law	$\left(\dfrac{a}{b}\right)^m = \dfrac{a^m}{b^m},\ b \neq 0$
Zero Exponent	$a^0 = 1,\ a \neq 0$
Negative Exponent	$a^{-m} = \dfrac{1}{a^m};\ \dfrac{1}{a^{-m}} = a^m;$ $\left(\dfrac{a}{b}\right)^{-m} = \left(\dfrac{b}{a}\right)^m;\ a \neq 0, b \neq 0$

Example 3

Evaluate.

a) $2^{-3} \times 2^4 \times 2^{-1}$ 　　　　 **b)** $4^3 \div 4^5$ 　　　　 **c)** $\left(\dfrac{4}{5}\right)^{-2}$

Solution

a) $2^{-3} \times 2^4 \times 2^{-1} = 2^{-3+4-1}$ 　　Use the multiplication law. Add the
$\qquad\qquad\qquad\qquad\quad = 2^0$ 　　　exponents. Then use the zero exponent rule.
$\qquad\qquad\qquad\qquad\quad = 1$

b) $4^3 \div 4^5 = 4^{3-5}$ 　　　Use the division law. Subtract the exponents.
$\qquad\qquad\quad = 4^{-2}$ 　　　Then use the negative exponent rule.
$\qquad\qquad\quad = \dfrac{1}{4^2}$
$\qquad\qquad\quad = \dfrac{1}{16}$

c) $\left(\frac{4}{5}\right)^{-2} = \left(\frac{5}{4}\right)^2$ Use the negative exponent rule.

$\qquad = \frac{5^2}{4^2}$ Then use the power of a quotient law.

$\qquad = \frac{25}{16}$

Example 4

Simplify.

a) $a^{-4} \times a^4$ **b)** $a^3 \div a^4$ **c)** $(a^{-3})^4$ **d)** $(a^{-1}b)^2$ **e)** $\left(\frac{a^{-2}}{b}\right)^{-5}$

Solution

a) $a^{-4} \times a^4 = a^{-4+4}$ Use the multiplication law. Add the

$\qquad = a^0$ exponents. Then use the zero exponent rule.

$\qquad = 1$

b) $a^3 \div a^4 = a^{3-4}$ Use the division law. Subtract the exponents.

$\qquad = a^{-1}$

c) $(a^{-3})^4 = a^{(-3)(4)}$ Use the power of a power law. Multiply the

$\qquad = a^{-12}$ exponents.

d) $(a^{-1}b)^2 = (a^{-1})^2 b^2$ Use the power of a product law.

$\qquad = a^{-2}b^2$

e) $\left(\frac{a^{-2}}{b}\right)^{-5} = \frac{(a^{-2})^{-5}}{b^{-5}}$ Use the power of a quotient law.

$\qquad = \frac{a^{10}}{b^{-5}}$

Discuss

We could have written the above answers with positive exponents.
For example, in the solution of part b, we could have written $a^{-1} = \frac{1}{a}$.
How can the expressions in the solutions of parts c, d, and e be written with
positive exponents?

Exercises

1. Write as a single power.

a) $2^{-2} \times 2^3$ **b)** $3^{-1} \times 3^4$ **c)** $10^{-2} \times 10^{-5}$

d) $\left(\frac{1}{2}\right)^3 \times \left(\frac{1}{2}\right)^{-5}$ **e)** $(-2)^{-2} \times (-2)^{-4}$ **f)** $\left(\frac{2}{5}\right)^{-6} \times \left(\frac{2}{5}\right)^{-2}$

2. Write as a single power.

a) $\dfrac{2^{-5}}{2^2}$ **b)** $\dfrac{2^{-5}}{2^{-2}}$ **c)** $\dfrac{2^{-2}}{2^5}$

d) $\dfrac{2^{-2}}{2^{-5}}$ **e)** $3^6 \div 3^{-3}$ **f)** $3^{-6} \div 3^{-3}$

3. Write as a single power.

a) $c^5 \times c^{-3}$ **b)** $a^2 \times a^{-3}$ **c)** $m^3 \times m^{-6}$

d) $c^{-5} \div c^3$ **e)** $a^{-2} \div a^{-2}$ **f)** $m^{-3} \div m^{-6}$

4. Simplify.

a) $\dfrac{x^3}{x^4}$ **b)** $\dfrac{m^{-3}}{m^{-3}}$ **c)** $\dfrac{n^{-10}}{n^{-5}}$

d) $m^{-3} \times m^{-2}$ **e)** $x^4 \times x^{-2}$ **f)** $b^3 \times b^4$

5. Write as a single power.

a) $(m^4)^{-2}$ **b)** $(m^{-4})^2$ **c)** $(m^{-4})^{-2}$

d) $(x^2)^{-3}$ **e)** $(x^{-2})^{-3}$ **f)** $(a^{-3})^{-5}$

6. Write as a product of powers.

a) $(xy)^3$ **b)** $(a^2b)^2$ **c)** $(5b^2)^2$

d) $(ab)^{-2}$ **e)** $(3b)^{-2}$ **f)** $(4x^{-1})^{-1}$

7. Write as a quotient.

a) $\left(\dfrac{2}{3}\right)^2$ **b)** $\left(\dfrac{a}{8}\right)^2$ **c)** $\left(\dfrac{1}{2}\right)^6$

d) $\left(\dfrac{3}{b^2}\right)^3$ **e)** $\left(\dfrac{3}{10}\right)^2$ **f)** $\left(\dfrac{a^5}{5}\right)^3$

8. Evaluate.

a) $2^{-2} \times 2^3 \times 2$ **b)** $6^4 \times 6^{-3}$ **c)** $6^4 \div 6^3$

d) $\left(\dfrac{2}{3}\right)^3$ **e)** $3^3 \times 3^{-4} \times 3^5$ **f)** $\left(\dfrac{2}{3}\right)^{-3}$

g) $5^{-2} \div 5^{-4}$ **h)** $\left(\dfrac{4}{3}\right)^2$ **i)** $\left(\dfrac{4}{3}\right)^{-2}$

9. Write as a quotient of powers.

a) $\left(\dfrac{a^3}{b^{-1}}\right)^2$ **b)** $\left(\dfrac{x^2}{y^2}\right)^2$ **c)** $\left(\dfrac{m^3}{n^{-2}}\right)^{-1}$

d) $\left(\dfrac{b^{-2}}{a^3}\right)^{-2}$ **e)** $\left(\dfrac{a^3}{b^2}\right)^{-1}$ **f)** $\left(\dfrac{m^{-1}}{n^{-2}}\right)^{-3}$

10. Write as powers with positive exponents.

a) $a^2 \times a^{-4}$ **b)** $a^3 \div a^5$ **c)** $(x^{-2})^3$

d) $a^{-5} \times a^{-2}$ **e)** $x^{-3} \div x^{-4}$ **f)** $(m^3)^{-4}$

g) $\dfrac{x^2}{x^{-4}}$ **h)** $a^{-5} \times a^3$ **i)** $(b^2)^{-5}$

j) $(a^3b^{-2})^3$ **k)** $\left(\dfrac{a^3}{b^{-2}}\right)^3$ **l)** $(x^{-1}y^{-2})^2$

m) $\left(\dfrac{a^{-2}}{b^{-2}}\right)^{-1}$ **n)** $\left(\dfrac{x^2}{y^2}\right)^{-3}$ **o)** $(f^2g^{-3})^{-2}$

Introduction to Exponential Functions

You first learned about exponents as a shortcut for repeated multiplication. Repeated multiplication occurs frequently in many real situations involving growth and decay, as shown by the following examples.

Compound Interest

In Chapter 2, you learned about compound interest, where an investment grows in value.

Suppose a $50 investment earns 8% interest compounded annually. The amount, A, of the investment at the end of each year is calculated using the formula $A = P(1 + i)^n$.

Year	Calculation ($)	Amount in exponential form ($)
1	$50(1 + 0.08)^1$	$50(1.08)^1$
2	$50(1 + 0.08)^2$	$50(1.08)^2$
3	$50(1 + 0.08)^3$	$50(1.08)^3$
4	$50(1 + 0.08)^4$	$50(1.08)^4$
$\vdots$	$\vdots$	$\vdots$
n	$50(1 + 0.08)^n$	$50(1.08)^n$

Each year, the amount is 1.08 times the amount from the previous year. The amount can be written as the product of the principal and a power of 1.08.

The amount, A dollars, at the end of n years is given by the equation $A = 50(1.08)^n$.

The graph on the next page shows the equation $A = 50(1.08)^n$ plotted for values of n from 0 to 20. Since a fractional number of years is not meaningful in this situation, the points on the graph are not joined with a solid curve. A broken curve shows the trend.

Year	Amount ($)
0	$50(1.08)^0 = 50$
4	$50(1.08)^4 \doteq 68.02$
8	$50(1.08)^8 \doteq 92.55$
12	$50(1.08)^{12} \doteq 125.91$
16	$50(1.08)^{16} \doteq 171.30$
20	$50(1.08)^{20} \doteq 233.05$

Amount of $50 Investment that Earns 8% Interest Compounded Annually

Number of Ancestors

Every person has 2 parents, 4 grandparents, 8 great-grandparents, and so on.

The number of ancestors doubles each generation back, and can be written as a power of 2.

Generations back	Number of ancestors	Number of ancestors in exponential form
1	2	2^1
2	4	2^2
3	8	2^3
4	16	2^4
5	32	2^5
$\vdots$	$\vdots$	$\vdots$
n		2^n

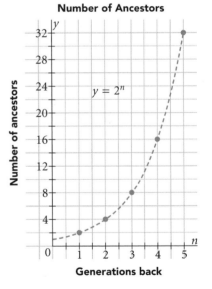

Number of Ancestors

The number of ancestors, y, at the end of n generations is given by the equation $y = 2^n$.

The graph shows the equation $y = 2^n$ plotted for values of n from 1 to 5. Since a fractional number of generations is not meaningful, the points on the graph are not joined. A broken curve shows the trend.

Depreciation

A computer sells for $2000.

Its value decreases, or depreciates, by 20% each year.

Therefore, at the end of each year, the computer is worth $100\% - 20\% = 80\%$, or 0.8 times its value the preceding year. This value can be written as the product of the initial value and a power of 0.8.

Year	Value of computer ($)	Value of computer in exponential form ($)
0	2000	$2000(0.8)^0$
1	$2000(0.8)$	$2000(0.8)^1$
2	$2000(0.8)(0.8)$	$2000(0.8)^2$
3	$2000(0.8)^2(0.8)$	$2000(0.8)^3$
4	$2000(0.8)^3(0.8)$	$2000(0.8)^4$
$\vdots$	$\vdots$	$\vdots$
t	$2000(0.8)^{t-1}(0.8)$	$2000(0.8)^t$

The value of the computer, V dollars, at the end of t years is given by the equation $V = 2000(0.8)^t$.

The graph shows the equation $V = 2000(0.8)^t$ plotted for values of t from 0 to 10. Since a fractional number of years is not meaningful in this situation, the points on the graph are not joined with a solid curve. A broken curve shows the trend.

Year	Value ($)
0	$2000(0.8)^0 = 2000$
2	$2000(0.8)^2 = 1280$
4	$2000(0.8)^4 = 819.20$
6	$2000(0.8)^6 \doteq 524.29$
8	$2000(0.8)^8 \doteq 335.54$
10	$2000(0.8)^{10} \doteq 214.75$

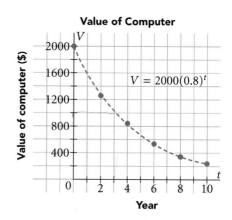

Bouncing Ball

A ball drops from a height of 5 m. On each bounce, the ball rises to 60% of the height from which it fell. That is, the ball's height is 0.6 times its height on the previous bounce. The height can be written as the product of the initial height and a power of 0.6.

Bounce number	Height of ball (m)	Height of ball in exponential form (m)
1	$5(0.6)$	$5(0.6)^1$
2	$5(0.6)(0.6)$	$5(0.6)^2$
3	$5(0.6)^2(0.6)$	$5(0.6)^3$
4	$5(0.6)^3(0.6)$	$5(0.6)^4$
$\vdots$	$\vdots$	$\vdots$
n	$5(0.6)^{n-1}(0.6)$	$5(0.6)^n$

The height of the ball, h metres, after n bounces is given by the equation $h = 5(0.6)^n$.

The graph shows the equation $h = 5(0.6)^n$ plotted for values of n from 0 to 5. Since it is not meaningful to have a fractional number of bounces, the points are not joined with a solid curve. A broken curve shows the trend.

Bounce number	Height (m)
0	$5(0.6)^0 = 5$
1	$5(0.6)^1 = 3$
2	$5(0.6)^2 = 1.8$
3	$5(0.6)^3 = 1.08$
4	$5(0.6)^4 \doteq 0.65$
5	$5(0.6)^5 \doteq 0.39$

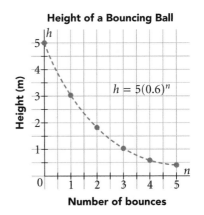

Height of a Bouncing Ball

Height (m) vs Number of bounces. $h = 5(0.6)^n$

Consider the equations from the above situations:

Compound interest $\qquad A = 50(1.08)^n$
Number of ancestors $\qquad y = 2^n$ or $y = 1(2)^n$
Depreciation $\qquad V = 2000(0.8)^t$
Bouncing ball $\qquad h = 5(0.6)^n$

Each equation is the product of a number and a power. In the power, the base is a number and the exponent is a variable. Equations of this type represent *exponential functions*.

Exponential Function

An exponential function has an equation of the form $y = Ab^x$.

  A is any non zero number.
  b is any positive number except 1.

Example 1

A computer sells for $3200. Each year, its value decreases by 20%. Its value after t years is given by the exponential function $V = 3200(0.8)^t$. Find the value of the computer after each time.

  a) 2 years   **b)** 5 years

Solution

a) Substitute $t = 2$ in the equation $V = 3200(0.8)^t$.

  $V = 3200(0.8)^2$ Key in: 3200 ⊗ 0.8 ⌃ 2 [ENTER]
      $= 2048$
In 2 years, the computer is worth $2048.

b) Substitute $t = 5$ in the equation $V = 3200(0.8)^t$.

  $V = 3200(0.8)^5$ Key in: 3200 ⊗ 0.8 ⌃ 5 [ENTER]
      $\doteq 1048.58$
In 5 years, the computer is worth approximately $1050.

Discuss

What would be the equation for the value of a computer that cost $2400? What would be the equation for the value of the computer if its value decreased by 30% each year?

Example 2

The first artificial satellites were put in orbit in the late 1950s. The total mass of all the satellites in orbit can be modelled by an exponential function. The equation of the function is $m = 120(1.12)^t$, where m is the mass in tonnes and t is the time in years since 1960.

  a) Graph the equation.

  b) Use the graph to estimate when the total mass was 4000 t.

Solution
Using paper and pencil

a) Make a table of values. Use values of t from 0 to 40 in steps of 10. Substitute for t in $m = 120(1.12)^t$, and use a calculator to evaluate. Then plot the points on grid paper.

t	$m = 120(1.12)^t$
0	$120(1.12)^0 = 120$
10	$120(1.12)^{10} \doteq 373$
20	$120(1.12)^{20} \doteq 1158$
30	$120(1.12)^{30} \doteq 3595$
40	$120(1.12)^{40} \doteq 11\ 166$

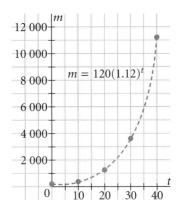

In the equation, t represents the number of years since 1960. Thus, t is a whole number. The graph is drawn as a broken curve.

b) On the graph, draw a horizontal line through $m = 4000$.

This line intersects the graph at $t \doteq 32$.

32 years after 1960 is 1992.

The total mass was 4000 t in approximately 1992.

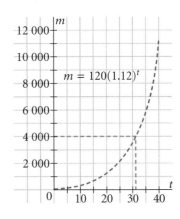

Using a graphing calculator
The key sequences are for the TI-83 and the TI-83 Plus.

- Press [Y=]. Use the arrow keys and [CLEAR] to remove any equation in the Y= list. If any of Plot1, Plot2, or Plot3 is highlighted, move the cursor to it, then press [ENTER] to turn it off.

a) Press ⌈ Y= ⌉, then input 120 ⌈ × ⌉ 1.12 ⌈ ^ ⌉ ⌈ X,T,θ,n ⌉.

Press ⌈WINDOW⌉ and change the settings to those shown below left.

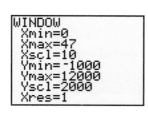

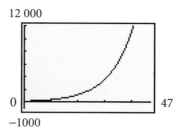

Press ⌈GRAPH⌉ to obtain the graph above right.

b) Press ⌈ Y= ⌉. Move the cursor to Y2=. Input 4000. Press ⌈GRAPH⌉.

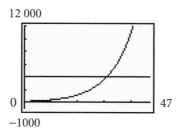

Press ⌈ 2nd ⌉ ⌈TRACE⌉ for CALC.

Press **5** for **intersect**.

Move the cursor to the left of the point of intersection.

Press ⌈ENTER⌉.

Move the cursor to the right of the point of intersection.

Press ⌈ENTER⌉ ⌈ENTER⌉.

The intersection point is (30.941486, 4000).

30.941 486 is approximately 31.

31 years after 1960 is 1991.

The total mass was 4000 t in approximately 1991.

Discuss

Why do the two solutions for part b produce different results?

Discuss

In *Example 2b*, could you use the substitution method of *Example 1* to obtain an answer? Explain.

A

✓ **1.** Which equations represent exponential functions? Explain.

a) $y = 4x$ b) $y = 5(2)^x$ c) $A = 900(1.05)^n$

d) $P = 25(5)^t$ e) $D = t^2$ f) $y = x^3$

✓ **2.** Use the graph on page 123. It shows the growth of $50 at 8% compounded annually.

a) Estimate the amount of the investment after 5 years.

b) Estimate how many years it takes for the investment to amount to $200.

✓ **3.** Use the graph on page 124. It shows how a computer depreciates in value over time.

a) Estimate the value after 3 years.

b) Estimate how long it takes before the computer is worth one-half of its original value.

B

✓ **4. Knowledge/Understanding** The approximate population of Ontario, P millions, can be represented by the exponential function $P = 10.1(1.016)^n$, where n is the number of years since 1991. Estimate the population of Ontario in each year.

a) 1995   b) 2000   c) 2005

5. Coffee, cola, and chocolate contain caffeine. When you consume caffeine, the percent, P, left in your body after n hours can be represented by the exponential function $P = 100(0.87)^n$. Suppose you drink a soft drink that contains caffeine. What percent remains in your body after each time?

a) 1 h   b) 3 h   c) 5 h

✓ **6.** A principal of $2000 is invested at 6% compounded annually. The amount, A dollars, after n years is represented by the exponential function $A = 2000(1.06)^n$. Find the amount after each time.

a) 3 years   b) 6 years   c) 10 years

✓ **7.** The growth of a bamboo plant over a 3-week period can be represented by the equation $h = 0.7(1.09)^n$, where h is the height of the plant in metres, n days after the start of the 3-week period.

a) What was the height of the plant at the start of the 3-week period?

b) What was the height of the plant at the end of the 3-week period?

8. **Communication** A principal of $700 is invested at 5% compounded annually. After n years, the amount, A dollars, is given by $A = 700(1.05)^n$.

a) Draw a graph to show the amount at the end of each of the first 10 years.

b) Estimate the value of n when $A = \$985$. Write to explain what this means.

c) Use a graphing calculator to confirm the result in part b.

 9. **Thinking/Inquiry/Problem Solving** The number of Canadian cellular phone subscribers, s, has grown according to the equation $s = 130\ 000(1.45)^t$, where t is the time in years since 1987.

a) Estimate when the number of subscribers will reach 12 000 000.

b) Will there ever be 50 000 000 subscribers? Explain.

10. **Application** A principal of $1200 is invested at 6% compounded annually. Let the amount after n years be represented by A dollars.

a) Write the equation of an exponential function to represent A.

b) What is the amount after 10 years?

c) When will the amount be $1800?

Career Profile

Retail Customer Service Representative

A Customer Service Representative (CSR) in the retail business is the key link between the customer and the company. To be successful in this field, a CSR must have a thorough knowledge of the company's products or services and possess outstanding communication, sales, and organizational skills. In addition, CSRs must be able to handle the pressures of a job that is completely dependent on the needs of another—the customer.

In the retail business, CSRs in a store have to learn to manage several tasks, such as attending to customers, answering the phone, checking the inventory, and arranging the display areas. CSRs in retail are constantly on their feet. Those who work in catalogue or telephone sales need excellent listening skills and telephone manners.

CSRs are trained to be courteous with people at all times. They work an eight-hour shift. However, as many businesses remain open 12 hours a day, seven days a week, shifts may vary. During the busiest shopping seasons, CSRs may work overtime.

Where's the Math?
CSRs must have calculation skills when asked to determine the final price of items for customers, especially when discounts are offered.

Powers with positive exponents were defined using repeated multiplication.

Powers with zero and negative exponents were defined so the exponent laws still apply. Powers with rational exponents can also be defined so the exponent laws still apply.

Remember that a rational number is a number that can be written as a fraction. A power with a rational exponent cannot be defined in terms of repeated multiplication. But, it can be defined so the exponent laws still apply.

Remember the rule for multiplying powers with the same base.
$$a^m \times a^n = a^{m+n}$$

We extend the exponent laws so they apply when m and n are rational numbers.

Then we can write:
$$5^{\frac{1}{2}} \times 5^{\frac{1}{2}} = 5^{\frac{1}{2} + \frac{1}{2}}$$
$$= 5^1$$
$$= 5$$

But it is also true that $\sqrt{5} \times \sqrt{5} = 5$

Therefore, the values of $5^{\frac{1}{2}}$ and $\sqrt{5}$ must be the same; that is, $5^{\frac{1}{2}} = \sqrt{5}$.

Similarly,
$$5^{\frac{1}{3}} \times 5^{\frac{1}{3}} \times 5^{\frac{1}{3}} = 5^{\frac{1}{3} + \frac{1}{3} + \frac{1}{3}}$$
$$= 5^1$$
$$= 5$$

But it is also true that $\sqrt[3]{5} \times \sqrt[3]{5} \times \sqrt[3]{5} = 5$

Therefore, the values of $5^{\frac{1}{3}}$ and $\sqrt[3]{5}$ must be the same; that is, $5^{\frac{1}{3}} = \sqrt[3]{5}$.

These examples suggest that an exponent of $\frac{1}{2}$ means the positive square root of the number, an exponent of $\frac{1}{3}$ means the cube root of the number, an exponent of $\frac{1}{4}$ means the positive fourth root of the number, and so on.

$$7^{\frac{1}{2}} = \sqrt{7} \qquad 7^{\frac{1}{3}} = \sqrt[3]{7} \qquad 7^{\frac{1}{4}} = \sqrt[4]{7}, \ldots$$

Thus, rational exponents and radical signs are different ways to express the same number.

You can use the exponent laws to evaluate some powers with rational exponents mentally.

Example 1 Evaluate without using a calculator.

  a) $16^{\frac{1}{2}}$ **b)** $27^{\frac{1}{3}}$

Solution

a) $16^{\frac{1}{2}}$ Write 16 as a power of 4: $16 = 4^2$

$16^{\frac{1}{2}} = (4^2)^{\frac{1}{2}}$ Use the power of a power law.

$\quad = 4^{2 \times \frac{1}{2}}$ Note: $2 \times \frac{1}{2} = \frac{2}{1} \times \frac{1}{2} = 1$

$\quad = 4^1$

$\quad = 4$

b) $27^{\frac{1}{3}}$ Write 27 as a power: $27 = 3^3$

$27^{\frac{1}{3}} = (3^3)^{\frac{1}{3}}$

$\quad = 3^{3 \times \frac{1}{3}}$ Note: $3 \times \frac{1}{3} = \frac{3}{1} \times \frac{1}{3} = 1$

$\quad = 3^1$

$\quad = 3$

When a power has a negative exponent, the first step is to write the power so the exponent is positive.

Example 2 Evaluate without using a calculator.

  a) $16^{-\frac{1}{2}}$ **b)** $27^{-\frac{1}{3}}$ **c)** $32^{-\frac{1}{5}}$

Solution

a) $16^{-\frac{1}{2}} = \dfrac{1}{16^{\frac{1}{2}}}$ **b)** $27^{-\frac{1}{3}} = \dfrac{1}{27^{\frac{1}{3}}}$ **c)** $32^{-\frac{1}{5}} = \dfrac{1}{32^{\frac{1}{5}}}$

$\quad = \dfrac{1}{(4^2)^{\frac{1}{2}}}$ $\quad = \dfrac{1}{(3^3)^{\frac{1}{3}}}$ $\quad = \dfrac{1}{(2^5)^{\frac{1}{5}}}$

$\quad = \dfrac{1}{4}$ $\quad = \dfrac{1}{3}$ $\quad = \dfrac{1}{2}$

We can extend the definition of rational exponents to include exponents with fractions that have numerators other than 1.

We use the power of a power law, $a^{mn} = (a^m)^n$.

For example, we can write $16^{\frac{3}{4}}$ as $(2^4)^{\frac{3}{4}} = 2^{4 \times \frac{3}{4}}$
$$= 2^3$$
$$= 8$$

That is, we write 16 as a power with an exponent 4, so when we multiply $4 \times \frac{3}{4}$, we get a whole number, 3.

Some powers with such rational exponents can be calculated mentally.

Example 3

Evaluate.

a) $16^{\frac{3}{2}}$ **b)** $27^{\frac{4}{3}}$ **c)** $32^{-\frac{2}{5}}$

Solution

a) $16^{\frac{3}{2}} = (4^2)^{\frac{3}{2}}$ Write 16 as a power with an exponent 2.
$$= 4^{2 \times \frac{3}{2}}$$ Note: $2 \times \frac{3}{2} = \frac{2}{1} \times \frac{3}{2} = 3$
$$= 4^3$$
$$= 64$$

b) $27^{\frac{4}{3}} = (3^3)^{\frac{4}{3}}$
$$= 3^{3 \times \frac{4}{3}}$$ Note: $3 \times \frac{4}{3} = \frac{3}{1} \times \frac{4}{3} = 4$
$$= 3^4$$
$$= 81$$

c) $32^{-\frac{2}{5}} = \dfrac{1}{32^{\frac{2}{5}}}$
$$= \frac{1}{(2^5)^{\frac{2}{5}}}$$ Note: $5 \times \frac{2}{5} = \frac{5}{1} \times \frac{2}{5} = 2$
$$= \frac{1}{2^2}$$
$$= \frac{1}{4}$$

Discuss

How are *Examples 2* and *3* similar? How are they different?

Most powers with rational exponents cannot be calculated mentally.

Example 4

Evaluate. Write each number to 2 decimal places.

a) $15^{0.5}$ **b)** $\left(\frac{1}{2}\right)^{\frac{1}{3}}$ **c)** $30^{-0.2}$

Solution

a) $15^{0.5}$

Key in: 15 ⌃ 0.5 ENTER= to display 3.872983346

$15^{0.5} \doteq 3.87$

b) $\left(\frac{1}{2}\right)^{\frac{1}{3}}$

Key in: (1 ÷ 2) ⌃ (1 ÷ 3) ENTER= to display 0.793700526

$\left(\frac{1}{2}\right)^{\frac{1}{3}} \doteq 0.79$

c) $30^{-0.2}$

Key in: 30 ⌃ (−) 0.2 ENTER= to display 0.506495684

$30^{-0.2} \doteq 0.51$

Discuss

Look at *Examples 1* to *4*. When you evaluate a power with a rational exponent, how do you know when to use a calculator?

 3.2 Exercises

A

1. Evaluate without using a calculator.

a) $16^{\frac{1}{2}}$ **b)** $36^{\frac{1}{2}}$ **c)** $4^{\frac{1}{2}}$ **d)** $100^{\frac{1}{2}}$

e) $25^{\frac{1}{2}}$ **f)** $49^{\frac{1}{2}}$ **g)** $64^{\frac{1}{2}}$ **h)** $81^{\frac{1}{2}}$

2. Evaluate without using a calculator.

a) $125^{\frac{1}{3}}$ **b)** $64^{\frac{1}{3}}$ **c)** $8^{\frac{1}{3}}$ **d)** $1000^{\frac{1}{3}}$

3. Evaluate without using a calculator.

a) $49^{-\frac{1}{2}}$ **b)** $4^{-\frac{1}{2}}$ **c)** $100^{-\frac{1}{2}}$ **d)** $25^{-\frac{1}{2}}$

e) $81^{-\frac{1}{2}}$ **f)** $36^{-\frac{1}{2}}$ **g)** $16^{-\frac{1}{2}}$ **h)** $9^{-\frac{1}{2}}$

B

4. Evaluate without using a calculator.

   a) $8^{-\frac{1}{3}}$ b) $1000^{-\frac{1}{3}}$ c) $64^{-\frac{1}{3}}$ d) $125^{-\frac{1}{3}}$

5. **Knowledge/Understanding** Evaluate without using a calculator.

   a) $4^{\frac{3}{2}}$ b) $9^{\frac{5}{2}}$ c) $64^{\frac{4}{3}}$ d) $16^{\frac{3}{4}}$

   e) $27^{\frac{2}{3}}$ f) $1000^{\frac{4}{3}}$ g) $8^{\frac{5}{3}}$ h) $25^{\frac{5}{2}}$

6. **Communication** Refer to exercise 5c. The number 64 can be written as a power several different ways. How do you know which base to use? Does the base matter? Explain.

7. Evaluate without using a calculator.

   a) $8^{-\frac{2}{3}}$ b) $10\ 000^{-\frac{3}{4}}$ c) $4^{-\frac{5}{2}}$ d) $64^{-\frac{5}{6}}$

   e) $125^{-\frac{2}{3}}$ f) $16^{-\frac{3}{2}}$ g) $16^{-\frac{5}{4}}$ h) $9^{-\frac{3}{2}}$

8. Evaluate. Write each number to 2 decimal places.

   a) $10^{0.5}$ b) $15^{\frac{1}{2}}$ c) $40^{\frac{1}{3}}$ d) $50^{0.1}$

   e) $3.5^{0.2}$ f) $0.6^{\frac{2}{3}}$ g) $146^{\frac{3}{2}}$ h) $2.9^{0.3}$

9. Evaluate. Write each number to 2 decimal places.

   a) $100^{-0.5}$ b) $26^{-\frac{1}{2}}$ c) $3.7^{-\frac{1}{3}}$ d) $356^{-0.1}$

   e) $0.8^{-\frac{3}{4}}$ f) $1.8^{-\frac{4}{3}}$ g) $17.1^{\frac{3}{5}}$ h) $17.1^{0.3}$

10. **Application** Draw a graph of the function $y = x^2$.

    a) Describe how to use this graph to estimate square roots of numbers.

    b) How does this graph relate to the work of this section?

11. **Thinking/Inquiry/Problem Solving**

    Evaluate and compare 2^1, $2^{\frac{1}{2}}$, $2^{\frac{1}{3}}$, $2^{\frac{1}{4}}$ and $\left(\frac{1}{2}\right)^1$, $\left(\frac{1}{2}\right)^{\frac{1}{2}}$, $\left(\frac{1}{2}\right)^{\frac{1}{3}}$, $\left(\frac{1}{2}\right)^{\frac{1}{4}}$.
    Describe the differences in the results for each base. Explain why you think this happens.

12. Evaluate. Write each number to 2 decimal places.

    a) $103.6^{0.7}$ b) $25.1^{-0.2}$ c) 1.006^{-3} d) $37^{0.75}$

    e) $0.1^{0.7}$ f) $0.1^{-0.1}$ g) $1.3^{1.3}$ h) $1.3^{-1.3}$

13. Evaluate. Write each number to 2 decimal places.

    a) $\left(\frac{1}{2}\right)^{\frac{1}{2}}$ b) $\left(\frac{1}{3}\right)^{\frac{1}{2}}$ c) $\left(\frac{3}{4}\right)^{\frac{1}{2}}$ d) $\left(\frac{3}{4}\right)^{\frac{1}{3}}$

    e) $\left(\frac{5}{4}\right)^{\frac{3}{2}}$ f) $\left(\frac{3}{2}\right)^{\frac{3}{2}}$ g) $\left(\frac{7}{10}\right)^{\frac{1}{10}}$ h) $\left(\frac{1}{2}\right)^{\frac{1}{4}}$

14. Evaluate. Write each number to 2 decimal places.

    a) $\left(\frac{1}{2}\right)^{-\frac{1}{4}}$ b) $\left(\frac{1}{4}\right)^{-\frac{1}{2}}$ c) $\left(\frac{3}{4}\right)^{-\frac{1}{2}}$ d) $\left(\frac{4}{5}\right)^{-\frac{2}{3}}$

    e) $\left(\frac{3}{8}\right)^{-\frac{3}{2}}$ f) $\left(\frac{2}{5}\right)^{-\frac{3}{4}}$ g) $\left(\frac{4}{3}\right)^{-\frac{5}{4}}$ h) $\left(\frac{5}{6}\right)^{-\frac{3}{4}}$

In Section 3.1, you graphed exponential functions of the form $y = Ab^x$, where x was an integer. For this reason, the points on the graphs were not joined. A broken curve was drawn to show the trend.

In Section 3.2, you extended the definition of an exponent to include rational exponents. In fact, an exponent can be any number that can be written as a decimal. Recall, from Necessary Skills, that these numbers are real numbers.

We shall look at graphs of exponential functions of the form $y = b^x$, where $b > 0$ and x is any real number.

Example 1

Without using a calculator, graph each exponential function. Use values of x between –3 and 3 inclusive.

a) $y = 2^x$ **b)** $y = \left(\frac{1}{2}\right)^x$

Solution

a) Complete a table of values. Plot the points on a grid.

Since the function is defined for all values of x, join the points with a smooth curve.

x	$y = 2^x$
–3	$2^{-3} = \frac{1}{2^3} = \frac{1}{8}$
–2	$2^{-2} = \frac{1}{2^2} = \frac{1}{4}$
–1	$2^{-1} = \frac{1}{2^1} = \frac{1}{2}$
0	$2^0 = 1$
1	$2^1 = 2$
2	$2^2 = 4$
3	$2^3 = 8$

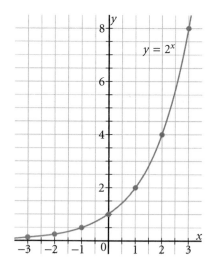

b) Complete a table of values. Plot the points on a grid. Join the points with a smooth curve.

x	$y = \left(\frac{1}{2}\right)^x$
−3	$\left(\frac{1}{2}\right)^{-3} = 2^3 = 8$
−2	$\left(\frac{1}{2}\right)^{-2} = 2^2 = 4$
−1	$\left(\frac{1}{2}\right)^{-1} = 2^1 = 2$
0	$\left(\frac{1}{2}\right)^{0} = 1$
1	$\left(\frac{1}{2}\right)^{1} = \frac{1}{2}$
2	$\left(\frac{1}{2}\right)^{2} = \frac{1}{4}$
3	$\left(\frac{1}{2}\right)^{3} = \frac{1}{8}$

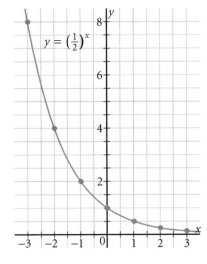

$y = \left(\frac{1}{2}\right)^x$

Discuss
How are the graphs similar?
How are the graphs different?
Do the graphs have any point in common? If so, why is this point common to both graphs?

In the following investigations, you will use a graphing calculator to further investigate the properties of an exponential function.

The key sequences are for the TI-83 and the TI-83 Plus.

- Press ⟨ Y= ⟩. Use the arrow keys and ⟨CLEAR⟩ to remove any equation in the Y= list. If any of Plot1, Plot2, or Plot3 is highlighted, move the cursor to it, then press ⟨ENTER⟩ to turn it off.

The graph of $y = b^x$, $b \geq 1$

1. Graph $y = 2^x$, $y = 5^x$, and $y = 1^x$ on the same screen. The cursor should be next to Y1 =.

   a) To enter $y = 2^x$, press 2 [^] [X,T,θ,n] [ENTER]

   b) To enter $y = 5^x$, press 5 [^] [X,T,θ,n] [ENTER]

   c) To enter $y = 1^x$, press 1 [^] [X,T,θ,n] [ENTER]

2. Press [WINDOW]. Change the settings to the ones shown below.

   ```
   WINDOW
    Xmin=-4.7
    Xmax=4.7
    Xscl=1
    Ymin=-1
    Ymax=10
    Yscl=1
    Xres=1
   ```

3. Press [GRAPH]. The three graphs are displayed. Explain why $y = 1^x$ is not an exponential function.

4. Press [Y=]. Use the arrow keys and [CLEAR] to remove the equations for $y = 5^x$ and $y = 1^x$. Do not clear the equation for $y = 2^x$.

5. Press [GRAPH]. The graph of $y = 2^x$ is displayed.
   To determine the y-intercept, press [TRACE] 0 [ENTER]. Record the corresponding y-value. This is the y-intercept.

6. To determine the x-intercept, press [TRACE] and the left arrow key. Keep the left arrow key pressed until at least $x = -10$. What do you notice about the value of y? What does this seem to indicate about the x-intercept?

7. a) Describe the graph as x increases.

   b) Describe the graph as x decreases.

8. Change the equation from $y = 2^x$ to $y = 5^x$.
   Repeat exercises 5 to 7 for $y = 5^x$.

9. Change the equation from $y = 5^x$ to $y = 10^x$.
   Repeat exercises 5 to 7 for $y = 10^x$.

10. a) What is the y-intercept of the graph of the exponential function
    $y = b^x$, $b > 1$?

    b) What is the x-intercept of this graph? Explain.

The graph of $y = b^x$, for $b > 0$ and $b < 1$

You will graph $y = \left(\frac{1}{2}\right)^x$, $y = \left(\frac{1}{5}\right)^x$, and $y = \left(\frac{1}{10}\right)^x$ to determine the x- and y-intercepts.

1. Press $\boxed{\text{WINDOW}}$. Change the settings to match those in *Investigation 1*.

2. To enter $y = \left(\frac{1}{2}\right)^x$, press $\boxed{\text{Y=}}$ $\boxed{\text{(}}$ 1 $\boxed{\div}$ 2 $\boxed{\text{)}}$ $\boxed{\frown}$ $\boxed{\text{X,T,θ,n}}$.

3. Press $\boxed{\text{GRAPH}}$. Use $\boxed{\text{TRACE}}$ to determine the y-intercept, then the x-intercept. What do you notice?

4. a) Describe the graph as x increases.

   b) Describe the graph as x decreases.

5. Repeat exercises 2 to 4 for $y = \left(\frac{1}{5}\right)^x$.

6. Repeat exercises 2 to 4 for $y = \left(\frac{1}{10}\right)^x$.

The results of *Investigations 1* and *2* are summarized below.

- As you trace along a graph, all values of x are possible for all the exponential functions. This set of numbers is called the *domain* of the exponential functions.
- As you trace along a graph, only positive values of y are possible for all the exponential functions. This set of numbers is called the *range* of the exponential functions.
- As you trace along a graph, the graph does not intersect the x-axis. The graph gets very close to the x-axis, but there is no x-intercept. The x-axis is an *asymptote*.
- All the graphs have a y-intercept of 1.
- For graphs of $y = b^x$ with b greater than 1 (such as $y = 2^x$, $y = 5^x$, and $y = 10^x$) as x increases, y also increases. That is, as x increases, the graph goes up to the right. These graphs illustrate *exponential growth*.
- For graphs of $y = b^x$, with b between 0 and 1 (such as $y = \left(\frac{1}{2}\right)^x$, $y = \left(\frac{1}{5}\right)^x$, and $y = \left(\frac{1}{10}\right)^x$) as x increases, y decreases. That is, as x increases, the graph goes down to the right. These graphs illustrate *exponential decay*.

Properties of the Graph of the Exponential Function $y = b^x$

- When $b > 1$, the graph goes up to the right – exponential growth
- When $b > 0$ and $b < 1$, the graph goes down to the right – exponential decay
- The y-intercept is 1.
- There is no x-intercept. The x-axis is an asymptote.
- The domain (the set of all possible x-values) is the real numbers.
- The range (the set of all possible y-values) is all positive real numbers.

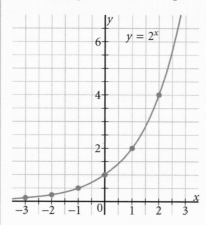
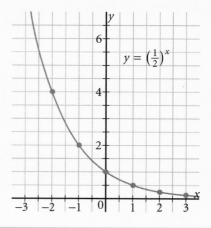

3.3 Exercises

A

1. Evaluate.

   a) i) 2^1 **ii)** 2^2 **iii)** 2^3 **iv)** 2^4 **v)** 2^5 **vi)** 2^{-1}

   b) i) 3^1 **ii)** 3^2 **iii)** 3^3 **iv)** 3^4 **v)** 3^5 **vi)** 3^{-1}

   c) i) 10^{-1} **ii)** 10^0 **iii)** 10^1 **iv)** 10^2 **v)** 10^3 **vi)** 10^4

2. Evaluate. Write each number to 2 decimal places if necessary.

   a) i) 4^{-3} **ii)** 4^{-2} **iii)** 4^{-1} **iv)** 4^0 **v)** 4^1

   b) i) $\left(\frac{1}{4}\right)^{-3}$ **ii)** $\left(\frac{1}{4}\right)^{-2}$ **iii)** $\left(\frac{1}{4}\right)^{-1}$ **iv)** $\left(\frac{1}{4}\right)^0$ **v)** $\left(\frac{1}{4}\right)^1$

B

3. Which equations represent exponential functions? Explain.

   a) $y = x^2$ **b)** $y = 2^x$ **c)** $y = 1.05^x$

   d) $P = 5^x$ **e)** $V = 4^t$ **f)** $r = 2x^3$

4. Identify the graph below that best represents each function.

a) $y = 3^x$ **b)** $y = 10^x$ **c)** $y = \left(\frac{1}{2}\right)^x$ **d)** $y = 5^x$

i)

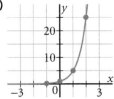

ii)

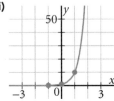

iii)

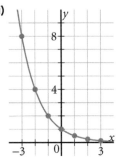

iv)

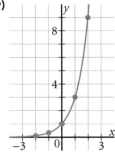

 5. a) Copy and complete this table of values for $y = 3^x$.

x	−1	0	1	3	5	7
y						

b) Use a whole sheet of grid paper. Graph $y = 3^x$.

c) Use the graph. Estimate the value of x for each value of y.

     i) 9   **ii)** 729   **iii)** 81

6. Knowledge/Understanding

a) Construct a table of values for the exponential function $y = 10^x$. Use values of x from −1 to 3.

b) Use a whole sheet of grid paper. Graph $y = 10^x$.

c) What is the x-intercept? What is the y-intercept?

d) What is the asymptote? How do you know?

e) Use the graph. Estimate the value of y when $x = 0.5$.

7. Communication

a) Graph these exponential functions on the same grid. Use values of x from −3 to 3. Round the values of y to 2 decimal places where necessary.

     i) $y = 4^x$ **ii)** $y = \left(\frac{1}{4}\right)^x$

b) Describe how the graphs are similar.

c) Describe how the graphs are different.

8. **a)** Make a table of values for each pair of exponential functions.

  i) $y = 5^x$, $y = \left(\frac{1}{5}\right)^x$ **ii)** $y = 6^x$, $y = \left(\frac{1}{6}\right)^x$

  b) How are the values in each table related?

  c) Graph each pair of exponential functions in part a.

  d) How are the graphs related?

9. A principal of $800 is invested at 5% compounded annually. After n years, the amount, A dollars, is given by $A = 800(1.05)^n$.

  a) Draw a graph to show the amount each year for up to 10 years.

  b) Estimate the number of years before the investment amounts to $1000.

  c) Use a graphing calculator to confirm the result in part b.

10. **Application** The Universal Insurance Company sells life insurance. For each $1000 of insurance, a person pays a premium depending on her or his age. This table shows the premiums for people between the ages of 16 and 60. For example, a person age 16 pays $2.40 per year for each $1000 of insurance.

Age (years)	16	20	24	28	32	36	40	44	48	52	56	60
Annual premium ($)	2.40	2.43	2.44	2.49	2.65	2.96	3.39	3.96	4.42	4.82	5.29	5.81

  a) Use a whole sheet of grid paper. Plot *Age* horizontally and *Annual premium* vertically. Join the points to form a smooth curve. Describe the curve.

  b) From the graph, determine the annual premium for $1000 of insurance for each age.

  i) 18   **ii)** 21   **iii)** 30   **iv)** 35   **v)** 50

  c) Extend the graph. What will be the cost of insurance for each age?

  i) 61   **ii)** 65   **iii)** 70   **iv)** 10   **v)** 0 (an infant)

  d) What assumption did you make in part c?

11. **Thinking/Inquiry/Problem Solving** Graph these functions on the same screen.

  $y = 2^x + 2^{-x}$, $y = 3^x + 3^{-x}$, $y = 4^x + 4^{-x}$

  a) Predict the characteristics of the curve $y = 5^x + 5^{-x}$.

  b) Use algebra to explain your answer to part a.

  c) Graph $y = \left(\frac{1}{2}\right)^x + \left(\frac{1}{2}\right)^{-x}$ on the same screen. What do you notice?

  d) Explain your answer to part c.

  e) Each curve is called a catenary. Describe a catenary.

1. Evaluate without using a calculator.

   a) 2^{-1} **b)** 3^{-2} **c)** $\left(\frac{1}{2}\right)^3$ **d)** $3(2)^0$

   e) $8^{\frac{1}{3}}$ **f)** $9^{\frac{1}{2}}$ **g)** $4^{-\frac{1}{2}}$ **h)** $81^{\frac{3}{4}}$

2. Evaluate using a calculator.

   a) 5^{-2} **b)** $3^{2.3}$ **c)** $5(1.02)^{-3}$ **d)** $2^{\frac{1}{5}}$

3. Write as a single power with positive exponents.

   a) $a^{-5} \times a^{11} \times a^0$ **b)** $x^4 \div x^{-2}$ **c)** $(b^2)^{-4}$ **d)** $\left(\frac{x^2}{y^{-1}}\right)^{-2}$

4. Which equations represent exponential functions?

   a) $y = \frac{1}{2}x$ **b)** $y = \left(\frac{1}{5}\right)^x$ **c)** $y = x^{\frac{1}{2}}$ **d)** $y = 3(2)^x$

5. The approximate population of Canada, P millions, is represented by the exponential function $P = 27.3(1.016)^n$, where n is the number of years since 1991. Estimate the population of Canada in each given year.

   a) 1991   **b)** 2001   **c)** 2011

6. A ball drops onto a concrete floor. Its height, h metres, after n bounces is represented by the exponential function $h = 4(0.5)^n$. Draw a graph to show the height of the ball for each of the first 5 bounces.

7. On the same grid, draw the graphs of $y = 2^x$ and $y = \left(\frac{1}{2}\right)^x$. Use values of x from −3 to 3.

   a) Which point is common to both graphs? Why is this point common to both graphs?

   b) Which graph is increasing? Which graph is decreasing?

   c) Which graph illustrates exponential growth? Which graph illustrates exponential decay? Explain.

Some of the bacteria that cause food poisoning are called salmonella. Under favourable conditions, one salmonella bacterium will divide every 20 min to form two new salmonella.

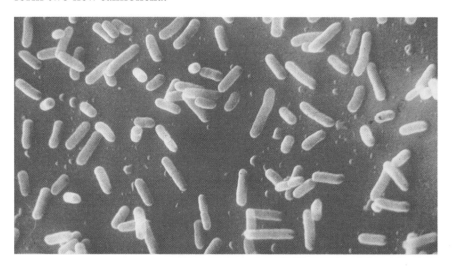

Suppose there are 400 salmonella to start.
Every 20 min, the population doubles and can be written using a power of 2.

Initially, there are 400 salmonella.

After 20 min, or 1 doubling period, there are 800 salmonella.

Number of salmonella $= 400 \times 2$
$$= 400(2)^1$$

After 40 min, or 2 doubling periods, there are 1600 salmonella.

Number of salmonella $= 400 \times 2 \times 2$
$$= 400(2)^2$$

After 60 min, or 3 doubling periods, there are 3200 salmonella.

Number of salmonella $= 400 \times 2 \times 2 \times 2$
$$= 400(2)^3$$

After 80 min, or 4 doubling periods, there are 6400 salmonella.

Number of salmonella $= 400 \times 2 \times 2 \times 2 \times 2$
$$= 400(2)^4$$

This pattern continues.

Thus, after n doubling periods, there are $400(2)^n$ salmonella.
The population, P, of salmonella can be represented by the exponential function $P = 400(2)^n$.

In the equation $P = 400(2)^n$,

P is the population after n doubling periods.

400 is the initial population of salmonella.

2 is called the *growth factor*, since the population grows by a factor of 2 each doubling period.

n is the number of doubling periods.

The equation $P = 400(2)^n$ represents an exponential function. The general exponential function has equation $y = Ab^x$. From Section 3.3, recall that when b is greater than 1, the function illustrates exponential growth.

Here is a graph of the function $P = 400(2)^n$. The shape of the graph is typical of a function that represents exponential growth.

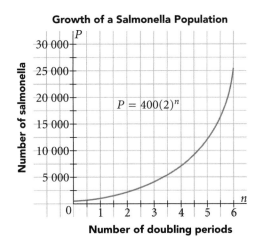

Growth of a Salmonella Population

Number of doubling periods

Discuss

Can the growth illustrated by the graph continue indefinitely? Explain.

TAKE NOTE

Modelling Exponential Growth

A quantity whose increase over time can be described by an exponential function exhibits exponential growth.

The equation $y = Ab^x$ can be used to describe the growth.

y is the amount after x time periods.

A is the initial amount.

b is the growth factor, the number that the amount is multiplied by in each time period. For exponential growth, b is greater than 1.

x is the number of time periods.

Example 1

A strain of yeast cells triples every hour. Suppose there are 60 cells now.

a) Write an equation to represent y, the number of yeast cells x hours from now.

b) Estimate how many cells there will be 5 h from now.

Solution

a) Use the equation $y = Ab^x$.

A is the initial amount. Since there are 60 cells initially, $A = 60$.

b is the growth factor. Since the number of cells grows by a factor of 3, $b = 3$.

Let x be the number of hours.

The required equation is $y = 60(3)^x$.

b) Substitute $x = 5$ in the equation $y = 60(3)^x$.

$$y = 60(3)^5$$
$$= 60(243)$$
$$= 14\ 580$$

There will be approximately 14 580 yeast cells 5 h from now.

In the preceding examples, the rate of growth of a population was expressed in terms of doubling and tripling times. The rate of growth can also be given as a percent.

Example 2

A school has an enrolment of 1200 students. The student population is expected to grow at a rate of 1.5% each year for the next 10 years.

a) What is the growth factor as a decimal?

b) Write an equation to represent y, the number of students enrolled x years from now.

c) Estimate the number of students enrolled 8 years from now.

Solution

a) Each year, the student population increases by 1.5%.

Population = 100% of population + 1.5% of population
at end of year   at beginning of year   at beginning of year

= 101.5% of population at beginning of year

= 1.015 times the population at beginning of year

Each year, the population increases by a factor 1.015.

Thus, the growth factor, b, is 1.015.

b) Use the equation $y = Ab^x$.

Let x represent the number of years.

Substitute $A = 1200$ and $b = 1.015$.

The required equation is $y = 1200(1.015)^x$.

c) Substitute $x = 8$ in the equation $y = 1200(1.015)^x$.

$$y = 1200(1.015)^8$$
$$\doteq 1351.791\ 104$$
$$\doteq 1352$$

There will be approximately 1352 students enrolled 8 years from now.

In *Example 2*, a population grew by 1.5% a year. As a decimal, 1.5% is 0.015. The growth factor, b, was 1.015, which is $1 + 0.015$.

This result is generalized below.

> **TAKE NOTE**
>
> **Growth Factor for Exponential Growth**
>
> For exponential growth, the growth factor, b, is given by $1 + r$, where r is the percent rate of increase expressed as a decimal.

Discuss

In Chapter 2, you learned the compound interest formula $A = P(1 + i)^n$. How is this equation related to $y = Ab^x$?

Example 3

The Petersons purchased their house for \$30 000 in 1970. Since then, the value of their house has increased 5% per year.

a) Write an equation to represent the value of the house, y dollars, as a function of x, the number of years since 1970.

b) Estimate the value of the house in the year 2001.

Solution

a) Use the equation $y = Ab^x$.

Substitute $A = 30\ 000$ and $b = 1 + 0.05 = 1.05$.

The required equation is $y = 30\ 000(1.05)^x$.

b) In the equation $y = 30\ 000(1.05)^x$, x is the number of years since 1970.

$$x = 2001 - 1970$$
$$= 31$$

Substitute $x = 31$ in the equation $y = 30\ 000(1.05)^x$.

$y = 30\ 000(1.05)^{31}$

$\doteq 136\ 141$

In 2001, the house was worth approximately $136 000.

Example 4

In 1995, Canada's population was approximately 29.6 million. It was growing at a rate of approximately 1.24% a year.

a) Write an equation to represent the population of Canada, y millions, as a function of x, the number of years since 1995.

b) Graph the equation in part a. Use values of x from 0 to 100 in steps of 20 years.

c) Estimate the doubling time for Canada's population.

Solution

a) Use the equation $y = Ab^x$.

Substitute $A = 29.6$ and $b = 1 + 0.0124 = 1.0124$.

The required equation is $y = 29.6(1.0124)^x$.

Using Pencil and Paper

b) Create a table of values. Draw a graph of y against x.

x	$y = 29.6(1.0124)^x$
0	$29.6(1.0124)^0 = 29.6$
20	$29.6(1.0124)^{20} \doteq 37.9$
40	$29.6(1.0124)^{40} \doteq 48.5$
60	$29.6(1.0124)^{60} \doteq 62.0$
80	$29.6(1.0124)^{80} \doteq 79.3$
100	$29.6(1.0124)^{100} \doteq 101.5$

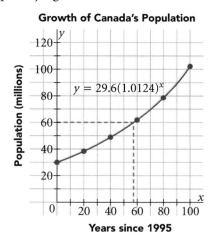

Growth of Canada's Population

$y = 29.6(1.0124)^x$

Population (millions)

Years since 1995

c) Canada's population in 1995 was approximately 30 million.

To find when Canada's population doubles to 60 million, draw a horizontal line from $y = 60$ to meet the graph. Then draw a vertical line. It meets the x-axis at $x \doteq 56$.

Canada's population doubles in about 56 years.

Using a Graphing Calculator

b) Press $\boxed{\text{Y=}}$. Use the arrow keys and $\boxed{\text{CLEAR}}$ to clear any equations.
Move the cursor next to Y1=.
Input 29.6 $\boxed{\times}$ 1.0124 $\boxed{\wedge}$ $\boxed{\text{X,T,θ,n}}$.
Press $\boxed{\text{WINDOW}}$. Use the window settings below left.
Press $\boxed{\text{GRAPH}}$ to obtain the screen below right.

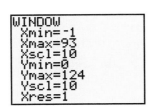

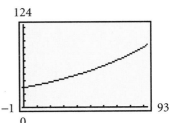

c) Press $\boxed{\text{TRACE}}$. Move the cursor as
close as possible to $y = 60$, for a
population of 60 million. Record
the x-value: $x \doteq 57$

Canada's population doubles in
about 57 years.

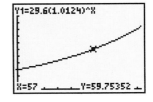

Discuss
How could you use the "intersect" method, page 128, to complete part c?

3.4 Exercises

A

1. A population increases at each rate shown. Determine the growth factor
for each rate of growth.

   a) 12%   **b)** 6%   **c)** 3.4%   **d)** 8.2%   **e)** 10.5%

 2. A population has each growth factor. What is the rate of growth as
a percent?

   a) 1.2   **b)** 1.05   **c)** 1.025   **d)** 1.004   **e)** 1.15

B

 3. Knowledge/Understanding There are 1200 bacteria in a culture. Write
an equation to represent the growth of the bacteria n days from now
under each given condition.

a) The population doubles every day.

b) The population triples every day.

c) The population grows by a factor of 5 every day.

4. The population , P million, of Alberta can be modelled by the equation $P = 2.238(1.014)^n$, where n is the number of years since 1981.

    a) What was the population of Alberta in 1981?

    b) At what annual rate, as a percent, has Alberta's population been increasing since 1981?

    c) Estimate the population in 2021. What assumption did you make?

    d) What factors might affect the accuracy of the model's estimation of the population?

5. Ontario's population in 1991 was approximately 10.1 million. The population has been increasing at a rate of 1.25% per year.

    a) Write an equation to represent the population of Ontario, y millions, as a function of the number of years, x, since 1991.

    b) Suppose the population continues to grow at this rate. Estimate the population in 2041.

6. In 1626, Manhattan Island in New York was purchased for goods worth about \$24. Suppose the \$24 had been invested at 6% interest compounded annually.

    a) Write an equation to represent the value of the investment, y dollars, as a function of the number of years, x, since 1626.

    b) What would the investment be worth at the end of the year 2000?

7. A strain of bacteria doubles every hour. Suppose there were 4000 bacteria at the start.

    a) Write an equation to represent y, the number of bacteria x hours from now.

    b) How many bacteria would be present after each time?

      i) 4 h   **ii)** 6 h   **iii)** 9 h

8. A rare stamp was worth \$65 in 1995. It was predicted to grow in value at a rate of 8% per year.

    a) Write an equation to represent the value of the stamp, y dollars, as a function of the number of years, x, since 1995.

    b) Graph the equation in part a. Use values of x from 0 to 10 in steps of 2 years.

    c) Use the graph. Estimate the number of years before the value of the stamp is double its value in 1995.

9. There are 800 caribou in a provincial park. The caribou population has been growing at an annual rate of 2%.

   a) Write an equation to represent y, the number of caribou in the park x years from now.

   b) Graph the equation in part a. Use values of x from 0 to 40 in steps of 5 years.

   c) Use the graph to estimate when the caribou population is 1000.

   d) Use the graph to estimate how long it will take for the current caribou population to double.

10. **Application** Mei Lin invested $600 in a GIC for several years. The interest rate was 5% compounded annually.

    a) Write an equation to represent the value, y dollars, of the GIC x years from now.

    b) Use the equation from part a. What is the value of the GIC after 7 years?

    c) Graph the equation in part a for values of x up to 20.

    d) Use the graph. Estimate when the value of the GIC is $1200.

    e) Use the graph. What is the doubling time for this investment?

✓ 11. **Communication** The table below shows the population of a town from 1993 to 1999.

Year	1993	1994	1995	1996	1997	1998	1999
Population	500 000	525 000	551 250	578 813	607 754	638 142	670 049

Write a question about the population that involves exponential growth. Answer the question. Show all your work.

✓ 12. A principal of $500 is invested at 3% compounded annually. Pose a problem about this investment that involves exponential growth. Solve the problem. Show all your work.

13. A principal of $20 000 is invested at 4% compounded annually.

    a) Write an equation to describe the growth of the investment.

    b) Write a problem about this investment that involves exponential growth. Solve the problem. Show all your work.

✓ 14. **Thinking/Inquiry/Problem Solving** In 1990, one estimate of the world's population was 5.28 billion, growing at a rate of 1.55% per year.

    a) Predict the world's population in 2010 according to the estimate in 1990.

    b) According to the United Nations, the maximum population Earth can be expected to support is between 8 and 28 billion people. Estimate when a population of 12 billion will be reached.

Exponential Decay

Iodine-131 is present in radioactive waste from the nuclear power industry. It has a *half-life* of about 8 days. This means that every 8 days, one-half of the iodine-131 decays to a form that is not radioactive.

Suppose there are 100 g of iodine-131 to start.
Every 8 days, the mass decreases by one-half. The table shows the mass remaining after several 8-day periods.

Number of days	0	8	16	24	32
Mass (g)	100	50	25	12.5	6.25

Initially, there are 100 g of iodine-131.

After 8 days, or 1 half-life, there are 50 g left.

$$\text{Mass of iodine-131} = 100 \times \tfrac{1}{2}$$
$$= 100\left(\tfrac{1}{2}\right)^1$$

After 16 days, or 2 half-lives, there are 25 g left.

$$\text{Mass of iodine-131} = 100 \times \tfrac{1}{2} \times \tfrac{1}{2}$$
$$= 100\left(\tfrac{1}{2}\right)^2$$

After 24 days, or 3 half-lives, there are 12.5 g left.

$$\text{Mass of iodine-131} = 100 \times \tfrac{1}{2} \times \tfrac{1}{2} \times \tfrac{1}{2}$$
$$= 100\left(\tfrac{1}{2}\right)^3$$

After 32 days, or 4 half-lives, there are 6.25 g left.

$$\text{Mass of iodine-131} = 100 \times \tfrac{1}{2} \times \tfrac{1}{2} \times \tfrac{1}{2} \times \tfrac{1}{2}$$
$$= 100\left(\tfrac{1}{2}\right)^4$$

This pattern continues.

Thus, after n half-lives, there are $100\left(\tfrac{1}{2}\right)^n$ g of iodine-131 left.
The mass of iodine-131 can be represented by the exponential function $A = 100\left(\tfrac{1}{2}\right)^n$. In the equation $A = 100\left(\tfrac{1}{2}\right)^n$,

A is the mass of iodine-131 left after n half-lives.

100 is the initial mass of iodine-131.

$\tfrac{1}{2}$ is called the *decay factor,* since the mass is halved (that is, multiplied by $\tfrac{1}{2}$) each half-life.

n is the number of half-lives.

Recall that the general exponential function has equation $y = Ab^x$. From Section 3.3, recall that when b is between 0 and 1, the function illustrates exponential decay.

The graph of the function $A = 100\left(\frac{1}{2}\right)^n$ is plotted for values of n from 0 to 5. The shape of the graph is typical of a function that represents exponential decay.

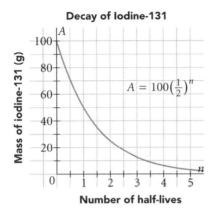

Decay of Iodine-131

Number of half-lives

Discuss

How are the equations and graphs that represent exponential growth and exponential decay similar? How are they different?

> ## TAKE NOTE
>
> ### Modelling Exponential Decay
>
> A quantity whose decrease over time can be described by an exponential function exhibits exponential decay.
>
> The equation $y = Ab^x$ can be used to describe the decay.
> y is the amount after x time periods.
> A is the initial amount.
> b is the decay factor, the number that the amount is multiplied by in each time period. For exponential decay, $b > 0$ and $b < 1$.
> x is the number of time periods.

Example 1

A radioactive substance has a half-life of 5 days. Suppose you have 70 g of this substance now.

a) Write an equation to represent the mass of the substance, y grams, after x half-lives.

b) Use the equation in part a to estimate the mass of the substance 30 days from now.

Solution

a) Use the equation $y = Ab^x$.

The initial amount is 70 g. Thus, $A = 70$

Every half-life, the amount decreases by $\frac{1}{2}$. Thus, $b = \frac{1}{2}$

The required equation is $y = 70\left(\frac{1}{2}\right)^x$.

b) The substance has a half-life of 5 days.

In 30 days, there are $\frac{30}{5}$, or 6 half-lives.

Substitute $x = 6$ in the equation $y = 70\left(\frac{1}{2}\right)^x$.

$y = 70\left(\frac{1}{2}\right)^6$

$ = 1.093\ 75$

There will be approximately 1.09 g of the substance 30 days from now.

As with exponential growth, in exponential decay the rate of decrease is often expressed as a percent.

Example 2

A photocopier sells for $12 000. Each year it depreciates, or decreases in value, by 15%.

a) Determine the decay factor, b.

b) Write an equation to represent the value, y dollars, of the photocopier when it is x years old.

c) Estimate the value of the machine when it is 5 years old.

Solution

a) Each year, the value of the photocopier decreases by 15%.

Thus, it is worth $100\% - 15\% = 85\%$ of its value the preceding year.

As a decimal, $85\% = 0.85$

The decay factor, b, is 0.85.

b) Use the equation $y = Ab^x$.

Substitute $A = 12\ 000$ and $b = 0.85$.

The required equation is $y = 12\ 000(0.85)^x$.

c) Substitute $x = 5$ in the equation $y = 12\ 000(0.85)^x$.

$y = 12\ 000(0.85)^5$

$ \doteq 5324.46$

The photocopier is worth approximately $5320 when it is 5 years old.

Decay Factor for Exponential Decay

For exponential decay, the decay factor, b, is given by $1 - r$, where r is the percent rate of decrease expressed as a decimal.

Example 3

Blue jeans fade with repeated washing. Suppose a pair of jeans loses 2% of its colour after each wash.

a) Write an equation to represent the percent of colour, y, after x washings.

b) How much of the original colour is left after 50 washings?

Solution

a) Use the equation $y = Ab^x$.

Initially, all the colour (100%) is present. Thus, $A = 100$

As a decimal, 2% = 0.02

Thus, $b = 1 - 0.02 = 0.98$

The required equation is $y = 100(0.98)^x$.

b) Substitute $x = 50$ in the equation $y = 100(0.98)^x$.

$y = 100(0.98)^{50}$

$\doteq 36.42$

About 36% of the original colour is left after 50 washings.

Example 4

Caffeine, found in pop, coffee, and tea, travels to your bloodstream after you consume it. After you drink a beverage that contains caffeine, 13% of the caffeine in your blood is removed every hour.

a) Write an equation to represent the percent of caffeine, y, that remains in your bloodstream x hours after you drink a can of pop.

b) What percent of the original amount of caffeine is left in your bloodstream 4 h after you drink a can of pop?

c) Graph the equation.

d) Estimate the time after which one-half the caffeine remains. This is the half-life of caffeine.

Solution

a) Use the equation $y = Ab^x$.

Initially, 100% of the caffeine is present. Thus, $A = 100$

As a decimal, $13\% = 0.13$; thus, $b = 1 - 0.13 = 0.87$

The required equation is $y = 100(0.87)^x$.

b) Substitute $x = 4$ in the equation $y = 100(0.87)^x$.

$$y = 100(0.87)^4$$
$$\doteq 57.3$$

About 57% of the original amount of caffeine is present 4 h after you drink a can of pop.

c) Make a table of values. Draw a graph of y against x.

x	$y = 100(0.87)^x$
0	$100(0.87)^0 = 100$
1	$100(0.87)^1 = 87$
2	$100(0.87)^2 \doteq 75.7$
3	$100(0.87)^3 \doteq 65.9$
4	$100(0.87)^4 \doteq 57.3$
5	$100(0.87)^5 \doteq 49.8$
6	$100(0.87)^6 \doteq 43.4$

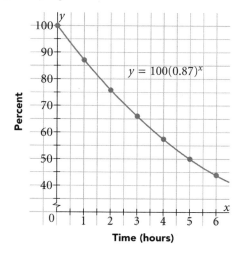

d) From the table and the graph, after 5 h, approximately one-half of the original caffeine remains.

 A

1. There are currently 1000 deer in a provincial park. Write an equation to represent y, the number of deer in the park x years from now, under each condition.

a) The population increases at a rate of 3% a year.

b) The population decreases at a rate of 3% a year.

2. A population decreases at each rate shown. Determine the decay factor for each rate of decrease.

    a) 12%   **b)** 6%   **c)** 3.4%   **d)** 8.2%   **e)** 10.5%

3. A population has each decay factor. What is the percent decrease in the population?

    a) 0.8   **b)** 0.95   **c)** 0.975   **d)** 0.96   **e)** 0.45

B

4. Knowledge/Understanding A radioactive isotope has a half-life of 1 day.

    a) Describe what is meant by the term "half-life" in this case.

    b) How much of a 1000-g sample would be left after each time? Use a table to organize your calculations.

        i) 1 day   **ii)** 2 days   **iii)** 3 days   **iv)** 4 days   **v)** n days

5. Radium-221 is a radioactive substance with a half-life of approximately 30 s.

    a) How many half-lives will have elapsed after each time?

        i) 30 s   **ii)** 60 s   **iii)** 90 s   **iv)** 120 s   **v)** 5 min

    b) How much of a 300-g sample would be left after each time? Use a table to organize your calculations.

        i) 30 s   **ii)** 60 s   **iii)** 90 s   **iv)** 120 s   **v)** 5 min

6. A laboratory has a 500-g sample of nitrogen-13. This substance has a half-life of approximately 10 min.

    a) Write an equation to represent the mass of the sample, y grams, left after x half-lives.

    b) How many half-lives will have elapsed in 1 h?

    c) How much of the sample is left after 1 h?

7. A radioactive isotope has a half-life of 5 years. A laboratory has a 24-g sample of the isotope.

    a) Write an equation to represent the mass of the sample, y grams, left after x half-lives.

    b) How many half-lives will have elapsed in 125 years?

    c) How much of the sample is left after 125 years?

8. A new car decreases in value exponentially after it is purchased. The value, V dollars, of a new car n years after it is purchased is given by the equation $V = 20\ 000(0.84)^n$.

    a) What was the purchase price of the car?

    b) By what percent does the value of the car decrease each year?

    c) Estimate the value of the car 6 years after it was purchased.

9. The infant mortality rate in Canada has been declining. An equation that models this situation is $D = 6(0.96)^n$, where D is the number of deaths per 1000 children under 1 year of age, and n is the number of years since 1995.

a) What does "infant mortality" mean?

b) In 1995, how many deaths were there per 1000 children under 1?

c) Estimate the number of deaths per 1000 children under 1 in 2000.

10. When light passes through ice, its intensity is reduced by 4% for every 1 cm thickness of ice.

a) Write an equation to express the percent of light, y, that penetrates x centimetres of ice.

b) What percent of light penetrates a sheet of ice 4.5 cm thick?

11. An endangered species of birds has a current population of 4000. Biologists estimate that the population decreases by 5% per year.

a) Write an equation to estimate y, the number of birds x years from now.

b) Estimate the number of birds at each time.

    i) 5 years from now   ii) 10 years from now

12. **Thinking/Inquiry/Problem Solving** An endangered whale species has a population of 1000. Biologists estimate that the population decreases by 5% per year. At this rate, how many years will it be before only 500 of the species remain?

13. Jean purchased a new car for $20 000 in 1990. Since then, the car has decreased in value by 12% per year.

a) Write an equation to represent the value, y dollars, of the car as a function of x, the number of years since 1990.

b) Graph the equation from part a for values of x up to 10.

c) Use the graph. How long does it take before the car is worth only one-half of its purchase price?

14. Application A cup of coffee contains approximately 100 mg of caffeine. After you drink a cup of coffee, the amount of caffeine in your bloodstream is reduced by about 13% per hour.

a) Write an equation to represent the mass of caffeine, y milligrams, in your bloodstream x hours after you drink a cup of coffee.

b) Graph the equation for values of x from 0 to 35 in steps of 5 h.

c) Use the graph to determine how many hours it takes for the mass of caffeine to be reduced to:

    i) 25 mg   **ii)** 10 mg   **iii)** 1 mg

d) Explain how this exercise is similar to, and different from *Example 4*.

15. A ball is dropped from a height of 4 m. After each bounce, the ball rises to 50% of its previous height.

    a) What is the height of the ball after the third bounce?

    b) After how many bounces will the ball's height be 0.125 m?

16. A ball is bounced straight down onto a concrete floor. After each bounce, the ball rises to 54% of the height from which it fell. Pose a problem about this situation that involves exponential decay. Solve the problem. Show all your work.

17. In 1990, the population of a small town was 22 234. Since then, the population has decreased by 4.2% per year.

    a) Write an equation that represents the population, y, as a function of x, the number of years since 1990.

    b) Write a problem about this situation that involves exponential decay. Solve the problem. Show all your work.

18. Communication

    a) Suppose you have a table of values that represents an exponential function. How do you know whether the table represents exponential growth or decay?

    b) Suppose you have an equation that represents an exponential function. How do you know whether the equation represents exponential growth or decay?

    c) Suppose you have a graph that represents an exponential function. How do you know whether the graph represents exponential growth or decay?

C

19. Several layers of glass are stacked. Each layer reduces the light that passes through it by 5%.

    a) Write an equation to represent y, the percent of light that passes through x layers of glass.

    b) Estimate the percent of light that passes through 5 layers of glass.

    c) Graph the equation. Use values of x from 0 to 14 in steps of 2 layers.

    d) Use the graph. Estimate the percent of light that passes through 7 layers of glass.

    e) Use the graph. Estimate the number of layers that will reduce the light by 50%.

In Chapter 1, you learned about linear growth. In Section 3.4, you learned about exponential growth. In this section, we will compare these and other models of growth.

Megan has just graduated from college. She has job offers from two different companies.

Company A: Starting salary of $30 000 plus a $1500 raise each year
Company B: Starting salary of $30 000 plus a 5% raise each year

Both jobs have good long-term prospects. If money is the only consideration, which job should Megan take?

In Company A, Megan's salary increases by $1500 each year.

In Company B, Megan's salary increases by 5% each year.
Each year, her salary is the preceding year's salary increased by 5%.
Salary = 100% of preceding year's salary + 5% of preceding year's salary
= 105% of preceding year's salary
Thus, each year, Megan's salary is 105%, or 1.05 times, her salary the preceding year.

We can use a table to compare the salaries Megan earns in the first 10 years at each job.

Year	Salary at Company A ($)	Yearly raise ($)
0	30 000	
		1500
1	30 000 + 1500 = 31 500	
		1500
2	31 500 + 1500 = 33 000	
		1500
3	33 000 + 1500 = 34 500	
		1500
4	34 500 + 1500 = 36 000	
		1500
5	36 000 + 1500 = 37 500	
		1500
6	37 500 + 1500 = 39 000	
		1500
7	39 000 + 1500 = 40 500	
		1500
8	40 500 + 1500 = 42 000	
		1500
9	42 000 + 1500 = 43 500	
		1500
10	43 500 + 1500 = 45 000	

Year	Salary at Company B ($)	Yearly raise ($)
0	30 000	
		1500
1	30 000 × 1.05 = 31 500	
		1575
2	31 500 × 1.05 = 33 075	
		1654
3	33 075 × 1.05 $\doteq$ 34 729	
		1736
4	34 729 × 1.05 $\doteq$ 36 465	
		1823
5	36 465 × 1.05 $\doteq$ 38 288	
		1914
6	38 288 × 1.05 $\doteq$ 40 202	
		2010
7	40 202 × 1.05 $\doteq$ 42 212	
		2111
8	42 212 × 1.05 $\doteq$ 44 323	
		2216
9	44 323 × 1.05 $\doteq$ 46 539	
		2327
10	46 539 × 1.05 $\doteq$ 48 866	

We can also compare the salaries by drawing a graph. The points are joined to show the trend.

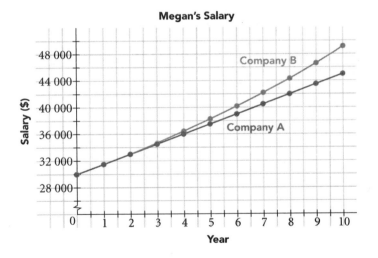

At Company A, Megan's salary increases by the same amount each year, $1500.
When we calculated her salary, we repeatedly added $1500.
When the salary is graphed, the points lie on a straight line.
Remember that these are the characteristics of linear growth.

At Company B, Megan's salary increases by the same percent each year, 5%.
When we calculated her salary, we repeatedly multiplied by 1.05.
When the salary is graphed, the points lie on a curve.
Remember that these are the characteristics of exponential growth.

At Company A, Megan's salary grows linearly. At Company B, Megan's salary grows exponentially.

Notice the difference between the rates of growth.

Under linear growth, Megan's salary grows by the same amount each year.

Under exponential growth, Megan's salary grows by an increasing amount each year. This is shown in the *Yearly raise* column of each table. For any year after the first year, the salary at Company B is greater than at Company A. Thus, growth occurs more rapidly under exponential growth than under linear growth.

Megan's salary grows more rapidly at Company B. If money is the only consideration, Megan should accept the job offer at Company B.

The differences between linear growth and exponential growth are summarized below.

TAKE NOTE

Comparison of Linear and Exponential Growth

Linear Growth

- The same number is repeatedly added.
- The rate of growth is constant.
- The graph is a straight line.

Exponential Growth

- The same number is repeatedly multiplied.
- The rate of growth is increasing.
- The graph is a curve.

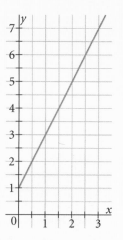

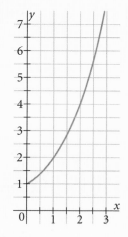

Example 1

A principal of $500 is invested at 5% annually for 20 years.

a) On the same grid, draw a graph to compare the growth of the investment under simple interest and under compound interest. For the compound interest, assume the interest is compounded annually.

b) What type of growth is illustrated by simple interest?

c) What type of growth is illustrated by compound interest?

d) Compare the rates of growth of the two investments.

Solution

a) Make a table of values. Use years from 0 to 20 in steps of 4.

For simple interest, use the formula $I = Prt$.

To calculate the interest earned every 4 years, substitute $P = 500$, $r = 0.05$, and $t = 4$.

$I = 500(0.05)(4)$
$\quad = 100$

$100 interest is earned every 4 years.

Every 4 years, $100 is added to the amount.

For compound interest, use the formula $A = P(1 + i)^n$.

Substitute $P = 500$ and $i = 0.05$.

$A = 500(1.05)^n$

In turn, substitute $n = 0, 4, 8, 12, 16, 20$ to determine A. The results are shown in the table.

Year	0	4	8	12	16	20
Simple interest amount ($)	500	600	700	800	900	1000
Compound interest amount ($)	500	607.75	738.73	897.93	1091.44	1326.65

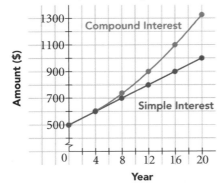

Amount of a $500 Investment under Simple and Compound Interest

b) The simple interest graph is a straight line. The growth of an investment under simple interest illustrates linear growth.

c) The compound interest graph is a curve. The growth of an investment under compound interest illustrates exponential growth.

d) Exponential growth is faster than linear growth. The investment that earns compound interest grows faster than the investment that earns simple interest.

In grade 10, you studied linear functions and quadratic functions.
The equation $y = 2x$ represents a linear function.
The equation $y = x^2$ represents a quadratic function.
The equation $y = 2^x$ represents an exponential function.

Compare the equation $y = x^2$ with the exponential function $y = 2^x$.
Both equations contain powers.
In the equation $y = x^2$, the base is a variable and the exponent is a number.
However, in the equation $y = 2^x$, the base is a number and the exponent is a variable.

We can compare the rates of growth of the three functions above.
One way to compare is with tables of values.

To compare the rates of growth, we calculate the differences between successive y-values.

x	y = 2x	Difference
0	0	
		2
1	2	
		2
2	4	
		2
3	6	
		2
4	8	
		2
5	10	
		2
6	12	

x	y = x²	Difference
0	0	
		1
1	1	
		3
2	4	
		5
3	9	
		7
4	16	
		9
5	25	
		11
6	36	

x	y = 2ˣ	Difference
0	1	
		1
1	2	
		2
2	4	
		4
3	8	
		8
4	16	
		16
5	32	
		32
6	64	

In the function $y = 2x$, the same number, 2, is repeatedly added. The differences are constant. This function illustrates linear growth.

In the function $y = x^2$, the differences increase by 2. This function illustrates *quadratic growth*.

In the function $y = 2^x$, the same number, 2, is repeatedly multiplied. The differences increase by a factor of 2. This function illustrates exponential growth.

We graph the functions on the same grid.

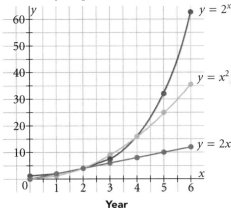

Comparing Rates of Growth

The tables and graphs show that the exponential function $y = 2^x$ grows the fastest, followed by the quadratic function $y = x^2$, then the linear function $y = 2x$.

The difference in the rates of growth is small at first, but increases as x increases.

In general, growth occurs most rapidly under exponential growth, followed by quadratic growth, and then linear growth.

Example 2

Compare the growth represented by each of these two equations.

$$y = 100x^2$$
$$y = 100(2)^x$$

a) Copy and complete the table of values for $y = 100x^2$.

x	0	1	2	3	4	5	6
y							

b) Copy the table in part a. Complete the table for $y = 100(2)^x$.

c) Graph the data from both tables on the same grid.

d) What type of growth does the graph of $y = 100x^2$ represent?

e) What type of growth does the graph of $y = 100(2)^x$ represent?

f) Which graph corresponds to a higher rate of growth?

Solution

a) For $y = 100x^2$

x	0	1	2	3	4	5	6
y	0	100	400	900	1600	2500	3600

b) For $y = 100(2)^x$

x	0	1	2	3	4	5	6
y	100	200	400	800	1600	3200	6400

c)

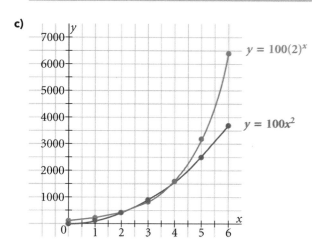

d) The equation $y = 100x^2$ represents a quadratic function. Its graph represents quadratic growth.

e) The equation $y = 100(2)^x$ represents an exponential function. Its graph represents exponential growth.

f) The rate of growth is greater under exponential growth.

3.6 Exercises

1. Which table of values illustrates the greatest rate of change? Explain how you know.

a)

x	0	1	2	3	4	5
y	0	3	6	9	12	15

b)

x	0	1	2	3	4	5
y	0	1	8	27	64	125

c)

x	0	1	2	3	4	5
y	1	3	9	27	81	243

2. Which table of values illustrates the least rate of change? Explain.

a)

x	0	1	2	3	4	5
y	0	1	4	9	16	25

b)

x	0	1	2	3	4	5
y	0	1	2	3	4	5

c)

x	0	1	2	3	4	5
y	0	1	8	27	64	125

3. Which graph, below left, illustrates the greatest rate of change for values of x between 0 and 5? Explain how you know.

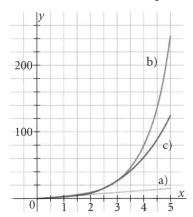
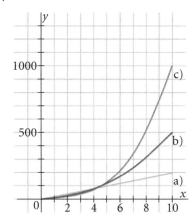

4. Which graph, above right, illustrates the least rate of change for values of x between 0 and 10? Explain.

5. Which situations illustrate linear growth? Which illustrate exponential growth? Explain.

a) John earns $8 per hour. How do his earnings grow?

b) Mika's short-term deposit pays 4% compounded monthly. How does the amount grow?

c) The student population at a school has increased by 100 students in each of the past 5 years. How does the population grow?

d) Guong's regular interest CSB pays 4.75% simple interest. How does the amount grow?

e) The population of Ontario has increased by 1.6% annually over the last 8 years. How has the population grown?

6. **Knowledge/Understanding** Compare the graphs of $y = 6x$, $y = 3(2x)^2$, and $y = 3(2)^x$.

a) Copy and complete the table.

x	0	1	2	3	4	5
$y = 6x$						
$y = 3(2x)^2$						
$y = 3(2)^x$						

b) Graph each function.

c) Use the table and the graph. Which function shows the greatest rate of change? Which shows the least rate of change? Explain.

7. Compare the graphs of $y = 3x$, $y = 3x^2$, and $y = 3^x$.

a) Copy and complete the table.

x	0	1	2	3	4	5
$y = 3x$						
$y = 3x^2$						
$y = 3^x$						

b) Graph the data in the table.

c) Use the table and the graph. Which function has the greatest rate of change? Which has the least rate of change? Explain.

8. **Communication** A city council wants to discourage illegal parking. It has two plans.

Plan A: A $10 fine for the first offence. The fine increases by $10 for each subsequent offence.

Plan B: A $10 fine for the first offence. The fines doubles for each subsequent offence.

a) For each plan, make a table of values to show the fines for 0 to 6 offences.

b) Graph the data from the tables on the same grid.

c) Which type of growth does each plan illustrate? Explain how you know.

d) Will the city receive greater revenue from Plan A or Plan B? Explain.

e) How likely is it that Plan B would be adopted? Explain.

9. John is starting a new job. He chooses his method of payment.

Option A: Starting salary of $10 per hour, a raise of $1 per hour each year

Option B: Starting salary of $10 per hour, a raise of 10% per hour each year

Suppose John stays at the job for 5 years.

a) Make a table of values to show John's earnings for Option A. Add a difference column to show the growth each year.

b) Make a table of values to show John's earnings for Option B. Add a difference column to show the growth each year.

c) What type of growth does Option A represent? Explain.

d) What type of growth does Option B represent? Explain.

e) With which type of growth will the salary grow faster? Explain.

10. A school has a population of 800 students.

a) Suppose the population grows by 80 students each year. Copy and complete this table.

Year, n	0	1	2	3	4	5
Population, P						

b) Suppose the population grows by 10% each year.

Copy the table in part a. Complete the table for a 10% annual growth.

c) Graph the data from both tables on the same grid.

d) What type of growth do the data in part a represent? Explain.

e) What type of growth do the data in part b represent? Explain.

f) With which type of growth will the population grow faster? Explain.

11. Application Canada has a population of approximately 30 000 000.

a) Suppose the population grows by 100 000 each year. Copy and complete this table.

Year, n	0	1	2	3	4	5	6	7	8
Population, P									

b) Suppose the population grows by 3.3% each year.

Copy the table in part a. Complete the table for a 3.3% annual growth.

c) Graph the data from both tables on the same grid.

d) What type of growth do the data in part a represent? Explain.

e) What type of growth do the data in part b represent? Explain.

f) With which type of growth will the population grow faster? Explain.

12. **Thinking/Inquiry/Problem Solving** A business owner must select a depreciation method for her business equipment. One method is straight-line depreciation, where the book value of the item decreases at the same rate each year over a period of years (the effective life of the equipment). The salvage value at the end of this time will be $0. A second method is a declining balance method of depreciation, where the book value decreases by 30% of its value the preceding year. Suppose an item that cost $8000 has an effective life of 5 years.

a) Draw a graph to represent each depreciation method.

b) Predict the value of each item after 5 years, under each method.

c) Compare the two graphs. Make a recommendation, with reasons, for the better method of depreciation.

Chef

For some people, cooking is a daily chore. For a chef or cook, however, cooking transcends everything— it is an art that encompasses taste, smell, texture, and presentation of food. The chef determines the direction of a restaurant's menu by creating a variety of dishes that give the establishment its reputation and character.

Chefs have other duties aside from cooking. They administer the kitchen, order the supplies, supervise staff, demonstrate new preparation techniques, and plan ahead for seasonal and special occasion menus. Quality control is an integral part of a chef's responsibilities as people's culinary tastes are more sophisticated and presentation has become a major part of the dining experience. In a big hotel kitchen, chefs may choose to specialize in one specific area, such as desserts, soups, sauces, or pastas.

A long-time chef of a fine restaurant says, "The restaurant business is very competitive today and customers have become very demanding. The dishes we serve have to be of exceptional quality and the presentation exquisite. A chef is ultimately responsible for the success or failure of a restaurant."

Most chefs put in long hours, and evenings and weekends are mandatory.

Where's the Math?
Chefs often have to adapt the ingredients of recipes for servings greater than those originally indicated. They use ratio and proportion and skill in calculation. Knowledge of the Imperial system of measurement is essential. When ordering food supplies, a chef must estimate and budget.

1. Explain the difference between exponential growth and exponential decay.

2. There are currently 50 sea turtles in a wildlife sanctuary. Write an equation to represent the number of turtles, y, in the sanctuary x years from now, in each case.

   a) The population increases at a rate of 2.5% a year.

   b) The population decreases at a rate of 2.5% a year.

3. The cost of a candy bar, C dollars, has increased according to the formula $C = 0.05(1.08)^n$, where n is the number of years since 1960.

   a) In 1960, what was the cost of a candy bar?

   b) Since 1960, what has been the annual percent increase in the cost of a candy bar?

   c) Suppose the cost continues to increase at the same rate. Estimate the cost of a candy bar in the year 2010.

4. In 1991, there were approximately 3.7 million computers in use in Canada. Since then, the number of computers in use has increased at an average rate of 17.1% per year.

   a) Write an equation to represent the number of computers in use in Canada, y million, as a function of x, the number of years since 1991.

   b) Estimate the number of computers in use in Canada in 2001.

5. For every 1 m descended under water, the intensity of light decreases by 2.5%.

   a) Write an equation to represent the percent of light intensity, y, at a depth of x metres.

   b) Graph the equation for depths of 0 to 100 m in steps of 10 m.

   c) Use the graph to estimate the depth at which the intensity of light is 50% of the intensity at the surface.

6. A radioactive isotope has a half-life of 4 days. How much of the isotope is left in a 20-mg sample after each time?

   a) 4 days   b) 8 days   c) 16 days

7. On the same grid, plot the graphs of $y = 2x$, $y = x^2$, and $y = 2^x$ for values of x between 0 and 5. Which graph represents the highest rate of growth? Explain.

To complete this project, you need current and reliable information. You can get this from the Internet, the library in your school, or a public library.

For the Internet, start your search from our web site: www.pearsoned.ca/onmath11

The national debt is the money owed by our government to its creditors. This debt is partly domestic and partly external. Domestic debt is owed to citizens of Canada. External debt is owed to foreigners, such as international banks, individuals, and other governments.

In October 2000, Canada's national debt was about $667 122 000 000. The population of Canada on that date was about 31 690 000.

1. What is the national debt per person?

2. To understand why our national debt is so high, we must consider how the national debt has grown over the years. Here are some questions for you to research.

   a) What was the national debt 35 years ago?

   b) What was the national debt in 1990? What will it be in 2010?

   c) At what rate has the debt grown over the last 40 years?

   d) What do these trends in the national debt mean to you?

   e) How much do we currently owe?

   f) What are the interest charges?

   g) Will I be paying the debt in future years?

3. The table shows how Canada's national debt has grown since 1970. Since 1995, the Canadian government has taken steps to reduce the growth of the national debt.

Year	1970	1975	1980	1985	1990	1995
National debt (billions $)	36	55	111	251	407	596

   a) Graph the data.

   b) Determine whether the data are closest to a model of linear growth, quadratic growth, or exponential growth. Explain how you know.

   c) Extend the graph. Estimate the national debt today.

   d) Research to determine the national debt today. How does it compare with the prediction in part c? Explain any differences.

   e) Estimate the national debt in 2025.

f) What assumptions are you making when you calculate the future national debt?

4. In Chapter 1, you learned about Canada Savings Bonds. These bonds are part of the domestic debt owed to Canadians. Research to investigate how this happens.

5. Write a report on the story of Canada's national debt. Include the results of exercises 1 to 4 in your report.

6. Research to investigate the provincial debt.

a) What is Ontario's total debt?

b) What is Ontario's debt per person?

c) Determine Ontario's debt for the years from 1970 to 1995. Compare these data with the data in exercise 3.

d) Are the data for Ontario's debt represented by a model of linear growth or exponential growth? Explain.

e) Predict Ontario's debt in 2025.

Career Profile

Automotive Service Technician

An auto technician inspects, diagnoses, repairs, and services motor vehicles. For those considering a career as an automotive technician: Are you good with your hands? Are you prepared to get your hands dirty? Are you willing to do a job that is very physical and may involve heavy lifting? Do you mind working some evenings and weekends?

Today's automotive technicians must be able to use computerized diagnostic equipment to fix the problem. This may involve disassembling, repairing, and reassembling the parts and systems of motor vehicles. The ability to read and understand manufacturers' and technical manuals is important. Often a technician chooses to specialize in one type of system, such transmission, brakes, fuel system, or built-in electronics.

An automotive technician says, "Today's auto techs have to be on the ball. They must be willing to continually upgrade both technical and product knowledge of motor vehicles by attending courses and clinics. There's always something new to do and learn in solving a vehicle's problems."

Where's the Math?
The repair process may involve taking careful measurements, then calculating using formulas for quantities such as volume, displacement, or airflow.

MATHEMATICS TOOLKIT

Algebra Tools

> The exponent laws

Multiplication Law	$a^m \times a^n = a^{m+n}$
Division Law	$a^m \div a^n = a^{m-n}, \ a \neq 0$
Power of a Power Law	$(a^m)^n = a^{mn}$
Power of a Product Law	$(ab)^m = a^m b^m$
Power of a Quotient Law	$\left(\frac{a}{b}\right)^m = \frac{a^m}{b^m}, \ b \neq 0$
Zero Exponent	$a^0 = 1, \ a \neq 0$

Negative Exponents
$$a^{-m} = \frac{1}{a^m}; \ \frac{1}{a^{-m}} = a^m; \ \left(\frac{a}{b}\right)^{-m} = \left(\frac{b}{a}\right)^m; \ a \neq 0, \ b \neq 0$$

Function Tools

> An exponential function has an equation of the form $y = Ab^x$, where A is any number and b is any positive number except 1.

> Properties of the exponential function $y = b^x$

When $b > 1$, the graph goes up to the right. This represents exponential growth.

When $b > 0$ and $b < 1$, the graph goes down to the right. This represents exponential decay.

The y-intercept is 1.

There is no x-intercept. The x-axis is an asymptote.

The domain (the set of all possible x-values) is the set of all real numbers. The range (the set of all possible y-values) is the set of all positive real numbers.

> The equation $y = Ab^x$ can be used to describe exponential growth or decay, where y is the amount after x time periods.

A is the initial amount.

b is the growth or decay factor: for growth, $b > 1$;
for decay, $b > 0$ and $b < 1$.

NS 1. Simplify. Express each answer with positive exponents.

   a) $a^{-5} \times a^6$ b) $\frac{x^4}{x^6}$ c) $(3ab)^3(3ab)^{-2}$

   d) $\left(\frac{3}{x^2}\right)^5$ e) $(2xy^4)^0$ f) $\left(\frac{x^{-3}}{x^{-4}}\right)^2$

2. Evaluate. Round to 2 decimal places where necessary.

   a) $5.1^{-2} \times 2.4^{-1}$ b) $4.8^3 + 6.9^{-2}$ c) $8^{-2} \times 2^5$

   d) $\left(\frac{1}{2}\right)^{-2} - \left(\frac{3}{4}\right)^{-1}$ e) $3^{-3} - 2^3$ f) $32^{-4} \div 16^{-5}$

3.1 3. A principal of $1500 is invested at 4.5% compounded annually. The amount, A dollars, after n years can be represented by the function $A = 1500(1.045)^n$. Calculate the amount after each time.

   a) 4 years   b) 6 years   c) 9 years

4. Refer to exercise 3.

   a) Graph the function $A = 1500(1.045)^n$.

   b) Estimate the value of n when $A = 1750$.

   c) Use the graph to determine how long it takes for the investment to double.

3.2 5. Evaluate without using a calculator.

   a) $100^{\frac{5}{2}}$ b) $64^{\frac{2}{3}}$ c) $36^{\frac{3}{2}}$

   d) $27^{\frac{4}{3}}$ e) $9^{\frac{5}{2}}$ f) $125^{\frac{4}{3}}$

6. Evaluate. Write each number to 2 decimal places.

   a) $119.25^{1.3}$ b) $3.06^{-2.3}$ c) $170.5^{\frac{2}{3}}$

   d) $1.2^{-0.5}$ e) $50^{\frac{5}{2}}$ f) $\left(\frac{3}{8}\right)^{\frac{1}{4}}$

3.3 7. a) Copy and complete this table of values for $y = 1.5^x$.

x	−1	0	1	2	3	4
y						

   b) Use a whole sheet of grid paper. Graph $y = 1.5^x$.

   c) What is the x-intercept? What is the y-intercept?

   d) What is the asymptote for the graph?

   e) Use the graph. Estimate the value of x for each value of y.

   i) 2.75   ii) 1.6   iii) 1.8

3.4 **8.** The population of a strain of bacteria doubles every 30 min. Suppose there are 100 bacteria at the start.

    a) Write an equation to represent y, the number of bacteria after x hours.

    b) How many bacteria are there after each time?

      i) 4 h   **ii)** 6 h   **iii)** 10 h

9. The table shows a school population.

Year	1995	1996	1997	1998	1999
Population	500	515	530	546	562

Write a problem about this population that involves exponential growth. Solve the problem. Show all your work.

3.5 **10.** An office machine is purchased for $5200. Its value each year is 80% of its value the preceding year. Its value, V dollars, after n years is given by the equation $V = 5200(0.8)^n$.

    a) Graph the equation for $n = 0$ to 16.

    b) Use the graph or the equation. Predict the value after 12 years.

    c) The owner of the machine decides to replace it when its value falls below $250. Estimate when the owner will replace the machine.

    d) If you have a graphing calculator, use it to graph the function, then check your answers to parts b and c.

11. A radioactive isotope has a half-life of 1 week. Suppose you have 100 g of the isotope now.

    a) Write an equation to represent the mass of the isotope, y grams, after x weeks.

    b) Use the equation in part a to estimate the mass of the isotope after 10 weeks.

3.6 **12.** Alun has a new job. He is given the choice of two methods of payment:
Method A: A starting wage of $12/h, with a raise of $0.50/h per year.
Method B: A starting wage of $12/h with a raise of 5%/h per year.
Alun expects to stay at the job for 6 years.

    a) Make a table to show Alun's earnings for each method of payment.

    b) Which type of growth does each method represent? Explain.

    c) Which method of payment should Alun choose? Explain.

1. Simplify. Express the answer with positive exponents.

   a) $(x^{-2}y)^4$

   b) $(a^3)^0$

   c) $(r^2s^{-3})^3$

   d) $\left(\dfrac{x^2}{y^3}\right)^4$

   e) $\left(\dfrac{a^{-1}}{a^2}\right)^3$

   f) $(x^4y^2)^{-3}$

2. Evaluate. Round to 3 decimal places if necessary.

   a) $6.3^{2.5} \times 1.02^{-1}$

   b) $27^{-3} + 16^{\frac{1}{4}}$

   c) $2.6^3 - 1.5^2$

3. **Knowledge/Understanding**

   a) Copy and complete this table of values for $y = 0.75^x$.

x	−1	0	1	2	3
y					

   b) Use a whole sheet of grid paper. Graph $y = 0.75^x$.

   c) Use the graph. Estimate the value of x for each value of y.

   i) 0.49

   ii) 1.15

   iii) 0.70

4. **Application** A company estimates that one-quarter of all the bottles it distributes are recycled each year. One year, it distributes 1 million bottles. The function that represents the number of bottles, N, still in use after t years is $N = 1\,000\,000\left(\dfrac{1}{4}\right)^t$.

   a) Graph the function.

   b) During which year after distribution are fewer than 1000 of the original bottles still in use?

5. **Thinking/Inquiry/Problem Solving** The world's population in 2000 was over 6 billion (6 000 000 000) people. Since 1650, the world's population has been growing exponentially.

Year	1650	1825	1880	1925	1955	1970	1998	2000
Population (billions)	0.5	1	1.5	2	2.9	3.6	4.8	6.0

   a) From 1650, how long did it take for the population to double?

   b) How long will it take for the population to double again?

6. **Communication** Suppose there are 50 bacteria in a culture. The number of bacteria doubles every day. Explain how you calculate the number of bacteria after 1 week.

4 Annuities

Curriculum Expectations

By the end of this chapter, you will:

> Solve exponential equations involving common bases.

> Determine whether a sequence is arithmetic or geometric, or neither.

> Solve problems related to the formulas for the nth term and the sum of n terms of geometric sequences and series.

> Solve problems involving the calculation of the amount and the regular payment in the formula for the amount of an ordinary annuity, using scientific calculators.

> Demonstrate an understanding of the relationships between compound interest, geometric sequences, and exponential growth.

> Determine the effect of compound interest on deposits made into savings accounts (for example, demonstrate the effect of saving a small amount on a regular basis, compare the effects of different compounding periods, and so on).

> Demonstrate, through calculation, the advantage of early deposits to long-term savings plans.

Necessary Skills

1 Review: Arithmetic Sequences

In Chapter 1, you learned about sequences.

Remember that a sequence is an ordered list of numbers.
A sequence can be defined by:

- a list of its terms; for example, 3, 8, 13, 18, …
- a formula for the general term, the nth term, of the sequence; for example, $t_n = 5n - 2$

In an arithmetic sequence, the same number is added to each term to get the next term. The number added is the common difference, d.

Here are two examples of arithmetic sequences.

$$3, 8, 13, 18, \ldots \qquad d = 5$$
$$35, 31, 27, 23, \ldots \qquad d = -4$$

The formula for the general term of an arithmetic sequence is $t_n = a + (n - 1)d$, where a is the first term, n is the position of the term in the sequence, and d is the common difference.

An arithmetic sequence with a positive common difference illustrates linear growth.

Example 1

a) Write the first 4 terms of the sequence with general term $t_n = 3n + 4$.

b) Is the sequence arithmetic? If so, state the common difference.

Solution

a) Substitute $n = 1,\ 2,\ 3$, and 4 into the formula $t_n = 3n + 4$.

$$t_1 = 3(1) + 4 = 7$$
$$t_2 = 3(2) + 4 = 10$$
$$t_3 = 3(3) + 4 = 13$$
$$t_4 = 3(4) + 4 = 16$$

The first 4 terms are 7, 10, 13, 16.

b) Each term after the first is 3 more than the preceding term.
The sequence is arithmetic with common difference 3.

Example 2 Determine the 62nd term of the arithmetic sequence 7, 12, 17, 22, ...

Solution

Use the formula $t_n = a + (n - 1)d$.

$d = 12 - 7$
$\quad = 5$

Substitute $a = 7$, $n = 62$, and $d = 5$.

$t_n = a + (n - 1)d$
$t_{62} = 7 + (62 - 1)(5)$
$\quad = 7 + 61(5)$
$\quad = 7 + 305$
$\quad = 312$

The 62nd term is 312.

Exercises

1. Write the first 4 terms of the sequence defined by each general term. Determine whether the sequence is arithmetic. If a sequence is arithmetic, state its common difference.

   a) $t_n = 3n$
   b) $t_n = 6n - 4$
   c) $t_n = \frac{1}{n}$
   d) $t_n = n^2 + 2$
   e) $t_n = -n + 7$
   f) $t_n = 2^n$
   g) $t_n = \frac{n}{3}$
   h) $t_n = 4(3)^n$

2. Calculate the indicated term for each arithmetic sequence.

   a) 98, 93, 88, 83, ...; t_{22}
   b) 7, 14, 21, 28, ...; t_{15}
   c) 2, 4, 6, 8, ...; t_{41}
   d) $-2, -12, -22, -32, ...$; t_{80}
   e) 16, 12, 8, 4, ...; t_{17}
   f) 2, 12, 22, 32, ...; t_{36}
   g) $-5, 2, 9, 16, ...$; t_{45}
   h) 205, 199, 193, 187, ...; t_{80}

2 New: Solving Exponential Equations

An equation where the variable is an exponent is called an *exponential equation*; for example, $2^x = 16$.

An exponential equation can sometimes be solved using the following property.

If two powers with the same base are equal, then the exponents are equal.

That is, if $a^m = a^n$, then $m = n$ ($a > 0$ and $a \neq 1$)

Example 1 Solve each equation.

a) $2^x = 2^5$ **b)** $3^x = 3^{-4}$

c) $5^{x-1} = 5^3$ **d)** $10^{2x} = 10^8$

Solution

a) $2^x = 2^5$ The powers are equal. Since they have the same base,

      $x = 5$ the exponents must be equal.

b) $3^x = 3^{-4}$

      $x = -4$

c) $5^{x-1} = 5^3$

    $x - 1 = 3$

        $x = 4$

d) $10^{2x} = 10^8$

     $2x = 8$

       $x = 4$

Sometimes, we rewrite an exponential equation so the bases are the same.

Example **2** Solve each equation.

   a) $2^x = 16$ **b)** $5^{2x} = 25$ **c)** $3^x = \frac{1}{9}$ **d)** $32^{x-1} = 4^{3x}$

Solution

a) $2^x = 16$

  Write 16 as a power with base 2; that is, $16 = 2^4$
  Then, both sides of the equation have the same base.
  $2^x = 2^4$
  $x = 4$

b) $5^{2x} = 25$ Write 25 as a power with base 5.
  $5^{2x} = 5^2$
  $2x = 2$
  $x = 1$

c) $3^x = \frac{1}{9}$ Write $\frac{1}{9}$ as a power with base 3; that is, $\frac{1}{9} = \frac{1}{3^2}$
  $3^x = 3^{-2}$
  $x = -2$

d) $32^{x-1} = 4^{3x}$

  Rewrite the equation so the bases are the same.
  Since $32 = 2^5$ and $4 = 2^2$, rewrite each power with base 2.
  $(2^5)^{x-1} = (2^2)^{3x}$ Use the power of a power law.
  $2^{5x-5} = 2^{6x}$ Multiply the exponents.
  $5x - 5 = 6x$
  $-5 = x$

Exercises

1. Solve each equation.

   a) $3^x = 3^3$ **b)** $2^x = 2^{-1}$ **c)** $4^x = 4^7$

   d) $10^x = 10^{-2}$ **e)** $7^x = 7^2$ **f)** $5^x = 5^{-4}$

2. Solve each equation.

   a) $2^{x+1} = 2^9$ **b)** $4^{x+3} = 4^8$ **c)** $3^{x+2} = 3^{-2}$

   d) $5^{x-2} = 5^4$ **e)** $3^{x-1} = 3^7$ **f)** $10^{x-3} = 10^{-4}$

3. Solve each equation.

   a) $4^{2x} = 4^{10}$ **b)** $3^{3x} = 3^{-9}$ **c)** $2^{2x} = 2^{-6}$

   d) $10^{4x} = 10^{16}$ **e)** $5^{-x} = 5^5$ **f)** $3^{-2x} = 3^{-8}$

4. Solve each equation.

   a) $10^{x+1} = 10^{2x-3}$ **b)** $5^{2x+1} = 5^{x-1}$ **c)** $3^{-2x+1} = 3^{x-2}$

   d) $6^{5x-1} = 6^{11-x}$ **e)** $2^{2x-1} = 2^{3x+4}$ **f)** $4^{x+6} = 4^{-3x-6}$

5. Solve each equation.

   a) $2^x = 8$ **b)** $3^x = 9$ **c)** $4^x = 16$

   d) $2^x = 32$ **e)** $10^x = 1000$ **f)** $3^x = 3$

   g) $6^x = 36$ **h)** $4^x = 64$ **i)** $7^x = 49$

6. Solve each equation.

   a) $10^{2x} = 10\ 000$ **b)** $3^{3x} = 27$ **c)** $2^{2x} = 64$

   d) $10^{3x} = 1000$ **e)** $3^{2x} = 9$ **f)** $4^{3x} = 64$

7. Solve each equation.

   a) $2^{x-6} = 64$ **b)** $2^{2x-1} = 128$ **c)** $3^{x-2} = 81$

   d) $2^{-x} = 4$ **e)** $3^{-x} = 27$ **f)** $5^{x+2} = 25^{6-x}$

8. Solve each equation.

   a) $2^x = \frac{1}{4}$ **b)** $3^x = \frac{1}{27}$ **c)** $10^x = \frac{1}{100}$

   d) $2^{x+2} = \frac{1}{8}$ **e)** $6^{x+1} = \left(\frac{1}{36}\right)^{x+1}$ **f)** $100^{2-x} = 0.01^{x+1}$

9. Solve each equation.

   a) $4^{3x-2} = 32^{x+1}$ **b)** $16^{2x-5} = 8^{3x+4}$ **c)** $25^{x+1} = 125^{x-2}$

   d) $3^{2x+8} = 9^{-x-2}$ **e)** $4^{2x-3} = 8^{x-1}$ **f)** $100^{2x-3} = 1000^{3x+1}$

In Chapter 3, you learned that money earning compound interest is an example of exponential growth.

Consider a $100 investment that earns 5% compounded annually. The amount, A, at the end of n years is given by the exponential function $A = 100(1.05)^n$.

Substitute $n = 1, 2, 3,$ and 4 into the equation $A = 100(1.05)^n$ to calculate the amount at the end of each of the first 4 years.

End of year 1: $A = 100(1.05)^1$
$= 105$

End of year 2: $A = 100(1.05)^2$
$= 110.25$

End of year 3: $A = 100(1.05)^3$
$\doteq 115.76$

End of year 4: $A = 100(1.05)^4$
$\doteq 121.55$

At the end of 4 years, the $100 investment amounts to $121.55.

The principal and amounts can be written as the sequence
100, 105, 110.25, 115.76, 121.55, ….

A sequence defined by an exponential function is called a *geometric sequence*. In a geometric sequence, each term is multiplied by the same number to get the next term.
The number that each term is multiplied by is called the *common ratio*. To calculate the common ratio, divide a term by its preceding term.

In the sequence above, each term is 1.05 times the preceding term. The sequence is geometric with common ratio 1.05.

Here are two other geometric sequences:

Geometric sequence	**Common ratio**
3, 12, 48, 192, …	$\frac{12}{3} = 4$
	$\frac{48}{12} = 4$
	$\frac{192}{48} = 4$
128, 64, 32, 16, …	$\frac{64}{128} = 0.5$
	$\frac{32}{64} = 0.5$
	$\frac{16}{32} = 0.5$

Example 1 Determine whether each sequence is geometric.
 a) 1, 10, 100, 1000, …
 b) 2, 4, 6, 8, …

Solution

Check to see if there is a common ratio. To calculate the common ratio, divide a term by its preceding term.

 a) 1, 10, 100, 1000, …

$$\frac{10}{1} = 10$$

$$\frac{100}{10} = 10$$

$$\frac{1000}{100} = 10$$

There is a common ratio of 10. The sequence is geometric.

 b) 2, 4, 6, 8, …

$$\frac{4}{2} = 2$$

$$\frac{6}{4} = 1.5$$

$$\frac{8}{6} \doteq 1.33$$

There is no common ratio. The sequence is not geometric.

Discuss
What kind of sequence is shown in part b? Explain.

Example 2 A geometric sequence has first term −2 and common ratio 3.
 a) Write the first 5 terms of the sequence.
 b) Determine the general term of the sequence.

Solution

 a) The common ratio is 3. Multiply each term by 3 to get the next term.

$$t_1 = -2$$
$$t_2 = -2 \times 3 = -6$$
$$t_3 = -6 \times 3 = -18$$
$$t_4 = -18 \times 3 = -54$$
$$t_5 = -54 \times 3 = -162$$

The first 5 terms are −2, −6, −18, −54, −162.

b) Look for a pattern in how each term was calculated.

$t_1 = -2$

$t_2 = -2(3)$

$t_3 = -2(3)^2$

$t_4 = -2(3)^3$

$t_5 = -2(3)^4$

In each term, the exponent is 1 less than the term number.

This pattern continues.

The general term, t_n, is the nth term of the sequence.

$t_n = -2(3)^{n-1}$

The general term is $t_n = -2(3)^{n-1}$.

We can generalize the pattern in *Example 2* to determine the general term of any geometric sequence.

The general geometric sequence has first term a and common ratio r.
Multiply each term after the first by r to get the next term.

$t_1 = a = ar^0$ Remember that $r^0 = 1$.

$t_2 = a \times r = ar^1$

$t_3 = ar^1 \times r = ar^2$

$t_4 = ar^2 \times r = ar^3$

$t_5 = ar^3 \times r = ar^4$

The number of common ratios in each term is 1 less than the term number.
This pattern continues.

So, the nth term has $(n-1)$ common ratios; that is, $t_n = ar^{n-1}$.

TAKE NOTE

General Geometric Sequence

The general geometric sequence is $a, \ ar, \ ar^2, \ ar^3, \ ar^4, \ \ldots$

The general term is $t_n = ar^{n-1}$.

    a is the first term.

    r is the common ratio.

    n is the term number; that is, the position of the term in the sequence.

    t_n is the value of the nth term.

Example 3

A geometric sequence is 3, 6, 12, 24, ….

a) Calculate the 14th term.

b) This sequence has the term 384. What is the position of this term?

Solution

Since $\frac{6}{3} = 2$, the common ratio, r, is 2. The first term, a, is 3.

Use the formula for the nth term: $t_n = ar^{n-1}$

a) Substitute $a = 3$, $r = 2$, and $n = 14$.

$$t_{14} = 3(2)^{14-1}$$
$$= 3(2)^{13}$$
$$= 24\ 576$$

The 14th term is 24 576.

b) We know the value of the nth term is 384.

Substitute $t_n = 384$, $a = 3$, and $r = 2$.

$$384 = 3(2)^{n-1}$$

This is an exponential equation.

$384 = 3(2)^{n-1}$ Divide each side by 3.

$128 = 2^{n-1}$ Write 128 as a power of 2.

$2^7 = 2^{n-1}$

The powers are equal. Since the bases are the same, the exponents are equal.

$$7 = n - 1$$
$$8 = n$$

384 is the 8th term of the sequence.

In Necessary Skills, you reviewed arithmetic sequences. *Example 4* illustrates how to generate an arithmetic sequence and a geometric sequence.

Example 4

The first two terms of a sequence are 2, 4, ….

a) Write the first 6 terms when the sequence is arithmetic.

b) Write the first 6 terms when the sequence is geometric.

Solution

a) Remember that an arithmetic sequence has a common difference.

Common difference $= 4 - 2$

$$= 2$$

Each term is 2 more than the preceding term.

The first 6 terms of the arithmetic sequence are 2, 4, 6, 8, 10, 12.

b) A geometric sequence has a common ratio.

Common ratio $= \frac{4}{2}$

$= 2$

Each term is 2 times the preceding term.

The first 6 terms of the geometric sequence are 2, 4, 8, 16, 32, 64.

We graph each sequence from *Example 4*. We plot the term value, t_n, against the term number, n.

Graph of the Arithmetic Sequence

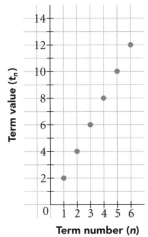

Graph of the Geometric Sequence

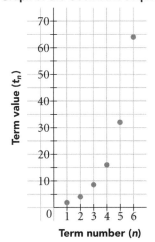

In the arithmetic sequence, the same number, 2, is repeatedly added. The graph of the sequence is a straight line.

In the geometric sequence, the same number, 2, is repeatedly multiplied. The graph of the sequence is an exponential curve.

TAKE NOTE

Properties of Arithmetic and Geometric Sequences

Arithmetic Sequence	**Geometric Sequence**
• The same number is repeatedly added. This number is the common difference.	• The same number is repeatedly multiplied. This number is the common ratio.
• The graph of an arithmetic sequence is linear.	• The graph of a geometric sequence is exponential.
• When the common difference is positive, the sequence illustrates linear growth.	• When the common ratio is positive, the sequence illustrates exponential growth.

A

1. State which sequences are geometric. For each sequence that is geometric, state the common ratio.

   a) 2, 4, 8, 16, …

   b) 1, 4, 7, 10, …

   c) 20, 10, 5, 1, …

   d) $\frac{1}{2}$, $\frac{1}{3}$, $\frac{1}{4}$, $\frac{1}{5}$, …

   e) 2, 3, 4.5, 6.75, …

   f) 27, 9, 3, 1, …

   g) $100, 100(1.07), 100(1.07)^2, 100(1.07)^3, …$

   h) 1, 4, 9, 16, …

 2. Is each sequence arithmetic, geometric, or neither? Explain how you know.

   a) 1, 2, 3, 4, 5, 6, …

   b) 2, 4, 6, 8, 10, 12, …

   c) 2, 4, 8, 16, 32, 64, …

   d) 1, 2, 4, 7, 11, 16, …

   e) 3, 6, 12, 24, 48, 96, …

   f) 1, 2, 6, 24, 120, 720, …

3. A geometric sequence has first term 2. Write the first 5 terms of the sequence for each geometric ratio.

   a) 2   b) −2   c) 3   d) −3   e) 4   f) −4

4. A geometric sequence has common ratio −2. Write the first 5 terms of the sequence for each first term.

   a) 1   b) −1   c) 2   d) −2   e) 3   f) −3

B

5. State the common ratio, then list the next 3 terms of each geometric sequence.

   a) 162, 54, 18, 6, …

   b) 1, 5, 25, 125, …

   c) 1, 1.5, 2.25, 3.375, …

   d) $\frac{1}{4}$, $\frac{1}{2}$, 1, 2, …

   e) −5, 20, −80, 320, …

   f) 96, 48, 24, 12, …

   g) 3, 15, 75, 375, …

   h) 10, 20, 40, 80, …

6. **Communication** Is each sequence arithmetic, geometric, or neither? Explain how you know.

   a) 2, 6, 18, 54, 162, …

   b) 1, 2, 5, 10, 17, …

   c) 5, 9, 13, 17, 21, …

   d) 2, 4, 16, 96, 768, …

   e) 100, 50, 25, 12.5, 6.25, …

   f) 99, 92, 85, 78, 71, …

7. Is each sequence arithmetic, geometric, or neither? Explain your choice.

a) 2, 20, 200, 2000, …

b) 1, 3, 6, 10, …

c) 1, 5, 9, 13, …

d) 1, 4, 9, 16, …

e) 22, 15, 8, 1, …

f) 4, 12, 36, 108, …

g) 1, −1, 1, −1, …

h) 8, 12, 16, 20, …

i) 24, 12, 6, 3, …

j) 2, 5, 8, 11, …

8. Write the first 4 terms of each geometric sequence.

a) The first term is 5 and the common ratio is 2.

b) The first term is 3 and the common ratio is −4.

c) The first term is −7 and the common ratio is 0.6.

d) The first term is $\frac{5}{8}$ and the common ratio is 4.

e) The first term is −1 and the common ratio is $\frac{1}{5}$.

f) The first term is 200 and the common ratio is 1.045.

g) The first term is −10 and the common ratio is −3.

h) The first term is 100 and the common ratio is 10.

i) The first term is −5 and the common ratio is $-\frac{1}{2}$.

9. For each geometric sequence in exercise 8, determine the general term.

10. Knowledge/Understanding For the geometric sequence 4, 8, 16, 32, …, determine each term.

a) t_n

b) t_7

c) t_{12}

11. For the geometric sequence 4, −8, 16, −32, …, determine each term.

a) t_n

b) t_7

c) t_{12}

12. Write the first 3 terms of the sequence defined by each general term. Is the sequence geometric? If it is, state the common ratio.

a) $t_n = 5n - 3$

b) $t_n = 2(3)^{n-1}$

c) $t_n = n^3$

d) $t_n = 5^{n-1}$

e) $t_n = 4(-2)^{n-1}$

f) $t_n = \frac{1}{2}(2)^{n-1}$

g) $t_n = 3^n$

h) $t_n = 0.5n$

13. Calculate the missing terms in each geometric sequence. Write the first 5 terms of each sequence.

a) __, 4, 8, __, __,

b) __, __, 9, 27, __,

c) __, __, __, −10, 20,

d) __, $\frac{1}{2}$, $\frac{1}{4}$, __, __,

e) __, __, 3.24, 5.832, __,

f) __, 1.7, 2.9, __, __,

g) __, __, −80, 400, __,

h) __, 48, 192, __, __,

14. For each geometric sequence, calculate t_n and t_8.

a) 4, 8, 16, 32 …

b) 10, −30, 90, −270, …

c) 11, 121, 1331, 14 641, …

d) −8, −4, −2, −1, …

e) 4, 12, 36, 108, …

f) $\frac{5}{3}$, 1, $\frac{3}{5}$, $\frac{9}{25}$, …

g) 2, 2(1.2), 2(1.2)^2, 2(1.2)^3, …

h) 50, 25, 12.5, 6.25, …

i) $\frac{1}{12}$, $\frac{1}{6}$, $\frac{1}{3}$, $\frac{2}{3}$, …

j) 4, 0.4, 0.04, 0.004, …

15. Determine the position of the last term in each geometric sequence; that is, the term number. How many terms are in the sequence?

a) 2, 4, 8, 16, …, 2048

b) 2, 6, 18, 54, …, 39 366

c) 1, −5, 25, −125, …, 15 625

d) 80, 40, 20, 10, …, $\frac{5}{16}$

e) 7, 14, 28, 56, …, 3584

f) −9, −3, −1, −$\frac{1}{3}$…, −$\frac{1}{243}$

g) 1, 1.5, (1.5)^2, (1.5)^3, …, (1.5)^{20}

h) 100, 10, 1, 0.1, …, 0.000 000 001

16. Application The population of a colony of insects doubles every week. The population now is 100.

a) Write a geometric sequence that lists the population every week for the next 4 weeks.

b) How many insects are there after 6 weeks?

17. The geometric sequence 1, 10, 100, … can be written as 1, 10, 10^2, …. Explain how this helps to determine the position of the term that has value 10 000 000 000 000.

18. Thinking/Inquiry/Problem Solving The second term of a geometric sequence is 6 and the fourth term is 54. Determine the common ratio.

19. A person has 2 parents, 4 grandparents, and 8 great-grandparents. How many great-great-great-great-great-grandparents does a person have?

20. I have a metre stick. I break off $\frac{1}{10}$ of it and throw the piece away. I then break off $\frac{1}{10}$ of what remains and throw that piece away. I repeat this process many times, each time breaking of $\frac{1}{10}$ of what remains and throwing the piece away.

a) What is the length of the piece I have after the first break? The second break? The third break?

b) Explain why the sequence of lengths of the pieces I have is geometric.

c) How long is the piece I have after the 10th break?

21. Determine the second and third terms of a geometric sequence that has a first term of 4 and a fourth term of 108.

Remember that an arithmetic series is the sum of the terms of an arithmetic sequence. Similarly, a *geometric series* is the sum of the terms of a geometric sequence.

Consider the series $1 + 3 + 9 + 27 + 81 + 243 + 729$.
We could use a calculator to add the terms. However, we can derive a formula to calculate the sum.
In the series above, each term is 3 times the preceding term.
The series is geometric with common ratio 3.
Since the series has 7 terms, its sum is denoted S_7.

We can calculate the sum of the series as follows.

Write the series.

$$S_7 = 1 + 3 + 9 + 27 + 81 + 243 + 729$$

Multiply each term by the common ratio, 3.

$$3S_7 = \qquad 3 + 9 + 27 + 81 + 243 + 729 + 2187$$

Subtract.

$$-2S_7 = 1 + 0 + 0 + 0 + 0 + 0 + 0 - 2187$$

Solve for S_7.

$$-2S_7 = -2186$$
$$S_7 = \frac{-2186}{-2}$$
$$= 1093$$

The sum of the 7 terms is 1093.

This method can be used to determine the sum, S_n, of the general geometric series $a + ar + ar^2 + ar^3 + \ldots + ar^{n-1}$.

The sum is $S_n = \frac{a(r^n - 1)}{r - 1}$.

TAKE NOTE

Sum of the General Geometric Series

The general geometric series with n terms is
$$a + ar + ar^2 + ar^3 + \ldots + ar^{n-1}$$

The sum of the general geometric series with n terms is:
$$S_n = \frac{a(r^n - 1)}{r - 1}, \quad r \neq 1$$
    a is the first term.
    r is the common ratio.

Discuss

In the formula for the sum of a geometric series, $r \neq 1$. Explain why r cannot equal 1.

Example 1

A geometric series has first term 2 and common ratio 3. Calculate the sum of the first 15 terms.

Solution

Use the formula $S_n = \frac{a(r^n - 1)}{r - 1}$.

We want to calculate S_{15}. Substitute $a = 2$, $r = 3$, and $n = 15$.

$$S_{15} = \frac{2(3^{15} - 1)}{3 - 1}$$

$$= \frac{2(3^{15} - 1)}{2}$$

Divide numerator and denominator by 2.

$$S_{15} = 3^{15} - 1$$

$$= 14\ 348\ 906$$

The sum of the first 15 terms is 14 348 906.

Example 2

Consider the geometric series $4 + 8 + 16 + 32 + \ldots + 512$.

a) Calculate the number of terms in the series.

b) Calculate the sum of the series.

Solution

Since $\frac{8}{4} = 2$, the common ratio, r, is 2. The first term, a, is 4.

a) To calculate the number of terms, use $t_n = ar^{n-1}$. We want to find the position (that is, the term number) of the last term 512.

Substitute $t_n = 512$, $a = 4$, and $r = 2$.

$512 = 4(2)^{n-1}$ Divide each side by 4.

$128 = 2^{n-1}$ Write 128 as a power of 2.

$2^{n-1} = 2^7$

$n - 1 = 7$

$n = 8$

There are 8 terms in the series.

b) To calculate the sum of the series, use $S_n = \frac{a(r^n - 1)}{r - 1}$.

Substitute $a = 4$, $r = 2$, and $n = 8$.

$$S_8 = \frac{4(2^8 - 1)}{2 - 1}$$

$$= 4(2^8 - 1)$$ Key in: 4 (2 ^ 8 − 1) ENTER

$$= 1020$$

The sum of the series is 1020.

(Remember that the keystrokes are for the TI-30X IIS calculator.)

We can use the sum of a geometric series to solve a financial problem.

Example 3

Which option amounts to more money?

Option A: $1 000 000, plus 10% simple interest for 30 days

Option B: a payment of 1¢ the 1st day, 2¢ the 2nd day, 4¢ the 3rd day, 8¢ the 4th day, and so on, for 30 days

Solution

The amount for option A is $1 000 000, plus 10% simple interest for 30 days. To calculate the interest, use the simple interest formula $I = Prt$.

Substitute $P = 1 000 000$, $r = 0.10$, and $t = \frac{30}{365}$.

$I = 1 000 000 \times 0.10 \times \frac{30}{365}$

$\doteq 8219.18$

The amount for option A is $1 000 000 + $8219.18 = $1 008 219.18$.

The amount, in cents, for option B is the sum of the first 30 terms of the geometric series $1 + 2 + 4 + 8 + \ldots$.

The common ratio, r, is $\frac{2}{1} = 2$. The first term, a, is 1.

Substitute $a = 1$, $r = 2$, and $n = 30$ in $S_n = \frac{a(r^n - 1)}{r - 1}$.

$S_{30} = \frac{1(2^{30} - 1)}{2 - 1}$

$= 2^{30} - 1$

$= 1 073 741 823$

The amount is 1 073 741 823¢.

To convert from cents to dollars, divide by 100.

The amount is $10 737 418.23.

This amount is approximately 10 times the amount in option A.

Option B amounts to more money.

Discuss

When do you think the two options might result in the same amount? How could you check?

Round answers to 2 decimal places where appropriate.

A

1. Use a calculator to determine the sum of each geometric series.
   a) $2 + 4 + 8 + 16 + 32$
   b) $2 - 4 + 8 - 16 + 32$
   c) $-2 + 4 - 8 + 16 - 32$
   d) $3 + 9 + 18 + 27 + 81$
   e) $3 - 9 + 18 - 27 + 81$
   f) $-3 + 9 - 18 + 27 - 81$

2. Calculate the sum of each geometric series.
   a) $1 + 2 + 4 + 8 + 16 + 32$
   b) $3 + 9 + 27 + 81 + 243 + 729$
   c) $2 + 8 + 32 + 128 + 512$
   d) $40 + 20 + 10 + 5 + 2.5$
   e) $1 - 2 + 4 - 8 + 16 - 32$
   f) $40 - 20 + 10 - 5 + 2.5$

3. Calculate the sum of the first 5 terms of each geometric series.
   a) $2 + 10 + 50 + \ldots$
   b) $4 + 12 + 36 + \ldots$
   c) $3 + 6 + 12 + \ldots$
   d) $24 + 12 + 6 + \ldots$
   e) $5 + 15 + 45 + \ldots$
   f) $80 - 40 + 20 - \ldots$

B

4. Calculate the sum of the first 10 terms of each geometric series.
   a) $2 + 4 + 8 + 16 + \ldots$
   b) $1 + 5 + 25 + 125 + \ldots$
   c) $-3 + 9 - 27 + 81 - \ldots$
   d) $2 + 6 + 18 + 54 + \ldots$
   e) $4 + 16 + 64 + 256 + \ldots$
   f) $800 + 400 + 200 + 100 + \ldots$
   g) $1 + 1.5 + 2.25 + 3.375 \ldots$
   h) $1 + 10 + 100 + 1000 + \ldots$

5. Determine the sum of the first 10 terms of each geometric series.
   a) $5 + 10 + 20 + 40 + \ldots$
   b) $5 - 10 + 20 - 40 + \ldots$
   c) $1 + \frac{1}{3} + \frac{1}{9} + \frac{1}{27} + \ldots$
   d) $1 - \frac{1}{3} + \frac{1}{9} - \frac{1}{27} + \ldots$
   e) $5 + \frac{5}{2} + \frac{5}{4} + \frac{5}{8} + \ldots$
   f) $5 - \frac{5}{2} + \frac{5}{4} - \frac{5}{8} + \ldots$

6. **Knowledge/Understanding** For the geometric series $1 + 3 + 9 + 27 + \ldots$, calculate:
   a) t_{10}
   b) S_8

7. For the geometric series $4 + 2 + 1 + 0.5 + \ldots$, calculate:
   a) the 9th term
   b) the sum of the first 9 terms

8. For each geometric series, determine the indicated sum.
   a) $15\ 625 + 3125 + 625 + 125 + \ldots;\ S_{11}$
   b) $4 + 1.6 + 0.64 + 0.256 + \ldots;\ S_7$
   c) $1 + \frac{1}{2} + \frac{1}{4} + \frac{1}{8} + \ldots;\ S_{14}$

d) $2 + 2(1.1) + 2(1.1)^2 + 2(1.1)^3 + \dots;\ S_8$

e) $18 + 4.5 + 1.125 + 0.281\ 25 + \dots;\ S_{15}$

f) $1.5 + 4.5 + 13.5 + 40.5 + \dots;\ S_{20}$

g) $1 - \frac{2}{3} + \frac{4}{9} - \frac{8}{27} + \dots;\ S_{10}$

h) $5 + 5(1.06) + 5(1.06)^2 + 5(1.06)^3 + \dots;\ S_{16}$

✓ **9. Communication** Consider the series

$100 + 100(1.04) + 100(1.04)^2 + 100(1.04)^3 + \dots.$

a) Identify the type of series.

b) Determine an expression for t_n.

c) Calculate S_{24}.

d) Write to explain how you completed parts a to c.

✓ **10.** Consider the sum of the geometric series $3 + 6 + 12 + 24 + \dots + 6144$.

a) Calculate the number of terms in the series.

b) Calculate the sum of the series.

11. Consider the geometric series $1 - 2 + 4 - 8 + \dots - 32\ 768$.

a) Calculate the number of terms in the series.

b) Calculate the sum of the series.

✓ **12.** Calculate the sum of the geometric series

$300 + 150 + 75 + 37.5 + \dots + 2.343\ 75$.

13. Calculate the sum of the geometric series $1 + \frac{1}{2} + \frac{1}{4} + \frac{1}{8} + \dots \frac{1}{2048}$.

✓ **14. Thinking/Inquiry/Problem Solving** A contest winner is given a choice of two prizes:

Prize 1: $1 today, $2 tomorrow, $4 on day 3, and so on, for 30 days. Each day the winner receives twice as much as the day before.

Prize 2: $1 today, $3 tomorrow, $9 on day 3, and so on, for 20 days. Each day the winner receives three times as much as the day before.

Which prize would you choose? Justify your answer.

✓ **15. Application** You have 2 parents, 4 grandparents, 8 great-grandparents, and so on.

a) How many ancestors do you have in the last 10 generations?

b) Why might you have fewer ancestors than the number you determined in part a? Explain.

C

16. Use the method on page 193. Show that the sum, S_n, of the general geometric series $a + ar + ar^2 + \dots + ar^{n-1}$ is given by $S_n = \frac{a(r^n - 1)}{r - 1}$.

1. Is each sequence arithmetic, geometric, or neither? If the sequence is arithmetic, state the common difference. If it is geometric, state the common ratio.

   a) 3, 6, 12, 24, ...　　　　　　　**b)** 3, 5, 7, 9, ...

   c) 27, 9, 3, 1, ...　　　　　　　**d)** 2, 3, 5, 8, ...

   e) 21, 19, 17, 15, ...　　　　　**f)** 1, 4, 9, 16, ...

2. Write the first 4 terms of each geometric sequence.

   a) The first term is 4 and the common ratio is 3.

   b) The first term is 2 and the common ratio is −5.

   c) The first term is −3 and the common ratio is −2.

3. Write the first 3 terms of the sequence defined by each general term. If the sequence is arithmetic, state the common difference. If the sequence is geometric, state the common ratio.

   a) $t_n = 3n - 1$　　　　　　　**b)** $t_n = 3(2)^{n-1}$

   c) $t_n = n^2$　　　　　　　　　**d)** $t_n = 4^{n-1}$

4. For each geometric sequence, find an expression for t_n, then calculate t_9.

   a) 2, 4, 8, 16, ...　　　　　　　**b)** 500, 100, 20, 4, ...

5. Calculate the missing terms in each geometric sequence.

   a) ___, 12, 48, ___, ___,　　　　**b)** ___, ___, 18, 36, ___,

   c) ___, ___, ___,−40, 20,　　　　**d)** ___, 3, 9, ___, ___,

6. Calculate the sum of the first 15 terms of each geometric series.

   a) 2 + 6 + 18 + 54 + ...　　　　**b)** 1024 + 512 + 256 + 128 + ...

   c) −1 + 3 − 9 + 27 − ...　　　　**d)** 1000 + 1500 + 2250 + 3375 + ...

7. Consider the geometric series 1 + 4 + 16 + 64 + ...

   a) Find an expression for t_n.

   b) Find an expression for S_n, then calculate S_9.

8. For each geometric series, calculate the indicated sum.

   a) 5 − 10 + 20 − 40 + ...; S_{12}

   b) 10 + 10(1.2) + 10(1.2)^2 + 10(1.2)^3 + ...; S_{40}

   c) 100 + 100(1.06) + 100(1.06)^2 + 100(1.06)^3 + ...; S_{24}

9. Calculate the sum of the geometric series 4 + 12 + 36 + ... + 236 196.

10. There are 128 people entered in a pool tournament. The loser after each round is eliminated. How many rounds are played in the tournament?

Ethan worked part-time during his teenage years to save for college. On each birthday, from his 13th to his 18th, inclusive, Ethan deposited $500 into a savings account. The account paid 6% compounded annually. What was the balance in the account on Ethan's 18th birthday?

Until now, you have calculated the amount of a single deposit. Now, more than one deposit is involved. To find the balance in the account, the amount of each deposit is calculated separately. Each amount can be found using the formula $A = P(1 + i)^n$.

On Ethan's 18th birthday:
The $500 deposited at age 13 has earned interest for 5 years.
The amount is $500(1.06)^5$.

The $500 deposited at age 14 has earned interest for 4 years.
The amount is $500(1.06)^4$.

The $500 deposited at age 15 has earned interest for 3 years.
The amount is $500(1.06)^3$.

The $500 deposited at age 16 has earned interest for 2 years.
The amount is $500(1.06)^2$.

The $500 deposited at age 17 has earned interest for 1 year.
The amount is $500(1.06)^1$.

The $500 deposited at age 18 has earned no interest.
The amount is $500.

A diagram called a *time line* can be used to organize the calculations. It shows the amount of each deposit on Ethan's 18th birthday.

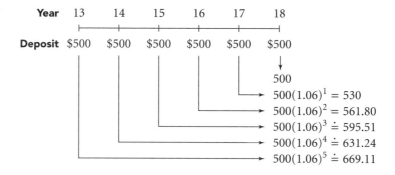

The balance in the account is the sum of the amounts.

Balance = 500 + 530 + 561.80 + 595.51 + 631.24 + 669.11
= 3487.66

On Ethan's 18th birthday, the balance in the account is $3487.66.

Ethan's deposits are an example of an *annuity*. The balance in the account on Ethan's 18th birthday is the amount of the annuity.

TAKE NOTE

Definition of an Annuity

An annuity is a series of equal deposits made at equal time intervals. Each deposit is made at the end of each time interval.

We can use geometric series to calculate the amount of an annuity.

The amount of Ethan's annuity is the sum of the amounts of the deposits. Write these amounts in exponential form.

$$500 + 500(1.06)^1 + 500(1.06)^2 + 500(1.06)^3 + 500(1.06)^4 + 500(1.06)^5$$

Each term in the series is 1.06 times the preceding term.
This is a geometric series with common ratio, r, is 1.06.
The first term, a, is 500.
The number of terms, n, is 6.

To calculate the sum of the series, use the formula $S_n = \frac{a(r^n - 1)}{r - 1}$.

Substitute $a = 500$, $r = 1.06$, and $n = 6$.
$$S_6 = \frac{500(1.06^6 - 1)}{1.06 - 1}$$
$$= \frac{500(1.06^6 - 1)}{0.06}$$
$$\doteq 3487.66$$

Key in: 500 (1.06 ^ 6 − 1) ÷ 0.06 ENTER =

The sum of the series is 3487.66.

We can use this method to obtain a formula for the amount, A, of an annuity with n regular deposits of R, and an interest rate of i per compounding period.

The amount of each deposit can be displayed on a time line.

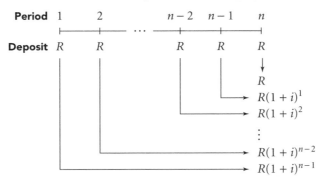

Thus, the amount of the annuity is the sum of the geometric series:

$$R + R(1 + i)^1 + R(1 + i)^2 + R(1 + i)^3 + \ldots + R(1 + i)^{n-1}$$

To calculate the sum, use the formula $S_n = \frac{a(r^n - 1)}{r - 1}$.

Substitute $S_n = A$, $a = R$, and $r = (1 + i)$.
There are n terms in the series.

$$A = \frac{R[(1 + i)^n - 1]}{(1 + i) - 1}$$
$$= \frac{R[(1 + i)^n - 1]}{i}$$

The amount, A dollars, of the annuity is $A = \frac{R[(1 + i)^n - 1]}{i}$.

TAKE NOTE

Amount of an Annuity

The amount of an annuity is:
$$A = \frac{R[(1 + i)^n - 1]}{i}$$

A is the amount in dollars.
R is the regular deposit in dollars.
i is the interest rate per compounding period, as a decimal.
n is the number of deposits.

A regular program of savings is an example of an annuity.

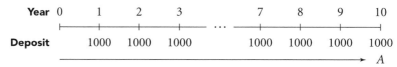

Example 1 Paul deposits $1000 at the end of each year in an account that pays 5% compounded annually. What is the amount in the account at the end of 10 years?

Solution

Paul's deposits form an annuity.

Draw a time line. Let A dollars represent the amount.

Year	0	1	2	3		7	8	9	10
Deposit		1000	1000	1000	...	1000	1000	1000	1000

Regular deposits of $1000 amount to $A in 10 years.

Use the formula $A = \dfrac{R[(1 + i)^n - 1]}{i}$.

Substitute $R = 1000$, $i = 0.05$, and $n = 10$.

$$A = \frac{1000[(1 + 0.05)^{10} - 1]}{0.05}$$

$$= \frac{1000(1.05^{10} - 1)}{0.05}$$

Key in: 1000 (1.05 ^ 10 − 1)

$$\doteq 12\ 577.89$$

÷ 0.05 ENTER/=

The amount at the end of 10 years is $12 577.89.

Example 2 Annika deposited $800 in an account at the end of every 6-month period for 7 years. The account paid 9% compounded semi-annually. Determine the amount in the account on the date of the last deposit.

Solution

Annika's deposits form an annuity.
Draw a time line.
Let A dollars represent the amount.

Year	0		1		2		6		7
Deposit		800	800	800	800	...	800	800	800	800

Regular deposits of $800 amount to $A in 14 periods.

Use the formula $A = \dfrac{R[(1 + i)^n - 1]}{i}$.

i is $\dfrac{0.09}{2} = 0.045$; n is $7 \times 2 = 14$.

Substitute $R = 800$, $i = 0.045$, and $n = 14$.

$$A = \frac{800[(1 + 0.045)^{14} - 1]}{0.045}$$

$$= \frac{800(1.045^{14} - 1)}{0.045}$$

$$\doteq 15\ 145.69$$

Key in: 800 (1.045 ^ 14 − 1
) ÷ 0.045 [ENTER]

The amount on the date of the last deposit is $15 145.69.

An annuity is often used to accumulate funds for a large purchase.

Example ③

Jill wants $1000 to buy a ring when she graduates from high school. She deposits $40 at the end of each month in an account that pays 6.5% compounded monthly. Jill will graduate in $2\frac{1}{2}$ years. Will she have enough money by then? Explain.

Solution

Calculate the amount after $2\frac{1}{2}$ years.

$2\frac{1}{2}$ years $= 2.5 \times 12$ months $= 30$ months

Draw a time line. Let A dollars represent the amount.

Month	0	1	2	3	4		27	28	29	30
Deposit		40	40	40	40	...	40	40	40	40

A

Regular deposits of $40 amount to $A in 30 months.

Use the formula $A = \frac{R[(1 + i)^n - 1]}{i}$.

Substitute $R = 40$, $i = \frac{0.065}{12}$, and $n = 30$.

$$A = \frac{40\left[\left(1 + \frac{0.065}{12}\right)^{30} - 1\right]}{\frac{0.065}{12}}$$

$$\doteq 1299.19$$

Key in: 40 ((1 + 0.065
÷ 12) ^ 30 − 1) ÷
(0.065 ÷ 12) [ENTER]

Jill will have about $1300 in the account. She will have enough money to buy the ring.

Discuss

How could you use the store and recall features of a calculator to simplify these calculations?

A

✓ 1. Use the formula $A = \frac{R[(1 + i)^n - 1]}{i}$. Calculate A for each set of values.

   a) $R = \$500$, $i = 0.04$, $n = 8$

   b) $R = \$1000$, $i = 0.04$, $n = 8$

   c) $R = \$500$, $i = 0.08$, $n = 8$

   d) $R = \$500$, $i = 0.04$, $n = 16$

2. Calculate the amount of each annuity. A deposit is made at the end of each year.

	Deposit	Deposit frequency	Length of annuity	Interest rate compounded annually
a)	$100	annual	5 years	4%
b)	$200	annual	6 years	3%
c)	$300	annual	3 years	5%
d)	$250	annual	4 years	4%
e)	$150	annual	7 years	6%
f)	$350	annual	8 years	3%

✓ 3. Calculate the amount of each annuity. A deposit is made at the end of each 6-month period.

	Deposit	Deposit frequency	Length of annuity	Interest rate compounded semi-annually
a)	$100	semi-annual	3 years	6%
b)	$150	semi-annual	5 years	4%
c)	$200	semi-annual	10 years	8%
d)	$250	semi-annual	7 years	5%
e)	$300	semi-annual	8 years	3%
f)	$350	semi-annual	4 years	2%

B

✓ 4. Calculate the amount of each annuity.

   a) $800 deposited at the end of each year for 5 years at 7% compounded annually

   b) $250 deposited at the end of each 6-month period for 3 years at 8% compounded semi-annually

c) $80 deposited at the end of each month for 2 years at 6% compounded monthly

d) $100 deposited at the end of each month for 10 years at 12% compounded monthly

e) $50 deposited at the end of each 6-month period for 9 years at 4% compounded semi-annually

f) $1000 deposited at the end of each year for 25 years at 8% compounded annually

5. Calculate the amount of each annuity.

a) $300 deposited at the end of each year for 4 years at $5\frac{1}{2}$% compounded annually

b) $1500 deposited at the end of each 6-month period for 7 years at 5.25% compounded semi-annually

c) $150 deposited at the end of each month for 3 years at 5% compounded monthly

d) $60 deposited at the end of each month for 25 years at 7% compounded monthly

e) $400 deposited at the end of each 6-month period for 12 years at $7\frac{3}{4}$% compounded semi-annually

f) $1000 deposited at the end of each 3-month period for 9.5 years at 7% compounded quarterly

 6. **Knowledge/Understanding** Calculate the amount of an annuity of $2000 deposited at the end of every year for 5 years at 6% compounded annually.

7. Calculate the amount of an annuity of $100 deposited at the end of every 6 months for 5 years at 6% compounded semi-annually.

8. Calculate the amount of an annuity of $50 deposited at the end of every month for 5 years at 6% compounded monthly.

9. Samantha saves $50 at the end of each month in an account that pays 9% compounded monthly. Calculate the amount in the account at the end of each time period.

a) 4 years   **b)** 18 months   **c)** $3\frac{1}{2}$ years   **d)** 10 years

 10. Bernard deposits $150 at the end of each quarter into an account that pays 8% compounded quarterly. Calculate the amount in the account at the end of each time period.

a) 3 years   **b)** 9 months   **c)** $5\frac{3}{4}$ years   **d)** $12\frac{1}{2}$ years

11. Rita's parents contributed $800 to a Registered Education Savings Plan at the end of every year for 18 years. The plan earned 6% compounded annually. What was the amount at the end of 18 years?

12. **Application** Mr. Dykstra opened a savings account for his granddaughter on the day she was born. He deposited $100. Each year on her birthday, Mr. Dykstra deposited another $100. The account pays 5% compounded annually. What is the amount in the account on his granddaughter's 10th birthday?

13. Olga is saving to buy a video camera. At the end of each month, she deposits $85 into a savings account that pays 4% compounded monthly. How much is in the account at the end of 1 year?

14. The Chens are saving to buy a house. They deposit $1000 at the end of each month in a savings account that pays 5.25% compounded monthly. How much is in the account after 4 years?

15. **Communication** Matt has contributed $1000 to his Registered Retirement Savings Plan at the end of each 6-month period for the past 40 years. During this time, the plan has earned an average of 9.5% compounded semi-annually. Explain how to calculate the amount in the plan and how much of the amount is interest.

16. John deposits $105 at the end of each month in a savings account that pays 4% compounded monthly. How much has John saved after 5 years?

17. A company plans to replace its computers in 3 years. To prepare for the expense, the company invests $5000 at the end of each month in an account that pays 4.5% compounded monthly. How much money will the company have available in 3 years?

18. **Thinking/Inquiry/Problem Solving**

    Which annuity has the greater amount at the end of 5 years? Why does this happen?

    Annuity A: $100 at the end of each month for 5 years at 6% compounded monthly

    Annuity B: $1200 at the end of each year for 5 years at 6% compounded annually

    Explain your answer. Include all necessary calculations.

19. Which annuity has the greater amount? Explain how you know.

    Annuity A: $100 at the end of each quarter for 10 years at 4% compounded quarterly

    Annuity B: $200 at the end of each quarter for 5 years at 4% compounded quarterly

20. Which annuity has the greater amount at the end of 5 years? Explain how you know.

    Annuity A: $100 at the end of each 6-month period for 5 years at 4% compounded semi-annually

    Annuity B: $200 at the end of each year for 5 years at 4.5% compounded annually

21. Beginning one month after the birth of their son, Zachary, the Petersons deposited $50 each month in an annuity for his college fund. The annuity earned interest at an average rate of 6.8% compounded monthly until Zachary's 18th birthday. What is the amount of Zachary's college fund?

22. Paula deposited $100 at the end of each month in an annuity that paid 7.5% compounded monthly. At the end of 6 years, the interest rate was increased to 8% compounded monthly. Paula continued the same deposit for another 5 years. What is the amount of the annuity on the date of the last deposit?

Electrician

Electricity is everywhere. Electricians lay out, assemble, repair, maintain, connect, and test a wide range of electrical fixtures, apparatus, control equipment, and wiring in both residential and commercial buildings. They also measure, cut, thread, bend, assemble, and install conduits and electrical conductor enclosures. Electricians are ultimately responsible for the proper and safe functioning of all electrical equipment and systems — from basic lighting to the complex security systems. In the initial phase of new construction work, highly skilled electricians lay the groundwork for all the necessary wiring through the structure, before the finishing touches can be made in installing the equipment and fixtures. As part of their training, electricians have to be proficient in reading electrical blueprints of buildings and instruction manuals of various appliances and equipment. Because of the dangers of working with electricity, electrician apprentices undergo 4 to 5 years of training to acquire sound knowledge and experience in the field.

The standard work week is 40 hours, and the work is done both indoors and outdoors in installation and repairs.

Where's the Math?
Mathematics is an essential component in the training of electricians, for example, in troubleshooting electrical alternating current (AC) circuit problems — whether series, parallel, or complex circuits. Knowledge of electrical theory, conduits, wire and cables, control devices, and systems involves mathematics.

Nancy is saving for the down payment on a car. She wants $3500 in her account 3 years from now. The account pays 6% compounded monthly. What regular deposit, to the nearest $10, must Nancy make at the end of each month?

Since Nancy makes equal deposits at equal time intervals, this situation represents an annuity.

This situation is different from those in Section 4.3 because the amount is known and the equal monthly deposits are not.

Let R dollars represent the monthly deposit.
Draw a time line.

In 3 years, Nancy will have made 3×12, or 36 monthly deposits.

Month	0	1	2	3		33	34	35	36
Deposit		R	R	R	...	R	R	R	R

$A = \$3500$

Regular deposits of $\$R$ grow to $\$3500$ in 36 months.

Use the formula $A = \dfrac{R[(1 + i)^n - 1]}{i}$. We want to calculate R.

The monthly interest rate is $\dfrac{6\%}{12} = 0.5\%$.

Substitute $A = 3500$, $i = 0.005$, and $n = 36$.

$$3500 = \frac{R[(1 + 0.005)^{36} - 1]}{0.005}$$

$$3500 = \frac{R(1.005^{36} - 1)}{0.005}$$

Solve the equation for R.

Multiply each side by 0.005.

$0.005 \times 3500 = R(1.005^{36} - 1)$

Divide each side by $1.005^{36} - 1$.

$\dfrac{0.005 \times 3500}{1.005^{36} - 1} = R$

$R \doteq 88.98$

Key in: 0.005 $\boxed{\times}$ 3500 $\boxed{\div}$ $\boxed{(}$

1.005 $\boxed{\wedge}$ 36 $\boxed{-}$ 1 $\boxed{)}$ $\boxed{\text{ENTER} =}$

The monthly deposit is $88.98.

Nancy should deposit $90 at the end of each month.

Example 1

An account pays 7.5% compounded semi-annually. What regular semi-annual deposit must be made to have $1800 in the account at the end of 6 years?

Solution

Draw a time line.

Let R dollars represent the regular deposit.

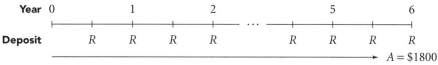

Regular semi-annual deposits of $R amount to $1800 in 6 years.

Use the formula $A = \dfrac{R[(1 + i)^n - 1]}{i}$.

The semi-annual interest rate is $\dfrac{7.5\%}{2} = 3.75\%$.

The number of deposits is $6 \times 2 = 12$.

Substitute $A = 1800$, $i = 0.0375$, and $n = 12$.

$1800 = \dfrac{R[(1 + 0.0375)^{12} - 1]}{0.0375}$

Solve for R. Multiply each side by 0.0375.

$0.0375 \times 1800 = R(1.0375^{12} - 1)$

Divide each side by $1.0375^{12} - 1$.

$\dfrac{0.0375 \times 1800}{1.0375^{12} - 1} = R$

$R \doteq 121.52$

Key in: 0.0375 $\boxed{\times}$ 1800 $\boxed{\div}$ $\boxed{(}$

1.0375 $\boxed{\wedge}$ 12 $\boxed{-}$ 1 $\boxed{)}$ $\boxed{\text{ENTER} =}$

The semi-annual deposit is $121.52.

Experts say that young people today cannot count on the government and employers to support them in their retirement. It is recommended that they plan for their retirement by saving early and regularly. One way is to make regular deposits into a retirement account.

Example 2

Amir is 25. He plans to have $500 000 in a retirement fund when he retires in 40 years. Assume that, on average, Amir's deposits earn 8% compounded annually for the next 40 years.

a) What regular annual deposit must Amir make to have the required amount at retirement?

b) How much does Amir contribute to the fund over the 40 years?

Solution

Draw a time line.

Let R dollars represent the annual deposit.

Year	0	1	2	3	...	37	38	39	40
Deposit		R	R	R		R	R	R	R

$A = \$500\ 000$

Regular deposits of $\$R$ amount to $500 000 in 40 years.

a) Use the formula $A = \dfrac{R[(1 + i)^n - 1]}{i}$.

Substitute $A = 500\ 000$, $i = 0.08$, and $n = 40$.

$$500\ 000 = \frac{R[(1 + 0.08)^{40} - 1]}{0.08}$$

Multiply each side by 0.08.

$$0.08 \times 500\ 000 = R(1.08^{40} - 1)$$

Divide each side by $1.08^{40} - 1$.

$$\frac{0.08 \times 500\ 000}{1.08^{40} - 1} = R$$

$$R \doteq 1930.08$$

The annual deposit at the end of each year is $1930.08.

b) Amir contributes $1930.08 at the end of each year.

In 40 years, he will have contributed $40 \times \$1930.08 = \$77\ 203.20$.

Discuss

What keystrokes were used to calculate R?

What is the total interest earned over the 40-year period?

A

1. Use the formula $A = \dfrac{R[(1 + i)^n - 1]}{i}$. Calculate R for each set of values.
   a) $A = \$2000$, $i = 0.005$, $n = 20$
   b) $A = \$10\ 000$, $i = 0.04$, $n = 10$
   c) $A = \$5000$, $i = 0.025$, $n = 40$

2. Calculate the regular deposit for each annuity. A deposit is made at the end of each year.

	Amount of annuity	Deposit frequency	Length of annuity	Interest rate compounded annually
a)	$1000	annual	4 years	6%
b)	$2000	annual	3 years	5%
c)	$3000	annual	8 years	4%
d)	$5000	annual	10 years	5%
e)	$10 000	annual	9 years	5%
f)	$25 000	annual	5 years	4%

3. Calculate the regular deposit for each annuity. A deposit is made at the end of each 6-month period.

	Amount of annuity	Deposit frequency	Length of annuity	Interest rate compounded semi-annually
a)	$1500	semi-annual	7 years	5%
b)	$2500	semi-annual	5 years	4%
c)	$3500	semi-annual	4 years	8%
d)	$5500	semi-annual	12 years	6%
e)	$13 500	semi-annual	6 years	4%
f)	$22 500	semi-annual	10 years	5%

B

4. Calculate the regular deposit for each annuity.
   a) an annual deposit to amount to $3000 in 4 years at 6% compounded annually
   b) a semi-annual deposit to amount to $5000 in 6 years at 8% compounded semi-annually
   c) a monthly deposit to amount to $4500 in 5 years at 6% compounded monthly

d) a quarterly deposit to amount to $9400 in 7 years at 8% compounded quarterly

5. Calculate the regular deposit for each annuity.

   a) an annual deposit to amount to $13 470 in 10 years at 6.5% compounded annually

   b) a semi-annual deposit to amount to $245 000 in 8 years at 7.5% compounded semi-annually

   c) a quarterly deposit to amount to $100 000 in 20 years at 5.5% compounded quarterly

   d) a monthly deposit to amount to $50 000 in 25 years at 7.75% compounded monthly

6. Alicia needs $2000 three years from now. How much should she deposit at the end of each year for the next 3 years in an account that pays 5% compounded annually?

7. Rafi needs $800 six months from now. How much should he deposit at the end of each month for the next 6 months in an account that pays 4% compounded monthly?

8. Jill needs $1200 two years from now. How much should she deposit at the end of each quarter for the next 2 years in an account that pays 4% compounded quarterly?

9. **Knowledge/Understanding** Diego needs $3500 two years from now. How much should he deposit at the end of each 6-month period for the next 2 years in an account that pays 8% compounded semi-annually?

10. Calculate the regular deposit for each annuity so the deposits accumulate to the given amount on the date of the last deposit. Each deposit is made at the end of the compounding period.

    a) $500 in 3 years at 8% compounded semi-annually

    b) $7000 in 10 years at 5% compounded annually

    c) $1000 in 4 years at 6% compounded monthly

11. Milan wants $5000 in an account 5 years from now. The account pays 6% interest. Calculate how much Milan must deposit at the end of each compounding period to have $5000 when the interest is compounded:

    a) annually   **b)** quarterly   **c)** monthly   **d)** semi-annually

12. Jennifer has started a savings program to have $1000 after 5 years. She saves the money in an investment account that pays 6.5% compounded monthly. How much should Jennifer deposit at the end of each month to meet her goal?

13. Application Josee is saving for a trip to the Caribbean. She needs $5000 in 3 years. What deposit, to the nearest $10, should Josee make at the end of each month in an account that pays 6% compounded monthly?

14. Jamie wants to buy a computer that will cost $1200 one year from now. How much should he deposit at the end of each month in an account that pays 7.35% compounded monthly?

15. Calculate the regular deposit for each annuity so the deposits accumulate to the given amount on the date of the last deposit. Each deposit is made at the end of the compounding period.
   a) $675 in 3.5 years at $4\frac{3}{4}$% compounded semi-annually
   b) $15 000 in 15 years at $5\frac{1}{4}$% compounded annually
   c) $1000 in 1 year at 6.7% compounded monthly
   d) $5500 in 6.5 years at 4.5% compounded quarterly

16. Communication The Millers need $10 000 for a down payment on a house. They would like to buy the house 5 years from now. Explain how the Millers calculate the regular deposit they need to make at the end of each month in an account that pays 6% compounded monthly.

17. Rachel is saving for a down payment for a car. She needs $6000 three years from now. How much money must she deposit at the end of each quarter in an account that pays 4.4% compounded quarterly?

18. Sergei wants to buy a CD player. He needs $249.50 six months from now. How much should Sergei deposit at the end of each month at 7% compounded monthly so he can buy the CD player on the date of his last deposit?

19. Sarah wants to save $5000 by her 18th birthday to help pay for her college tuition. She has just turned 13. To reach her goal, how much should Sarah deposit at the end of each month in an account that pays 6.5% compounded monthly?

20. Lim plans to have $250 000 in his retirement account when he turns 65. He is now 25. On average, he expects to earn 6% interest compounded monthly. How much money should Lim deposit at the end of each month in his retirement account?

21. a) What deposit made at the end of each month will amount to $1 000 000 forty years from now? Assume the money earns, on average, 8% compounded monthly.
   b) How much was deposited over the 40 years?
   c) How much interest was earned over the 40 years?

22. Thinking/Inquiry/Problem Solving Elizabeth plans to go to college 5 years from today. She estimates she will need $10 000 at that time. Elizabeth will make equal deposits regularly into a bank account. She has two options.

Option A: A deposit made at the end of each month into an account that pays 5.5% compounded monthly

Option B: A deposit made at the end of each 6-month period into an account that pays 6% compounded semi-annually

Which option should Elizabeth choose? Explain.

23. Suppose you make equal monthly payments for 3 years into an account that pays 6% compounded monthly. At the end of that time, you have $4000 in the account. Determine how much you will have invested.

Career Profile

Child Care Worker

In Canadian households where both adults work outside the home, parents often rely on child care workers to ensure a safe and comfortable environment for their children during the work day. The demand for quality child care is increasing.

Child care is essentially about relationship. As Gillian Doherty*, an expert in this field, states, "The interaction between caregiver and child is probably the most important indicator of quality."

Child care workers have to constantly engage children in activities to stimulate their physical, emotional, intellectual, and social growth. These may range from reading, singing, painting, and playing, to teaching them some basic behavioural and personal hygiene skills. To be a successful child care worker, a knowledge of early childhood development is essential. Child care workers must really love children and

enjoy being with them. They must be sensitive, thoughtful, and reliable; have lots of initiative and energy; and be extremely patient in responding to the needs of children. In their care, children must experience a sense of belonging—they learn to trust and develop a sense of security.

Child caregivers may work in established day-care centres, nursery schools, or family day-care homes. Their work week may range from 40 to 50 hours. Because of the challenging and physical nature of the work, the turnover in this occupation is high.

Where's the Math?

Basic estimation and problem solving skills are needed when budgeting for food, activities, and supplies. A strong sense of number will enhance the play activities that help the preschool child learn to count and use numbers.

*Gillian Doherty. "Factors Related to Quality in Child Care." Toronto, 1990.

In this section, you will study different investment options. Your task is to select the best option.

Example 1

Jonas plans to surprise his wife with a trip to Hawaii 10 years from now. He needs $10 000 for the trip. Jonas can afford to invest $720 per year. He has 2 choices:

- Invest $60 at the end of each month in an account that pays 6.5% compounded monthly.
- Invest $360 at the end of each 6-month period in an account that pays 6.7% compounded semi-annually.

a) Calculate the amount if Jonas invests the money in the monthly annuity.

b) Calculate the amount if Jonas invests the money in the semi-annual annuity.

c) Which investment should Jonas choose? Explain.

Solution

To calculate the amount of each annuity, use the formula $A = \dfrac{R[(1 + i)^n - 1]}{i}$.

a) There are 10×12, or 120 deposits.

Substitute $R = 60$, $i = \dfrac{0.065}{12}$, and $n = 120$.

$$A = \frac{60\left[\left(1 + \frac{0.065}{12}\right)^{120} - 1\right]}{\frac{0.065}{12}}$$

Key in: 60 ( ) ( ) 1 + 0.065
÷ 12) ^ 120 − 1) ÷
(0.065 ÷ 12) ENTER =

$$\doteq 10\ 104.19$$

The amount of the monthly annuity is $10 104.19.

b) The semi-annual interest rate is $\frac{6.7\%}{2} = 3.35\%$.

There are 10×2, or 20 deposits.

Substitute $R = 360$, $i = 0.0335$, and $n = 20$.

$$A = \frac{360[(1 + 0.0335)^{20} - 1]}{0.0335}$$

$$= \frac{360(1.0335^{20} - 1)}{0.0335}$$

$$\doteq 10\ 025.21$$

The amount of the semi-annual annuity is \$10 025.21.

c) The difference in the amounts is \$10 104.19 − \$10 025.21 = \$78.98.
Jonas earns more money with the monthly annuity, so he should invest in it.

Example 2

Celine is saving for a down payment on a car. She needs \$3500 in $2\frac{1}{2}$ years. Celine has 2 choices for saving the money.

- A regular deposit at the end of each month into an account that pays 7.2% compounded monthly
- A regular deposit at the end of each 6-month period into an account that pays 7.5% compounded semi-annually

a) What would be Celine's regular monthly deposit?

b) What would be Celine's regular semi-annual deposit?

c) Celine can afford to make either deposit. Which is the better choice? Justify your answer.

Solution

Use the formula $A = \frac{R[(1 + i)^n - 1]}{i}$.

a) The monthly interest rate is $\frac{7.2\%}{12} = 0.6\%$.

There are 2.5×12, or 30 deposits.

Substitute $A = 3500$, $i = 0.006$, and $n = 30$.

$$3500 = \frac{R[(1 + 0.006)^{30} - 1]}{0.006}$$

Multiply each side by 0.006.

$$0.006 \times 3500 = R(1.006^{30} - 1)$$

Divide each side by $1.006^{30} - 1$.

$$\frac{0.006 \times 3500}{1.006^{30} - 1} = R$$

$$R \doteq 106.83$$

Key in: 0.006 $\boxed{\times}$ 3500 $\boxed{\div}$ $\boxed{(}$
1.006 $\boxed{\wedge}$ 30 $\boxed{-}$ 1 $\boxed{)}$ $\boxed{\text{ENTER}}$

The regular monthly deposit would be \$106.83.

b) The semi-annual interest rate is $\frac{7.5\%}{2} = 3.75\%$.

There are 2.5×2, or 5 deposits.

Substitute $A = 3500$, $i = 0.0375$, and $n = 5$.

$$3500 = \frac{R[(1 + 0.0375)^5 - 1]}{0.0375}$$

Multiply each side by 0.0375.

$$0.0375 \times 3500 = R(1.0375^5 - 1)$$

Divide each side by $1.0375^5 - 1$.

$$R = \frac{0.0375 \times 3500}{1.0375^5 - 1}$$

$$\doteq 649.43$$

The regular semi-annual deposit would be $649.43.

c) To find the better investment, compare the total deposits.

Total of monthly deposits = 106.83×30 = $3204.90

Total of semi-annual deposits = 649.43×5 = $3247.15

The total deposit is less for monthly deposits.

Celine should choose the monthly deposit.

4.5 Exercises

1. Calculate the investment that provides the greater amount on maturity. For each investment, the deposit is made at the end of the compounding period.

a) i) $100 per month at 5% compounded monthly for 5 years
   ii) $300 per quarter at 5.5% compounded quarterly for 5 years

b) i) $1000 per year at 6% compounded annually for 10 years
   ii) $500 every 6 months at 5.8% compounded semi-annually for 10 years

c) i) $2400 per year at 8% compounded annually for 15 years
   ii) $200 per month at 7.25% compounded monthly for 15 years

d) i) $800 every 6 months at 7% compounded semi-annually for 9 years
   ii) $400 per quarter at 6.75% compounded quarterly for 9 years

e) i) $75 per month at 4.5% compounded monthly for 20 years
   ii) $225 per quarter at 5% compounded quarterly for 20 years

f) i) $20 per month at 8% compounded monthly for 5 years
   ii) $240 per year at 8.75% compounded annually for 5 years

2. For each amount of an annuity, find the option that requires the lesser total deposit. The number of payments is equal to the number of compounding periods.

    a) $20 000 after 15 years at 9% compounded monthly or 9.5% compounded semi-annually

    b) $7000 after 8 years at 6% compounded quarterly or 6.5% compounded semi-annually

    c) $1500 after 3 years at 5% compounded monthly or 5.5% compounded quarterly

    d) $5600 after 7 years at 4.5% compounded monthly or 5.25% compounded annually

    e) $18 000 after 12 years at 7.4% compounded quarterly or 8.1% compounded annually

3. Knowledge/Understanding Marcel wants to save $10 000 in 7 years. He has 3 options.

Option A pays 6% compounded monthly with monthly deposits.

Option B pays 6.2% compounded quarterly with quarterly deposits.

Option C pays 6.35% compounded annually with annual deposits.

Determine the total cost of each option. Which option should Marcel choose?

4. Communication Melanie is 18. She considers whether to start a savings plan now or to wait a few years. Melanie can save $20 per month if she starts now. She can save $40 per month if she starts in 5 years. Money can be invested at 6% compounded monthly for the next 10 years. Should Melanie start to save now or wait for 5 years? Explain your decision.

5. Application Consider these two options:

    i) Invest $50 per month for 20 years at 5% compounded monthly. Start to invest at the end of next month.

    ii) Wait 10 years. Invest $100 at the end of each month for 10 years at 5% compounded monthly.

    a) Which option earns more money?

    b) How much more is earned by the option in part a?

6. Thinking/Inquiry/Problem Solving When you double the time of an annuity, do you double the amount at maturity? Write a short explanation. Include examples to justify your answer.

7. When the deposit made each payment period into an annuity is doubled, is the amount at maturity doubled? Write a short explanation. Include examples to justify your answer.

1. Calculate the amount of each annuity on the date of the last deposit.

   a) A deposit of $1000 at the end of each year for 6 years at 7% compounded annually

   b) A deposit of $450 at the end of each 6-month period for 5 years at 6.5% compounded semi-annually

   c) A deposit of $180 at the end of each month for 4 years at $5\frac{1}{2}$% compounded monthly

   d) A deposit of $300 at the end of each quarter for 7 years at 6.75% compounded quarterly

2. William saves $60 at the end of each month in an account that pays 5.5% compounded monthly. Calculate the amount in his account at the end of each time.

   a) 15 months   b) 3 years   c) 4.5 years   d) 8 years

3. Calculate the regular deposit for each annuity. The deposits accumulate to the amount indicated on the date of the last deposit. Each deposit is made at the end of the compounding period.

   a) An amount of $1250 in 3 years at 4.8% compounded annually

   b) An amount of $12 000 in 9 years at 5.25% compounded semi-annually

   c) An amount of $1500 in 2 years at 6% compounded monthly

   d) An amount of $4500 in 5 years at 7% compounded quarterly

   e) An amount of $1700 in 2.5 years at 5.3% compounded monthly

   f) An amount of $5000 in 6.5 years at 4.9% compounded quarterly

4. Matt wants $4000 in an account 3 years from now. He considers monthly or semi-annual deposits. Matt can invest his money at 5% compounded monthly or at 5.2% compounded semi-annually.

   a) Calculate Matt's monthly deposit for the monthly option.

   b) Calculate Matt's semi-annual deposit for the semi-annual option.

   c) Which option should Matt choose? Explain.

5. Renee is saving for a trip to Australia. She wants $10 000 in 5 years. How much should Renee deposit at the end of each month into an account that pays 6.4% compounded monthly?

6. Suppose you make a deposit at the end of each month into an account that pays 7.6% compounded monthly for 7 years. The amount at the end of the 7 years is $10 000. How much do you invest?

Canadians who earn employment income must pay into the Canada Pension Plan (CPP). Your employer pays one-half the contribution and you pay the other half. If you are self-employed, you pay the whole contribution. The CPP provides a retirement pension for the contributor.

The pension pays about 25% of the earnings on which you paid into the plan. In 1999, this meant a maximum pension of about $9000 per year at age 65. If a person retires earlier than age 65, the amount is reduced by 0.5% for each month the person receives a pension before her or his 65th birthday. For example, a person aged 60 who retired in 1999 would receive a pension of about $6300 per year.

Because the CPP replaces only a small percent of a person's income, it is that person's responsibility to replace all or most of the remainder. This may be done in different ways, such as a company or private pension plan. Also, each person should contribute to a Registered Retirement Savings Plan (RRSP) to supplement retirement income.

When you invest in an RRSP, you do not pay taxes now on money you save. Contributions to your RRSP are deducted from your taxable income for the year and may result in a tax refund. The income tax is paid when the money is withdrawn from the plan. This provides substantial tax savings because your income will be lower when you retire, and thus taxed at a lower rate.

An RRSP can be opened at most financial institutions. We shall consider what we can contribute and how these contributions grow. In 2000, a person who earned employment income could contribute to an RRSP until the end of the year in which he or she turns 69. The person could contribute 18% of her or his income to a maximum of $13 500 per year.

To complete this project, you may need to use the Internet. You can start your search from our web site:

www.pearsoned.ca/onmath11

Example 1

Anne has an annual earned income of $30 000, and does not have a company pension plan.

a) How much can Anne contribute to an RRSP?

b) Anne pays income tax at 29%. How much is Anne's income tax rebate on this contribution?

Solution

a) Anne can contribute 18% of her earnings.

18% of $30 000 = 0.18 × $30 000
= $5400

Anne can contribute $5400.

b) Anne gets an income tax rebate of 29% of $5400.

That is, 0.29 × $5400 = $1566

Anne's income tax rebate is $1566.

Example 2

Refer to *Example 1*.

Suppose Anne's RRSP contribution earns interest at an average rate of 8% compounded annually.

a) What will the contribution amount to in 40 years?

b) Suppose Anne invests $5400 each year in an RRSP, for 40 years, at the same average interest rate. What will the amount be at the end of 40 years?

Solution

a) Use the formula $A = P(1 + i)^n$.

Substitute $P = 5400$, $i = 0.08$, and $n = 40$.

$A = 5400(1 + 0.08)^{40}$
$= 5400(1.08)^{40}$
$\doteq 117\ 312.42$

The amount after 40 years is $117 312.42.

b) Annual payments for 40 years represent an annuity.

Use the formula $A = \frac{R[(1 + i)^n - 1]}{i}$.

Substitute $R = 5400$, $i = 0.08$, and $n = 40$.

$A = \frac{5400[(1 + 0.08)^{40} - 1]}{0.08}$

$= \frac{5400(1.08^{40} - 1)}{0.08}$

$\doteq 1\ 398\ 905.20$

The amount after 40 years is $1 398 905.20.

Example 2 assumes that the contribution is affordable and the interest rate is maintained for 40 years. This may not be the case. However, *Example 2* does show how money can grow over an extended period of time. The more often interest compounds, the faster money grows. People should start to contribute as much as they can afford to an RRSP as early as possible.

Complete the following exercises to learn how different RRSP contributions can grow.

1. During the year she was 20 years old, Celeste worked in a far north community. She received a lump sum isolation bonus of $12 000 when she returned home. To save paying the income tax on the bonus, Celeste deposited the bonus in an RRSP.

  a) Celeste was in the 40% tax bracket. How much less tax did she pay for the year by investing in the RRSP?

  b) Celeste left the money in her RRSP for 35 years. Her RRSP earned interest at an average rate of 10% compounded annually. How much was in the RRSP account at the end of the 35 years?

  c) Celeste invested her tax rebate from part a in another RRSP account the next year. This account also earned an average of 10% compounded annually over the next 34 years. How much was there in this account at the end of the 34 years?

  d) Determine the total amount in the RRSPs in part b and c.

2. Maurice started an RRSP when he began his part-time job at age 16. Maurice invested $20 at the end of each month in an RRSP, starting the month following his birthday. Maurice made the same monthly deposit until his 50th birthday. The account paid interest at an average rate of 8.5% compounded monthly. How much did Maurice have in the RRSP on his 50th birthday?

3. Nabita entered the workforce at age 40. She immediately began to invest the maximum contribution in an RRSP. Her average salary over the next 20 years was $38 000 per year.

a) What was the average contribution Nabita made to her RRSP each year?

b) Assume Nabita made her average contribution at the end of each year and it earned an average rate of 12% compounded annually. How much did Nabita have in her RRSP account at the end of the 20 years?

4. Pete started an RRSP account when he was 21 years old. He deposited $50 in the account at the end of each month. Pete started investing one month after he turned 21, and continued until his 50th birthday. His account earned an average of 9.6% compounded monthly.

a) How much was in the account on his 50th birthday?

b) Suppose Pete had made $100 contributions instead of $50. How much would be in the account on his 50th birthday?

c) By doubling a contribution, does the amount in the RRSP double? Explain.

5. Anders started to make yearly contributions to his RRSP at age 20. At the end of the year, he contributed $3000 to his RRSP and continued to do so for the next 10 years. At age 30, Anders' income had grown. He increased his annual contribution to $7000, which continued for another 10 years. At age 40, Anders was again able to increase his annual contribution to $10 000 for another 10 years. At age 50, Anders increased his annual contribution to $15 000 for another 5 years, then he retired. Anders' RRSP earned an average of 10% compounded annually.

a) Calculate the amount in the RRSP at the end of the first 10 years. What will this amount to at the end of 25 years?

b) Calculate the amount of the $7000 contributions at the end of the 10 years. What will this amount to at the end of 15 years?

c) Calculate the amount of the $10 000 contributions at the end of the 10 years. What will this amount to at the end of 5 years?

d) Calculate the amount of the $15 000 contributions at the end of the 5 years.

e) Calculate the total amount Anders had in his RRSP at retirement.

A general statement concerning RRSPs is that you should start to contribute as early as possible (although the contribution may be small) and as often as possible, rather than wait until later and make larger contributions. After you complete the case studies that follow, write a report that discusses the validity of this statement.

Case Study 1

Helga began to contribute to an RRSP monthly, one month after her 19th birthday. She contributed $150 at the end of each month until her 60th birthday. Helga's RRSP earned an average of 10% compounded monthly. How much did Helga have in her RRSP on her 60th birthday? How much did Helga contribute to her RRSP?

Case Study 2

Tim waited until he was 32 years old before he started to contribute to his RRSP. He contributed $225 at the end of each month, starting one month after his 32nd birthday, until his 60th birthday. Tim's RRSP earned an average of 10% compounded monthly. How much did Tim have in his RRSP on his 60th birthday? How much did Tim contribute to his RRSP?

Case Study 3

Jessica waited until she was 40 years old before she opened an RRSP. One month after her 40th birthday, Jessica began to contribute $310 per month to her RRSP. She continued until her 60th birthday. Jessica's RRSP earned an average of 10% compounded monthly. How much did Jessica have in her RRSP on her 60th birthday? How much did Jessica contribute to her RRSP?

Case Study 4

Eric began to contribute to an RRSP one month after his 50th birthday. He continued to contribute $650 at the end of each month to the RRSP until his 60th birthday. Eric's RRSP earned an average of 10% compounded monthly. How much did Eric have in his RRSP on his 60th birthday? How much did Eric contribute to his RRSP?

Investigation 1   RRSPs

Visit a financial institution of your choice (or go to its web site) to obtain information on RRSPs. Prepare a written report, using this information, that also includes answers to these questions:

- In your words, what is an RRSP? Who can contribute to an RRSP?
- How much can a person contribute?
- How often should a person contribute?
- What happens if I can't contribute for a period of time?
- What happens if I need some of my RRSP for an emergency?
- When do I make contributions?
- How do I delay paying income tax with an RRSP?
- Where is my money invested in an RRSP?
- Are my investments safe in an RRSP?
- How many RRSP plans can I have?

Review Exercises

MATHEMATICS TOOLKIT

Sequences and Series Tools

> The general geometric sequence is a, ar, ar^2, ar^3, ..., ar^{n-1}.
>> a is the first term.
>> r is the common ratio.
>> n is the number of terms.

> The general term is $t_n = ar^{n-1}$.

> The general geometric series is $a + ar + ar^2 + ar^3 + ... + ar^{n-1}$.

> The sum of the first n terms of a geometric series is $S_n = \frac{a(r^n - 1)}{r - 1}$.

> Geometric sequences and series describe exponential growth.

Financial Tools

Annuities

> The amount of an annuity is given by $A = \frac{R[(1 + i)^n - 1]}{i}$.
>> A is the amount in dollars.
>> R is the regular deposit in dollars.
>> i is the interest rate per compounding period, as a decimal.
>> n is the number of deposits.

NS

1. Solve each equation.

   a) $2^{3x+1} = 4^2$ **b)** $2^{x-1} = 8^3$ **c)** $3^{x-5} = 9^{x+1}$

   d) $5^{x+3} = 25^{2x}$ **e)** $8^x = 4^{x+3}$ **f)** $2^{2x+3} = 8$

4.1

2. State which sequences are geometric. For each that is, state its common ratio.

   a) 5, 10, 20, 40, ...   **b)** 2, 7, 12, 17, ...

   c) 30, 15, 7.5, 3.75, ...   **d)** $\frac{1}{3}$, $\frac{1}{4}$, $\frac{1}{5}$, $\frac{1}{6}$, ...

   e) 50, 50(1.04), 50(1.04)^2, 50(1.04)^3, ...   **f)** 16, 8, 4, 2, ...

   g) 7, −21, 63, −189, ...   **h)** 2, 8, 18, 32, ...

3. Write the first 4 terms of each geometric sequence.

   a) The first term is 9 and the common ratio is 4.

   b) The first term is 5 and the common ratio is −3.

   c) The first term is 40 and the common ratio is 1.6.

   d) The first term is $-\frac{3}{8}$ and the common ratio is 2.

   e) The first term is −8 and the common ratio is −0.5.

4. Write the first 3 terms of the sequence defined by each general term. Determine whether the sequence is geometric. If it is, state its common ratio.

   a) $t_n = 2n + 7$ b) $t_n = 5(2)^{n-1}$

   c) $t_n = 3(-2)^{n-1}$ d) $t_n = 7^{n-1}$

   e) $t_n = n^4$ f) $t_n = \frac{1}{2}(5)^{n-1}$

5. Calculate the missing terms in each geometric sequence.

   a) __, 7, 14, __, __,   b) __, __, 1.7, 17, __,

   c) __, __, __, −160, 800,   d) __, $\frac{1}{8}$, $\frac{1}{16}$, __, __,

6. For each geometric sequence, find an expression for t_n, then calculate the value of t_{10}.

   a) 2, 8, 32, 128, …

   b) 100 000, −120 000, 144 000, −172 800, …

   c) −729, −243, −81, −27, …

   d) $\frac{1}{96}$, $\frac{1}{48}$, $\frac{1}{24}$, $\frac{1}{12}$, …

   e) 3, 3(1.1), $3(1.1)^2$, $3(1.1)^3$, …

   f) 12 345, 1234.5, 123.45, 12.345, …

7. Determine the number of terms in each geometric sequence.

   a) 4, 8, 16, 32, …, 8192   b) 1, 1.4, $(1.4)^2$, $(1.4)^3$, …, $(1.4)^{45}$

   c) $\frac{1}{25}$, $-\frac{1}{5}$, 1, −5, …, −78 125   d) 810, 270, 90, 30, …, $\frac{10}{81}$

4.2 8. Determine the sum of the first 12 terms of each geometric series.

   a) $4 + 8 + 16 + 32 + …$

   b) $1 + 4 + 16 + 64 + …$

   c) $-1 + 3 - 9 + 27 - …$

   d) $10 + 10(1.06) + 10(1.06)^2 + 10(1.06)^3 + …$

   e) $6 + 24 + 96 + 384 + …$

   f) $100\ 000 + 10\ 000 + 1000 + 100 + …$

9. For the geometric series $1 + 2 + 4 + 8 + \ldots$,

   a) Find an expression for t_n.

   b) Find an expression for S_n, then calculate S_8.

10. For the geometric series $128 + 64 + 32 + 16 + \ldots$,

   a) Calculate the 9th term.

   b) Calculate the sum of the first 9 terms.

11. For each geometric series, calculate the indicated sum.

   a) $7 + 28 + 112 + 448 + \ldots; S_{15}$

   b) $1 + 9 + 81 + 729 + \ldots; S_9$

   c) $80 + 80(1.3) + 80(1.3)^2 + 80(1.3)^3 + \ldots; S_9$

   d) $8 + 8(0.9) + 8(0.9)^2 + 8(0.9)^3 + \ldots; S_{10}$

12. Calculate the sum of the geometric series $4 + 8 + 16 + 32 + \ldots + 32\ 768$.

13. Calculate the sum of each series.

   a) $2 + 4 + 8 + \ldots + 128$

   b) $\frac{1}{25} + \frac{1}{5} + 1 + 5 \ldots + 3125$

   c) $4 + 12 + 36 + \ldots + 2916$

   d) $\frac{1}{4} + \frac{1}{2} + 1 + 2 + \ldots + 1024$

14. Calculate the sum of the geometric series $1 - 3 + 9 - 27 + \ldots - 177\ 147$.

4.3   **15.** What is an annuity?

16. Calculate the amount of each annuity on the date of the last deposit.

   a) A deposit of $1700 at the end of each year for 8 years at 6.7% compounded annually

   b) A deposit of $400 at the end of each 6-month period for 5 years at 6% compounded semi-annually

   c) A deposit of $60 at the end of each month for 3.5 years at 5.75% compounded monthly

   d) A deposit of $500 at the end of each quarter for 10 years at 4.8% compounded quarterly

   e) A deposit of $20 at the end of each month for 15 years at 7.2% compounded monthly

4.4 **17.** Calculate the regular deposit for each annuity so the deposits accumulate to the given amount on the date of the last deposit. Each deposit is made at the end of the compounding period.

a) $1575 in 5 years at $4\frac{3}{4}$% compounded semi-annually

b) $5000 in 3 years at $6\frac{1}{4}$% compounded monthly

c) $1000 in 2 years at 5.8% compounded annually

d) $2900 in 3.5 years at 6.6% compounded monthly

e) $1200 in 2.5 years at $5\frac{5}{8}$% compounded quarterly

f) $7500 in 7.5 years at 5.5% compounded monthly

18. Suppose you make a regular deposit at the end of each month into an account that pays 8.2% compounded monthly for 15 years. The amount in the account on the date of your last deposit is $15 000. How much do you invest in total?

4.5 **19.** Calculate the investment that provides the greater amount on maturity. For each investment, the deposit is made at the end of the compounding period.

a) **i)** $200 per month at 6% compounded monthly for 8 years
ii) $600 per quarter at 6.4% compounded quarterly for 8 years

b) **i)** $1500 per year at 7% compounded annually for 12 years
ii) $750 every 6 months at 6.8% compounded semi-annually for 12 years

c) **i)** $3600 per year at 5.5% compounded annually for 15 years
ii) $300 per month at 5.25% compounded monthly for 15 years

20. Irina deposited $200 at the end of each month in an annuity that pays 6.5% compounded monthly. At the end of 5 years, the interest rate increased to 7.75% compounded monthly. Irina continued the same deposit for another 7 years. What is the amount of Irina's annuity on the date of her last deposit?

21. Mark deposited $150 at the end of each month in an annuity that pays 4.5% compounded monthly. At the end of 4 years, the interest rate increased to 9% compounded monthly. Mark continued the same deposit for another 6 years. What is the amount of Mark's annuity on the date of his last deposit?

1. A geometric sequence has first term 5 and common ratio -2. Write the first 4 terms of the sequence.

2. Write the first 3 terms of the sequence with each general term. Determine whether the sequence is geometric. If it is, state the common ratio.

   a) $t_n = 3(2)^{n-1}$ b) $t_n = 2n + 5$ c) $t_n = 3^{n-1}$

3. **Knowledge/Understanding** Calculate the number of terms in the geometric sequence 1024, 512, 256, 128, …, $\frac{1}{16}$.

4. For the geometric series $1 - 3 + 9 - 27 + \ldots$,

   a) Find an expression for t_n.

   b) Find an expression for S_n, then calculate S_9.

5. **Communication** Explain how to calculate the sum of the geometric series $4 + 6 + 9 + 13.5 + \ldots + 102.515\,625$.

6. Calculate the amount of each annuity on the date of the last deposit.

   a) $2000 deposited at the end of each year for 12 years at 7.3% compounded annually

   b) $750 deposited at the end of each quarter for 8.5 years at 6.5% compounded quarterly

7. Calculate the regular deposit for each annuity so the deposits accumulate to the given amount on the date of the last deposit. Each deposit is made at the end of the compounding period.

   a) $900 in 2 years at 5.2% compounded monthly

   b) $5500 in 6.5 years at 4.5% compounded semi-annually

8. **Application** Suppose you make a deposit at the end of each month for 8 years in an account that pays 7% compounded monthly. After 8 years, the amount is $13 500. How much do you invest in total?

9. **Thinking/Inquiry/Problem Solving** Which investment provides the greater amount on maturity? Justify your decision.

   • A deposit of $400 at the end of each month, beginning one month from now, invested at 7.25% compounded monthly for 8 years

   • A semi-annual deposit of $2400, starting 6 months from now, invested at 7.5% compounded semi-annually for 8 years

5 Annuities: The Cost of Credit

Debit and Credit Cards

The project in Section 5.7 provides an opportunity to investigate the nature of debit and credit cards.

Curriculum Expectations

By the end of this chapter, you will:

> Solve problems involving the calculation of the present value and the regular payment in the formula for the present value of an ordinary annuity, using scientific calculators.

> Demonstrate, through calculation, the advantages of early deposits to long-term savings plans.

> Demonstrate, through calculations, using technology, the effect on interest paid of retiring a loan before it is due.

> Demonstrate, using technology, the effects of delayed payment on a credit card balance, on the basis of current credit card rates and regulations.

> Determine, through investigation, the features of various credit and debit cards.

> Calculate the cost of borrowing to purchase a costly item.

> Explain the process used in making a decision and justify the conclusions reached.

1 Review: Present Value

In Section 2.4, you learned that the *present value* of an amount is the principal that must be invested today to obtain that amount in the future.

The formula for present value is $P = \dfrac{A}{(1 + i)^n}$.

P is the present value or principal in dollars.

A is the amount in dollars.

i is the interest rate per compounding period, as a decimal.

n is the number of compounding periods.

Example 1

Calculate the present value of $3000 in 4 years at 4.5% compounded monthly.

Solution

Think: What principal will amount to $3000 in 4 years at 4.5% compounded monthly?

Use the formula $P = \dfrac{A}{(1 + i)^n}$.

Substitute $A = 3000$, $i = \dfrac{0.045}{12}$, and $n = 4 \times 12 = 48$.

$P = \dfrac{3000}{\left(1 + \dfrac{0.045}{12}\right)^{48}}$

$\doteq 2506.65$

Key in: 3000 ÷ (1 + 0.045
÷ 12) ^ 48 ENTER
=

The present value is $2506.65.

Exercises

1. Calculate the present value of each amount.

a) $900 in 4 years at 8% compounded annually

b) $500 in 3 years at 4.5% compounded annually

c) $1850 in 8 years at 7% compounded semi-annually

d) $350 in 5 years at 3.25% compounded semi-annually

e) $460 in 7 years at 6% compounded quarterly

f) $1250 in 4 years at 7.3% compounded quarterly

g) $950 in 2 years at 6% compounded monthly

2 Review: The Sum of a Geometric Series

The geometric series $a + ar + ar^2 + ar^3 + \ldots + ar^{n-1}$ has n terms.
The sum of the series is $S_n = \dfrac{a(r^n - 1)}{r - 1}$.

a is the first term.

r is the common ratio.

n is the number of terms.

Example 1

Calculate the sum of this geometric series to 9 terms.

$300 + 150 + 75 + \ldots$

Solution

$300 + 150 + 75 + \ldots$

The number of terms $n = 9$

The first term $a = 300$

The common ratio $r = \dfrac{150}{300} = 0.5$

Use the formula $S_n = \dfrac{a(r^n - 1)}{r - 1}$.

Substitute $a = 300$, $r = 0.5$, and $n = 9$.

$S_9 = \dfrac{300\left(0.5^9 - 1\right)}{0.5 - 1}$ Use a calculator.

$\doteq 598.83$

The sum of the series is approximately 598.83.

Exercises

1. Calculate the sum of each geometric series to the number of terms indicated. Write each sum to 2 decimal places where necessary.

a) $300 + 30 + 3 + \ldots$ to 10 terms

b) $242.5 + 97 + 38.8 + \ldots$ to 8 terms

c) $125 + \dfrac{125}{2} + \dfrac{125}{4} + \ldots$ to 9 terms

d) $75 + \dfrac{75}{5} + \dfrac{75}{5^2} + \ldots$ to 7 terms

Megan's parents plan to set up an annuity to help Megan when she attends college. The annuity will allow Megan to withdraw $2700 at the end of each year for 4 years. The first withdrawal will be made 1 year from now, when Megan starts college. The annuity pays interest at 6.5% compounded annually. How much money should Megan's parents invest now to provide the annuity?

The principal that must be invested now to provide an annuity is called the *present value of an annuity*.

Megan's annuity is 4 payments of $2700.
The first payment will be made 1 year from now.
Since the money earns interest, Megan's parents do not have to deposit $2700 now to have $2700 a year from now.
They only need to deposit the present value of the $2700.
This is also true for the remaining planned payments.

To calculate the present value of each payment, use the present value formula $P = \dfrac{A}{(1 + i)^n}$.

The present value, P_1, of $2700 in 1 year at 6.5% compounded annually is:
$$P_1 = \frac{2700}{(1 + 0.065)^1}$$
$$= \frac{2700}{1.065}$$

The present value, P_2, of $2700 in 2 years at 6.5% compounded annually is:
$$P_2 = \frac{2700}{(1 + 0.065)^2}$$
$$= \frac{2700}{1.065^2}$$

Continuing this pattern, the present value, P_3, of $2700 in 3 years at 6.5% compounded annually is:
$$P_3 = \frac{2700}{1.065^3}$$

Similarly, the present value, P_4, of $2700 in 4 years at 6.5% compounded annually is:
$$P_4 = \frac{2700}{1.065^4}$$

A time line is used to illustrate the annuity.

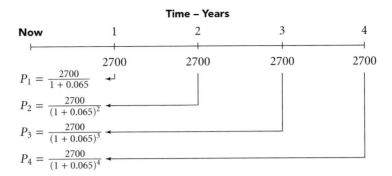

Time – Years

The present value of the annuity, PV, is the sum of the present values of the 4 payments.

$$PV = P_1 + P_2 + P_3 + P_4$$

$$= \frac{2700}{1.065} + \frac{2700}{1.065^2} + \frac{2700}{1.065^3} + \frac{2700}{1.065^4}$$

$$\doteq 2535.21 + 2380.48 + 2235.19 + 2098.77$$

$$\doteq 9249.65$$

Megan's parents must deposit $9249.65 now to provide the annuity for her college expenses.

We could have calculated the present value of the annuity in another way.

$$PV = \frac{2700}{1.065} + \frac{2700}{1.065^2} + \frac{2700}{1.065^3} + \frac{2700}{1.065^4}$$

This is a geometric series with common ratio $r = \frac{1}{1.065}$.

The first term $a = \frac{2700}{1.065}$

The number of terms $n = 4$

The present value of the annuity is the sum of the geometric series.

To calculate the sum of the series, use the formula $S_n = \frac{a(r^n - 1)}{r - 1}$.

Substitute the values above.

$$S_4 = \frac{\frac{2700}{1.065}\left[\left(\frac{1}{1.065}\right)^4 - 1\right]}{\frac{1}{1.065} - 1}$$

$$\doteq 9249.66$$

Key in: 2700 ÷ 1.065 × ((1 ÷ 1.065) ^ 4 − 1) ÷ (1 ÷ 1.065 − 1) ENTER =

The present value of the annuity is $9249.66.

This method can be generalized to calculate the present value of an annuity with n regular payments of R dollars per period at an interest rate of i per period. The formula for the present value of an annuity is shown in the Take Note that follows.

The present value of an annuity is:

$$PV = \frac{R[1 - (1 + i)^{-n}]}{i}$$

PV is the present value in dollars.

R is the regular payment in dollars.

i is the interest rate per compounding period, as a decimal.

n is the number of payments.

This formula is valid when:

- The payment period is the same as the compounding period.
- The payment is made at the end of the compounding period.

We will use the formula to verify the present value of Megan's annuity.

Example 1

Recall from page 234, Megan's annuity pays $2700 at the end of each year for 4 years, starting 1 year from now. The annuity earns 6.5% compounded annually. Determine the present value of the annuity.

Solution

Draw a time line to illustrate the annuity.

Time – Years

Now	1	2	3	4
	2700	2700	2700	2700

$PV \longleftarrow$ Present Value

Use the formula $PV = \frac{R[1 - (1 + i)^{-n}]}{i}$.

Substitute $R = 2700$, $i = 0.065$, and $n = 4$.

$$PV = \frac{2700[1 - (1 + 0.065)^{-4}]}{0.065}$$

$$= \frac{2700(1 - 1.065^{-4})}{0.065}$$

$$\doteq 9249.66$$

Key in: 2700 ⌐(⌐ 1 ⌐-⌐ 1.065 ⌐^⌐ ⌐(-)⌐ 4 ⌐)⌐ ⌐÷⌐ 0.065 (ENTER)

The present value of the annuity is $9249.66.

Discuss

The present value obtained here is 1¢ more that the first value obtained on page 235. Explain why.

Example 2

Fai's grandparents set up an annuity for him. He will be paid $500 at the end of each month for the next 5 years. The first payment will be made 1 month from now. How much must Fai's grandparents deposit to provide the annuity? Assume the money earns 5.7% compounded monthly.

Solution

Draw a time line to illustrate the annuity.

The number of payments is $5 \times 12 = 60$.

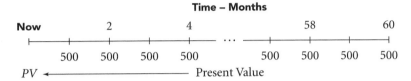

Use the formula $PV = \dfrac{R[1 - (1 + i)^{-n}]}{i}$.

Substitute $R = 500$, $i = \dfrac{0.057}{12}$, and $n = 60$.

$$PV = \frac{500\left[1 - \left(1 + \frac{0.057}{12}\right)^{-60}\right]}{\frac{0.057}{12}}$$

$\doteq 26\ 050.33$

Key in: 500 (1 − (1 + 0.057
÷ 12) ^ (−) 60) ÷
(0.057 ÷ 12) ENTER/=

Fai's grandparents must deposit $26 050.33 to provide the annuity.

Discuss

How can you use the store and recall features of a calculator to simplify the calculation?

It may be many years before you retire, but annuities are often used to provide income after retirement. If you understand the mathematics, you can make choices when you plan for retirement.

Example 3

Maurice is converting his RRSP into an income fund. He wishes to receive $1500 every six months for the next 20 years, starting 6 months from now. He is guaranteed an interest rate of 6.25% compounded semi-annually.
  a) How much must Maurice deposit now to pay for the annuity?
  b) How much interest does the annuity earn over the 20 years?

Solution

Draw a time line to illustrate the annuity.

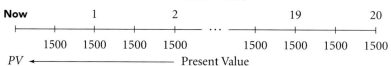

Time – Years

| Now | 1 | 2 | ... | 19 | 20 |

1500 1500 1500 1500   1500 1500 1500 1500

PV ← ——————— Present Value

a) The amount to be deposited now is the present value of the annuity.

Use the formula $PV = \dfrac{R[1 - (1 + i)^{-n}]}{i}$.

The number of payments is $20 \times 2 = 40$.

Substitute $R = 1500$, $i = \dfrac{0.0625}{2}$, and $n = 40$.

$$PV = \frac{1500\left[1 - \left(1 + \dfrac{0.0625}{2}\right)^{-40}\right]}{\dfrac{0.0625}{2}}$$

$$\doteq 33\,982.11$$

Maurice must deposit \$33 982.11 now to pay for the annuity.

b) Maurice receives 40 payments of \$1500.

The total amount received is $40 \times \$1500 = \$60\,000$.

Maurice paid \$33 982.11 for the annuity.

Thus, the interest earned is $\$60\,000 - \$33\,982.11 = \$26\,017.89$.

The annuity earns \$26 017.89 interest.

5.1 Exercises

A

1. Evaluate each expression. Write each answer to 2 decimal places.

   a) $\dfrac{200(1 - 1.2^{-5})}{0.2}$ **b)** $\dfrac{450(1 - 1.06^{-8})}{0.06}$ **c)** $\dfrac{225(1 - 1.075^{-15})}{0.075}$

 2. Determine the present value of each annuity.

	Regular payment, R (\$)	Interest rate per period, i (%)	Number of payments, n
a)	1800	4	8
b)	2000	7	10
c)	350	8	36
d)	200	6	36
e)	1200	5	14
f)	10 000	8.5	10
g)	1000	9.25	60
h)	1500	3.6	24

3. Determine the present value of each annuity. Each payment is made at the end of the compounding period.

a) \$475 per year for 16 years at $5\frac{3}{4}\%$ compounded annually

b) \$5500 every 6 months for 4.5 years at $6\frac{1}{4}\%$ compounded semi-annually

c) \$1365 per quarter for 11.5 years at 6.7% compounded quarterly

d) \$425 per month for 3.5 years at $7\frac{1}{2}\%$ compounded monthly

e) \$5000 every 6 months for 8.5 years at 5.25% compounded semi-annually

f) \$2500 per year for 7 years at $4\frac{3}{4}\%$ compounded annually

g) \$3275 per month for 5.25 years at 7.72% compounded monthly

h) \$985 per quarter for 6.75 years at $6\frac{1}{2}\%$ compounded quarterly

4. An account pays 6% compounded monthly. How much must be deposited in the account now to provide a regular payment of \$100 at the end of each month for the next 3 years, starting 1 month from now?

5. Knowledge/Understanding Fatima will need \$2500 per year for 3 years for college tuition. She will start college in 1 year. Fatima can invest her money at 5.4% compounded annually. How much will an annuity cost to pay for her tuition?

6. Tom has recently sold his business. He sets up an annuity that will pay him \$3000 per month for the next 15 years. The first payment is to be made 1 month from now. Tom can invest his money at 6.5% compounded monthly. How much does the annuity cost today?

7. Lindsay would like to withdraw \$700 every 3 months for 6 years. The first withdrawal will be 3 months from now. Money can be invested at $7\frac{1}{2}\%$ compounded quarterly. How much should Lindsay deposit now to pay for the annuity?

8. Application Yasser won a lottery. He will receive a payment of \$2000 per month for the next 5 years. The first payment will be made 1 month from now. What amount must the lottery company invest today at 8% compounded monthly to provide Yasser's prize?

9. Genine contributes to a scholarship fund set up by the college she attended. She will donate \$50 at the end of each year for the next 10 years, starting 1 year from now. The scholarship fund earns 7.2% compounded annually. What is the present value of Genine's contributions?

10. Josh has inherited a sum of money. He wants to buy an annuity that will pay him $300 per month for 25 years, starting 1 month from now. Josh can invest his money at 8.5% compounded monthly. How much will the annuity cost?

11. Communication Each part of exercise 1 is an expression that represents the present value of an annuity. Choose one expression from exercise 1. Pose a problem whose solution would result in the evaluation of the expression.

12. Emma has purchased an annuity that will allow her to withdraw $600 per month for the next 4 years. The first withdrawal will be 1 month from now. The money is invested at 7.5% compounded monthly.

a) Determine the cost of the annuity.

b) Determine the interest earned over the term of the annuity.

13. An annuity pays $1000 per year for 20 years. The money is invested at 5.8% compounded annually. The first payment is made 1 year after the purchase of the annuity. Determine the interest earned by the annuity over the 20 years.

14. Thinking/Inquiry/Problem Solving

Derek wants to buy a 10-year annuity. He has 2 options.

- Option A pays $1000 at the end of each year, starting 1 year from now. It earns interest at 6.25% compounded annually.
- Option B pays $500 every 6 months, starting 6 months from now. It earns interest at 6.25% compounded semi-annually.

Which annuity should Derek buy? Write an explanation that includes calculations to support your choice.

15. Consider these three annuities.

Annuity A: $400 per month for 5 years at 6% compounded monthly

Annuity B: $200 per month for 10 years at 6% compounded monthly

Annuity C: $100 per month for 20 years at 6% compounded monthly

The total of all the payments is the same for each annuity.

a) Which annuity has the greatest present value, or are all the present values the same? Explain.

b) Carry out calculations to confirm your prediction in part a.

When equal regular payments are needed, an annuity may be set up. The amount that is deposited to start the annuity must be sufficient to provide for the payments. After the last payment there is no money, or very little money, in the account. Often, the amount to be invested is known. When you know the interest rate and the period of the annuity, you can calculate the regular payment.

Example 1

Dimitri used the $20 000 his grandfather gave him, to set up an annuity that earns 7.2% compounded monthly. Dimitri will receive equal monthly payments from the annuity for the next 2 years, starting 1 month from now. What will be Dimitri's monthly payment?

Solution

Draw a time line.

The number of payments is $2 \times 12 = 24$.

Let R dollars represent the monthly payment.

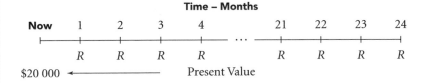

Time – Months

Now	1	2	3	4		21	22	23	24
	R	R	R	R	⋯	R	R	R	R

$20 000 ← Present Value

The $20 000 is the present value of the annuity; that is, $PV = 20\ 000$.

The interest rate $i = \frac{0.072}{12} = 0.006$, and $n = 24$.

Substitute these values in the formula $PV = \frac{R[1 - (1 + i)^{-n}]}{i}$. Solve for R.

$$PV = \frac{R[1 - (1 + i)^{-n}]}{i}$$

$$20\ 000 = \frac{R[1 - (1 + 0.006)^{-24}]}{0.006}$$

$$20\ 000 = \frac{R(1 - 1.006^{-24})}{0.006} \qquad \text{Multiply each side by 0.006.}$$

$$120 = R(1 - 1.006^{-24}) \qquad \text{Divide each side by } (1 - 1.006^{-24}).$$

$$R = \frac{120}{1 - 1.006^{-24}} \qquad \text{Key in: } 120 \; \boxed{\div} \; \boxed{(} \; 1 \; \boxed{-} \; 1.006$$

$$\doteq 897.27 \qquad\qquad\qquad \boxed{\wedge} \; \boxed{(-)} \; 24 \; \boxed{)} \; \boxed{\text{ENTER}}$$

Dimitri will receive a monthly payment of $897.27.

Discuss

In *Example 1*, when you enter the expression in the calculator, why must the denominator of the expression be enclosed within brackets?

Example 2

Anna won $25 000 in a lottery. The winnings will be paid in equal monthly installments for the next 4 years, starting 1 month from now. The money earns $7\frac{1}{2}\%$ compounded monthly. Determine the monthly installment.

Solution

Draw a time line.
Let R dollars represent the monthly installment.
The number of payments is $4 \times 12 = 48$.

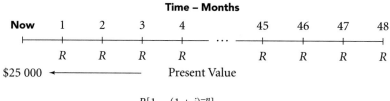

Use the formula $PV = \frac{R[1 - (1 + i)^{-n}]}{i}$.

Substitute $PV = 25\ 000$, $i = \frac{0.075}{12}$, and $n = 48$.

$$25\ 000 = \frac{R\left[1 - \left(1 + \frac{0.075}{12}\right)^{-48}\right]}{\frac{0.075}{12}} \quad \text{Multiply each side by } \frac{0.075}{12}.$$

$$156.25 = R\left[1 - \left(1 + \frac{0.075}{12}\right)^{-48}\right] \quad \text{Divide each side by } 1 - \left(1 + \frac{0.075}{12}\right)^{-48}.$$

$$R = \frac{156.25}{1 - \left(1 + \frac{0.075}{12}\right)^{-48}}$$

Key in: 156.25 $\div$ (1 − (1 + 0.075 $\div$ 12) ^ (−) 48) ENTER =

$$\doteq 604.47$$

The monthly installment is $604.47.

Example 3

Alexandra has $60 000 saved in her RRSP. She will use the money to buy an annuity that pays 6.8% compounded semi-annually. She will receive semi-annual payments for the next 20 years. The first payment will be made 6 months from now.

a) Determine the semi-annual payment.

b) Determine the interest earned during the term of the annuity.

Solution

Draw a time line.
Let R dollars represent the semi-annual payment.
The number of payments is $20 \times 2 = 40$.

The semi-annual interest rate is $\frac{6.8\%}{2} = 3.4\%$.

Time – Years

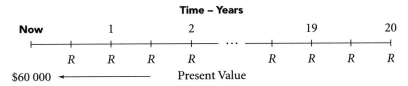

$60 000 \longleftarrow$ Present Value

a) Use the formula $PV = \frac{R[1 - (1 + i)^{-n}]}{i}$.

Substitute $PV = 60\ 000$, $i = 0.034$, and $n = 40$.

$60\ 000 = \frac{R[1 - (1 + 0.034)^{-40}]}{0.034}$

$60\ 000 = \frac{R[1 - 1.034^{-40}]}{0.034}$ Multiply each side by 0.034.

$2040 = R[1 - 1.034^{-40}]$ Divide each side by $1 - 1.034^{-40}$.

$R = \frac{2040}{1 - 1.034^{-40}}$ Key in: 2040 ÷ (1 −

$\doteq 2766.21$ 1.034 ^ (−) 40) ENTER =

The semi-annual payment is $2766.21.

b) Alexandra receives 40 payments of $2766.21.

The total amount received is $2766.21 \times 40 = \$110\ 648.40$.

Alexandra paid $60 000 for the annuity.

Thus, the interest earned is $110\ 648.40 - \$60\ 000 = \$50\ 648.40$.

The interest earned is $50 648.40.

A

1. Solve each equation for R. Write each answer to 2 decimal places.

   a) $40\ 000 = \dfrac{R(1 - 1.005^{-12})}{0.005}$ **b)** $2500 = \dfrac{R(1 - 1.0035^{-10})}{0.0035}$

   c) $2000 = \dfrac{R[1 - (1 + 0.025)^{-8}]}{0.025}$ **d)** $1200 = \dfrac{R[1 - (1 + 0.056)^{-4}]}{0.056}$

2. Determine the regular payment from each annuity. Each payment is made at the end of the compounding period.

	Present value, PV ($)	Interest rate per period, i (%)	Number of payments, n
a)	8000	5	6
b)	3000	3	10
c)	5000	2	16
d)	4000	1	36
e)	6000	4	20
f)	1000	1.5	8
g)	10 000	0.75	24
h)	7000	1.25	48

B

3. Determine the regular payment from each annuity. Each payment is made at the end of the compounding period.

   a) Present value of $7835 at 6.77% compounded annually for 15 years

   b) Present value of $8900 at $4\frac{3}{4}$% compounded semi-annually for 8.5 years

   c) Present value of $7500 at 7% compounded quarterly for 6.5 years

   d) Present value of $2000 at 7.25% compounded monthly for 1.5 years

   e) Present value of $15 500 at 4.85% compounded semi-annually for 11.5 years

   f) Present value of $20 000 at 5.1% compounded monthly for 9.25 years

4. You deposit $3500 in an account that pays 5.8% compounded monthly. What equal withdrawals can you make each month for the next 3 years?

5. **Knowledge/Understanding** Megan's trust fund has a present value of $15 000. She purchases an annuity that pays 6.4% compounded semi-annually. How much can Megan withdraw every 6 months for the next 8 years?

6. Jeremy is a triathlete. His parents deposited $15 000 in an account that pays 7.25% compounded monthly to help Jeremy with his training expenses. What equal monthly payment can Jeremy withdraw at the end of each month for the next 1.5 years?

7. Denise has $2000 to invest in an annuity that pays 6% compounded monthly. She will make equal monthly withdrawals for the next 3 years, starting 1 month from now.

a) Determine Denise's monthly withdrawal.

b) Determine the interest earned over the term of the annuity.

8. Oren has $5000 to invest. He decides to purchase an annuity that pays 8% compounded semi-annually for 12 years. His first withdrawal is 6 months from now. How much interest will he receive over the term of the annuity?

9. Application On John's 17th birthday, his grandparents put $10 000 in a trust fund that earns 5% compounded annually. John can make equal annual withdrawals from the fund starting on his 18th birthday. Determine each annual withdrawal when the money in the fund (principal and interest) must last each given time.

a) 5 years   b) 8 years   c) 12 years

10. Communication Karl has $3000 to invest in an annuity that pays 6.5% compounded monthly for 3 years. His first withdrawal will be 1 month from now. Sandra has $6000 to invest in annuity with identical conditions to Karl's. Will Sandra's monthly withdrawal be twice Karl's? Write a brief explanation of your answer and include calculations.

11. Suppose the interest rate on a $10 000 annuity that pays 4% compounded annually for 5 years is doubled. Will the annual withdrawal double? Write a brief explanation of your answer and include calculations.

12. Suppose the interest rate on a $4000 annuity that pays 3% compounded annually for 8 years is doubled. Will the interest earned over the term of the annuity double? Write a brief explanation of your answer including calculations.

13. Thinking/Inquiry/Problem Solving Suppose you have $20 000 to purchase an annuity for the next 5 years. The interest rate is 8% but the compounding period is flexible. You can choose monthly, quarterly, semi-annual or annual payments and compounding.

a) Determine the regular payment for each compounding period.

b) Determine the total amount received for each compounding period.

c) Which investment would you choose? Justify your choice.

Most of us borrow money at some time to finance the purchase of items we wish to have now, but cannot afford to pay in full. Loans are commonly repaid by making equal monthly payments for a fixed period of time. When all the payments have been made, both the original loan and the accumulated interest have been paid.

Colin borrowed $684.25 to buy a television. To repay the loan, he will make 24 equal monthly payments starting 1 month from now. He is charged interest at 12% compounded monthly. How much is Colin's monthly payment?

The equal monthly payments Colin makes form an annuity.

A single payment of $684.25 today would pay off the loan.
Thus, $684.25 is the present value of the loan.
That is, $PV = 684.25$
The number of payments is 24.
The monthly interest rate is $\frac{12\%}{12} = 1\%$.

To calculate the monthly payment, solve for R in the formula
$PV = \frac{R[1 - (1 + i)^{-n}]}{i}$.

Substitute $PV = 684.25$, $i = 0.01$, and $n = 24$.

$$684.25 = \frac{R[1 - (1 + 0.01)^{-24}]}{0.01}$$

$$684.25 = \frac{R(1 - 1.01^{-24})}{0.01}$$ Multiply each side by 0.01.

$$6.8425 = R(1 - 1.01^{-24})$$ Divide each side by $1 - 1.01^{-24}$.

$$R = \frac{6.8425}{1 - 1.01^{-24}}$$ Key in: 6.8425 ÷ (1 −

$$\doteq 32.21$$ 1.01 ^ (-) 24) ENTER=

Colin's monthly payment is $32.21.

When a loan is repaid by a series of equal regular payments, the payments form an annuity whose present value is the original loan.

Example **1**
Sophie bought a car for $23 477.50. She made a down payment of $2500. Sophie financed the rest through her car dealer at 8.9% compounded monthly. She will make monthly payments for the next 3 years. Her first payment is due 1 month from now. Estimate Sophie's monthly payment.

Solution

Sophie made a down payment of $2500.
So, the amount financed is $23 477.50 − $2500.00 = $20 977.50.
This is the present value of the loan.

To estimate the monthly payment, first estimate the interest.

The 1st month's interest is $20\ 977.50 \times \dfrac{0.089}{12} \doteq \$155.58$.

The last month's interest is $20\ 977.50 \times 0 = \$0$

The approximate total interest is the mean of the 1st and last months' interest multiplied by the number of months (payments).

The approximate total interest is $\left(\dfrac{\$155.58 + \$0}{2}\right) \times 36 = \$2800.44$.

The average monthly payment is $\dfrac{\text{Present value} + \text{Interest}}{36} \doteq \dfrac{\$20\ 978 + \$2800}{36}$
$$= \$660.50$$

Sophie's monthly payment is approximately $660.

The equivalent cash price of an item is what you pay to buy the item today instead of financing it.

Example **2**
A DVD player can be purchased for no money down and 24 equal monthly payments of $23. The interest charged is 10% compounded monthly. Determine the equivalent cash price of the DVD player.

Solution

The equivalent cash price is the cost of the DVD player today.
It is the present value of an annuity of 24 payments of $23 at 10% compounded monthly.

Use the formula $PV = \dfrac{R[1 - (1 + i)^{-n}]}{i}$.

Substitute $R = 23$, $i = \dfrac{0.1}{12}$, and $n = 24$.

$$PV = \dfrac{23[1 - (1 + \frac{0.1}{12})^{-24}]}{\frac{0.1}{12}}$$

$$\doteq 498.43$$

The equivalent cash price of the DVD player is $498.43.

A

1. Determine the monthly payment for each loan. The first payment is made 1 month after the date of the loan. Each interest rate is compounded monthly.

   a) $500 for 1 year at 6%

   b) $2000 for 3 years at 9%

   c) $20 875 for 5 years at 8%

   d) $1389 for 2 years at 12%

   e) $5000 for 3 years at 7%

   f) $4875 for 4 years at 5%

   g) $7000 for 5 years at 6%

   h) $1200 for 1 year at 12%

2. Refer to *Example 1*. Estimate how much Sophie paid for her car.

3. Estimate the monthly payment on a car loan of $32 967 for 48 months at 15% compounded monthly.

B

4. Determine the equivalent cash price of a "boom box" that can be purchased with 18 monthly payments of $24.09. The interest charged is 14% compounded monthly.

5. A laptop computer can be purchased for 36 monthly payments of $70. The interest charged is 12% compounded monthly. What is the equivalent cash price of the computer?

6. **Knowledge/Understanding** Sami has taken out a loan at 6% compounded monthly for 2 years. His monthly payment is $155.12. The first payment is due 1 month from today. How much did Sami borrow?

7. Rachel will repay a debt by making a payment of $1000 every 6 months for 5.5 years. Payments will start 6 months from today. The interest rate charged is 11% compounded semi-annually. What sum paid today would clear the debt?

8. **Application** Anna is planning to buy a car. She can afford to make a payment of $650 per month for the next 4 years. The first payment will be made 1 month from the date she buys the car. The interest rate on car loans is 9.5% compounded monthly. What is the maximum amount Anna can afford to pay for a car?

9. Communication Suppose Javier has saved $4500 for a down payment for a car. He can afford to make a payment of $600 per month for the next 3.5 years. The first payment will be made 1 month from the date he buys the car. The interest rate for his loan is 5.9% compounded monthly. Present a clear calculation that shows the maximum amount Javier can afford to pay for a car today. Show all your reasoning.

10. Simon plays in a band. He is updating his keyboard. A new keyboard costs $3975. The music store will take his old keyboard as a trade-in, and give him a credit of $1150 toward the price of the new one. He can finance the rest by making monthly payments for 2.5 years, starting 1 month from the purchase date. Estimate Simon's monthly payment when he is charged 10% compounded monthly.

11. When Paul was in college, he took out a student loan for $12 680 at 7.5% compounded monthly. Paul is working now, and wants to pay off the loan as quickly as possible. Estimate the monthly payment when Paul repays the loan in each given time. He will make his first payment in 1 month.

a) 4 years	**b)** 4.5 years	**c)** 5 years
d) 5.5 years	**e)** 6 years	**f)** 10 years

12. The bank has announced a rate increase for consumer loans. Effective tomorrow, the interest rate will increase from 8.5% to 9.25%. Leslie plans to buy a stereo system that costs $2799. The bank will loan her money to buy the stereo. The loan must be repaid in 30 equal monthly payments, at the current rate of interest, compounded monthly. The payments start 1 month from the date of the loan. What would be the difference in the monthly payment if Leslie buys the stereo tonight instead of tomorrow?

13. Gunnar wants to finance a car loan of $18 650 at 9.2% compounded monthly. He can choose a term of either 36 months or 48 months. Estimate how much more Gunnar pays per month if he chooses a term of 36 months instead of 48 months.

14. Thinking/Inquiry/Problem Solving Rosina spent $4689 to buy furniture for her new apartment. She made a down payment of $850, and financed the rest at 8.4% compounded monthly. She can choose to repay the loan in 24 months or in 36 months. How much will Rosina save if she repays the loan in 24 months instead of 36 months?

15. Huda purchased a new boat at a total price of $15 800. She received a trade-in allowance of $3700 for her old boat, and financed the rest at 12.6% compounded monthly. Huda can repay the loan in 36 months or 48 months. How much interest will Huda save if she repays the loan in 36 months instead of 48 months?

5.4 The Cost of Borrowing

When you take a loan to finance the purchase of a costly item, you repay not only the original amount borrowed, but also accumulated interest. The interest you pay is the cost of borrowing the money. This cost depends on the amount borrowed, the rate charged, and the term of the loan.

Example 1

Mila borrows $3500 from her bank to buy a new computer system. She will repay the loan in 36 equal monthly payments. The first payment will be 1 month from now. The bank charges 9.5% compounded monthly. How much interest does Mila pay over the lifetime of the loan?

Solution

To determine the total amount Mila repays, calculate her monthly payment.

Use the formula $PV = \frac{R[1 - (1 + i)^{-n}]}{i}$.

Substitute $PV = 3500$, $i = \frac{0.095}{12}$, and $n = 36$. Then solve for R.

$$3500 = \frac{R[1 - (1 + \frac{0.095}{12})^{-36}]}{\frac{0.095}{12}}$$

Multiply each side by $\frac{0.095}{12}$.

$$3500 \times \frac{0.095}{12} = R[1 - (1 + \frac{0.095}{12})^{-36}]$$

Divide each side by $1 - (1 + \frac{0.095}{12})^{-36}$.

$$R = \frac{3500 \times \frac{0.095}{12}}{1 - (1 + \frac{0.095}{12})^{-36}}$$

$$\doteq 112.12$$

Mila's monthly payment is $112.12.
She makes 36 payments.
The total amount repaid is $36 \times \$112.12 = \$4036.32$.
The original loan was $3500.
The difference between the two amounts is $\$4036.32 - \$3500 = \$536.32$.
Mila pays $536.32 interest on the loan.

Discuss

Use the method of *Example 1*, page 247, to estimate the interest on the loan. How do the estimated and calculated values compare?

Example 2 A bank advertises car loans at 8% compounded monthly for 48 months. There is a $\frac{1}{2}$% reduction in the rate if you apply for the loan through the Internet. Suppose you wish to borrow $35 000.

a) Calculate the regular monthly payment at each interest rate.

b) What is the total amount repaid for each loan?

c) How much interest do you save by applying through the Internet?

Solution

a) Use the formula $PV = \frac{R[1 - (1 + i)^{-n}]}{i}$.

To calculate the monthly payment at 8%, substitute $PV = 35\ 000$, $i = \frac{0.08}{12}$, and $n = 48$.

$$35\ 000 = \frac{R[1 - (1 + \frac{0.08}{12})^{-48}]}{\frac{0.08}{12}}$$

$$35\ 000 \times \frac{0.08}{12} = R[1 - (1 + \frac{0.08}{12})^{-48}]$$

$$R = \frac{35\ 000 \times \frac{0.08}{12}}{1 - (1 + \frac{0.08}{12})^{-48}}$$

$$\doteq 854.45$$

The monthly payment at 8% is $854.45.

When the loan is applied for through the Internet, the interest rate is 7.5%. To calculate the monthly payment at 7.5%, substitute $PV = 35\ 000$, $i = \frac{0.075}{12}$, and $n = 48$.

$$35\ 000 = \frac{R[1 - (1 + \frac{0.075}{12})^{-48}]}{\frac{0.075}{12}}$$

$$R = \frac{35\ 000 \times \frac{0.075}{12}}{1 - (1 + \frac{0.075}{12})^{-48}}$$

$$\doteq 846.26$$

The monthly payment at 7.5% is $846.26.

b) For each interest rate, 48 payments were made.

The total amount repaid at 8% is $48 \times \$854.45 = \$41\ 013.60$.

The total amount repaid at 7.5% is $48 \times \$846.26 = \$40\ 620.48$.

c) The difference in the total amounts repaid is

$\$41\ 013.60 - \$40\ 620.48 = \$393.12$.

$393.12 would be saved by applying through the Internet.

Discuss

Check the result of part c by subtracting the monthly payments, then multiplying by 48. Which method is easier?

A

1. For each loan, the payment is made at the end of the compounding period. Determine the payment per compounding period and the total interest paid.

	Amount borrowed	Payment period	Interest rate	Term
a)	$1500	semi-annually	11%	3 years
b)	$7000	quarterly	13%	5 years
c)	$18 000	monthly	10%	4 years
d)	$2000	annually	9%	2 years
e)	$900	monthly	12%	1 year
f)	$5000	semi-annually	8%	3 years
g)	$3000	quarterly	12%	4 years
h)	$6000	monthly	10%	2 years

B

2. Sharon takes a personal loan of $5000 for 4 years at 9% compounded monthly. The first payment will be made 1 month from now.
   a) Estimate Sharon's monthly loan payment.
   b) Estimate the interest Sharon pays over the term of the loan.

3. **Knowledge/Understanding** Ling takes a car loan of $21 000 for 3 years at 13.5% compounded monthly. The first payment will be made 1 month from now.
   a) What is Ling's monthly car payment?
   b) How much interest does Ling pay over the term of the loan?

4. Michael has a student loan of $8900 at 8.5% compounded monthly. He will pay off the loan over the next 4 years. The first payment will be made 1 month from now.
   a) Estimate Michael's monthly loan payment.
   b) Estimate the interest Michael pays over the term of the loan.

5. A bank advertises personal loans at 9.75% compounded monthly for 60 months. There is a $\frac{1}{2}$% reduction in the rate if you apply for the loan through the Internet. Suppose you borrow $12 000. The first payment will be made 1 month from now. How much interest do you save by applying for the loan through the Internet?

6. The Kongs are having a swimming pool built in their backyard. They borrowed $19 500 at 9.54% compounded monthly to finance the construction. They will pay back the loan with monthly payments for the next 10 years. The first payment will be made 1 month from now. Estimate the interest they will pay over the 10 years.

7. James buys a snowmobile for $4897. He pays 7% PST and 8% GST. James makes a down payment of $800 and finances the remainder. He will make monthly payments for the next 3 years at 10.8% compounded monthly. The first payment will be made 1 month from now. How much interest does James pay on the loan?

8. Application An automobile dealership has a year-end sale to make room for the new models. If you buy the current year model in the year-end sale, you will get financing at 2.9% compounded monthly. The regular cost of financing is 11.75% compounded monthly. Determine how much you save in interest on each vehicle listed below if you buy in the year-end sale. A payment is made each month, starting 1 month from the date of purchase.

	Amount financed	Term
a)	$18 760	2.5 years
b)	$31 978	48 months
c)	$24 852	3 years
d)	$13 595	3.5 years
e)	$9073	2 years
f)	$43 687	36 months

9. Communication When you buy car insurance, your driving record is taken into account when the premium is established. The better the driving record, the lower the premium charged. A similar situation exists with loans. Each person establishes a credit rating through payment history on loans, credit card balances, and so on. When you apply for a loan, the better your credit rating the lower the interest rate you may be charged.

A lender advertises car loans of $35 000 or more, at interest rates of 8% to 12.25%, compounded monthly, depending on credit worthiness. Calculate the interest paid on a $35 000 loan compounded monthly for 4 years at 8% and at 12.25%. Then calculate the difference in the interest paid. Show all your thinking when solving this problem.

10. Due to their credit ratings, Bill can borrow money at 9.45% compounded monthly but Sam must pay 11.3% compounded monthly. How much more interest would Sam pay than Bill on a $8650 loan with monthly payments for 3 years?

11. **Thinking/Inquiry/Problem Solving** Maya borrowed $5000. The terms of the loan were equal monthly payments at 12% compounded monthly for 3 years. The first payment was made 1 month after Maya took the loan. After making payments for 1 year, Maya decided to pay off the balance of the loan.

  a) What was Maya's monthly payment?

  b) How much must Maya pay at the end of 1 year to pay off the balance of the loan?

  c) How much interest did Maya save by repaying the loan in 1 year?

12. Investigate how a credit rating is established. Report your findings.

Career Profile

Credit Counsellor

The "purchasing" power of credit cards has had a dramatic effect in our society. The availability of "easy credit" has driven thousands of Canadians seriously into debt, causing disruption in the home and workplace. Under these circumstances, credit counsellors help find a solution to a person's financial situation.

Clients seek the advice of a credit counsellor when their debts are out of control and they need their finances to be restructured. To begin, a credit counsellor studies a person's whole financial picture, and focuses on the person's gross debt service ratio. This is the amount of the person's debt compared to her or his gross monthly income. This ratio will determine the regular monthly payment of the debt when the credit counsellor draws up the debt consolidation plan. A credit counsellor also provides the emotional support a client needs under such circumstances. Sometimes, a credit counsellor may educate the client in sound budgeting and money management techniques to avoid a repeat of the debt crisis.

Credit counsellors work regular hours when employed in banks and credit card companies or agencies specializing in credit assistance.

Where's the Math?

A credit counsellor uses basic math every day with each client. Most of the computations, such as calculating the gross debt service ratio, are done using a software program or calculator. The real skill comes in using these numbers to create suitable payment options for the client.

1. Determine the present value of each annuity. Each payment is made at the end of the compounding period.

   a) $1500 per year for 6 years at 5.6% compounded annually

   b) $600 every 6 months for 4 years at 8% compounded semi-annually

   c) $750 per quarter for 10 years at 7% compounded quarterly

   d) $300 per month for 5 years at 6.4% compounded monthly

2. Quentin purchased an annuity that will pay him $1000 per month for the next 3 years, starting 1 month from now. The money is invested at 7% compounded monthly.

   a) Determine the cost of the annuity.

   b) Determine the interest earned over the term of the annuity.

3. Determine the regular payment from each annuity. Each payment is made at the end of the compounding period.

   a) Present value of $7580 at 4.6% compounded annually for 4 years

   b) Present value of $6500 at 7% compounded semi-annually for 5.5 years

   c) Present value of $3000 at 5.75% compounded quarterly for 5 years

   d) Present value of $9000 at 6.8% compounded monthly for 4.5 years

4. Donna invests $5000 in an annuity that pays 7.2% compounded monthly. She will make equal monthly withdrawals for the next 4 years, starting 1 month from now.

   a) Determine Donna's monthly withdrawal.

   b) Determine the interest earned over the term of the annuity.

5. Suppose the rate on an $8000 annuity at 3.5% compounded annually for 6 years is doubled. Will the annual withdrawal double? Write a brief explanation of your answer and include calculations.

6. Spencer is taking out a personal loan of $6800. He will be charged interest at 12.8% compounded monthly. The loan is to be repaid in 48 monthly payments, starting 1 month from now. Determine Spencer's monthly payment.

7. Tamara borrowed $29 000 from her credit union to buy a car. She is charged 9.9% compounded monthly. Tamara will repay the loan with monthly payments for the next 3 years, starting 1 month from now.

   a) Determine Tamara's monthly payment.

   b) How much interest will Tamara pay over the term of the loan?

In this section, you will investigate how making more than the necessary monthly payments on a loan will affect the interest you pay.

A loan of $10 000 at 12% compounded monthly is to be repaid with 24 monthly payments of $470.73. The first payment is to be made 1 month from the date the loan was taken. (Recall, from Section 5.3, that the monthly payment is calculated using the present value formula, and solving for R.)

Using a Spreadsheet

When you take out a loan, you may obtain a *repayment schedule* for the loan. The schedule lists each payment and shows how much of each payment is interest and how much goes to reduce the principal. It also shows the outstanding balance (that is, the amount still owed) after each payment.

A repayment schedule is usually generated using a spreadsheet. The repayment schedule for the loan above is shown on the facing page.

Each month, a payment of $470.73 is made.
The annual interest rate is 12% compounded monthly.
Thus, the interest rate per month is $\frac{12\%}{12} = 1\%$. As a decimal, 1% = 0.01

For Payment 1:
When payment 1 is made, 1 month's interest is due on $10 000.
The interest for the month is $10 000 \times 0.01 = \$100$.
The remainder of the payment, $470.73 - \$100 = \$370.73$, reduces the principal.
Thus, the outstanding balance on the loan is $10 000 - \$370.73 = \$9629.27$.

For Payment 2:
When payment 2 is made, 1 month's interest is due on $9629.27.
The interest for the month is $9629.27 \times 0.01 \doteq \$96.29$.
The principal owed is reduced by $470.73 - \$96.29 = \$374.44$.
The outstanding balance on the loan is $9629.27 - \$374.44 = \$9254.83$.

The remaining payments are calculated in a similar fashion. The amount that goes toward paying interest decreases with each payment, while the amount that goes to reduce the principal increases with each payment.

The last payment is slightly larger than the rest. This final payment is adjusted to account for rounding errors, and to ensure the outstanding balance is $0.

Repayment Schedule

Amount of Loan: $10 000
Annual interest rate: 12%
Issue date (yyyy/mm/dd): 2000/10/22

Number of payments: 24
Monthly payment: $470.73

Payment number	Payment due date	Monthly payment	Interest paid	Principal paid	Outstanding balance
0	–	–	–	–	$10 000.00
1	2000/11/22	$470.73	$100.00	$370.73	$9629.27
2	2000/12/22	$470.73	$96.29	$374.44	$9254.83
3	2001/01/22	$470.73	$92.55	$378.18	$8876.65
4	2001/02/22	$470.73	$88.77	$381.96	$8494.69
5	2001/03/22	$470.73	$84.95	$385.78	$8108.91
6	2001/04/22	$470.73	$81.09	$389.64	$7719.27
7	2001/05/22	$470.73	$77.19	$393.54	$7325.73
8	2001/06/22	$470.73	$73.26	$397.47	$6928.26
9	2001/07/22	$470.73	$69.28	$401.45	$6526.81
10	2001/08/22	$470.73	$65.27	$405.46	$6121.35
11	2001/09/22	$470.73	$61.21	$409.52	$5711.83
12	2001/10/22	$470.73	$57.12	$413.61	$5298.22
13	2001/11/22	$470.73	$52.98	$417.75	$4880.47
14	2001/12/22	$470.73	$48.80	$421.93	$4458.54
15	2002/01/22	$470.73	$44.59	$426.14	$4032.40
16	2002/02/22	$470.73	$40.32	$430.41	$3601.99
17	2002/03/22	$470.73	$36.02	$434.71	$3167.28
18	2002/04/22	$470.73	$31.67	$439.06	$2728.22
19	2002/05/22	$470.73	$27.28	$443.45	$2284.77
20	2002/06/22	$470.73	$22.85	$447.88	$1836.89
21	2002/07/22	$470.73	$18.37	$452.36	$1384.53
22	2002/08/22	$470.73	$13.85	$456.88	$927.65
23	2002/09/22	$470.73	$9.28	$461.45	$466.20
24	2002/10/22	$470.86	$4.66	$466.20	$0.00
	Total	**$11 297.65**	**$1297.65**	**$10 000.00**	

Use this schedule to complete *Investigation 1*, exercises 1 to 6.

Using a Spreadsheet to Investigate a Loan

1. **a)** How much principal was paid in the 4th payment?

   b) What was the outstanding balance after the 9th payment?

   c) How much interest was paid in the 5th payment?

   d) Compare the interest paid in the 7th and 8th payments. Why are the amounts different?

   e) Compare the principal paid in the 10th payment to the principal paid in the 11th payment. Why do they differ?

   f) Does the outstanding balance decrease by the same amount after each payment? Explain.

   g) What is the due date of the 15th payment?

   h) What is the total interest paid over the term of the loan?

2. Suppose a person could pay off the loan entirely with the 13th payment.

   a) How much would it cost to do this?

   b) How much interest would the person save by paying off the loan early?

3. Repeat exercise 2. Assume each following payment is the last regular payment.

   a) 17th payment   **b)** 20th payment   **c)** 8th payment   **d)** 5th payment

4. What advice would you give a person who has a loan and suddenly comes into some extra cash? Why?

With some loans, you can pay an additional amount with any regular payment. This extra amount is a *lump sum* payment. It reduces the outstanding balance. You will now investigate how this affects the above loan.

5. **a)** A lump sum payment is made. Assume the monthly payment remains the same. What will happen to the number of payments required to pay off the loan?

   b) Suppose the number of payments is reduced. How will the total interest paid over the term of the loan be affected?

6. **a)** What is the outstanding balance after the 7th payment has been made?

   b) Suppose an additional payment of $1204.38 is made with the 7th payment. What is the new outstanding balance?

   c) Locate the new outstanding balance in the schedule. At what payment number is it located?

   d) How many more payments are now needed to pay off the loan?

   e) How many payments were not required because of the lump sum payment?

   f) What is the total interest saved by not making these payments?

7. Work with a partner. Use a spreadsheet to create a repayment schedule for a loan of $40 000 at 15% compounded monthly. The loan is repaid with equal monthly payments over 5 years.

a) Calculate the monthly payment. (Refer to Section 5.3, page 246.)

b) Vary the amount of a lump sum payment and its position in the repayment schedule. Investigate the savings obtained by shortening the length of time to pay off a loan. Choose at least 6 different cases. Alternate between one person who selects the amount of the lump sum payment and the other who determines the interest saved.

c) Write a report on your findings.

Using a Graphing Calculator

Refer to the loan at the top of page 256: a loan of $10 000 at 12% compounded monthly is repaid with 24 monthly payments of $470.73.

You can use the TVM Solver on the TI-83 Plus calculator to determine the monthly payment for a loan, and the outstanding balance after a given number of payments. If you have a different calculator, consult its manual. For more information on the TVM Solver, refer to *Utility 3*, page 390.

To access the TVM Solver, press APPS 1 1. To calculate the monthly payment, enter the values shown, below left, in the TVM Solver. Since the payment and compounding period are monthly, both P/Y and C/Y = 12.

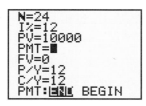

Move the cursor to PMT. Press ALPHA ENTER to obtain the screen above right.

The monthly payment is $470.73.

Consider the outstanding balance on the loan after 6 payments have been made. It is the present value of the remaining 18 payments.

Move the cursor to N. Enter 18.
Move the cursor to PV. Press ALPHA
ENTER to obtain this screen.

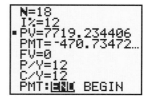

The outstanding balance after 6 payments have been made is $7719.23.

Discuss

Why is this outstanding balance different from the corresponding balance in the schedule on page 257?

Consider the interest paid in the first 6 months. The interest paid is the difference between the total amount paid and the principal paid.

6 payments of $470.73 are made.
The total amount paid is 6 × $470.73 = $2824.38.
The original loan is $10 000.
The outstanding balance is $7719.23.
Thus, the principal paid is $10 000 − $7719.23 = $2280.77.
The interest paid is $2824.38 − $2280.77 = $543.61.

The interest paid in the first 6 months is $543.61.

Investigation 2

Using a Graphing Calculator to Investigate a Loan

Use the TVM Solver. Exercises 1 to 3 refer to the loan at the top of page 256: a loan of $10 000 at 12% compounded monthly is repaid with 24 monthly payments of $470.73.

1. **a)** What is the outstanding balance after 8 payments have been made?
   b) How many payments remain when the outstanding balance is $6928.21?
   c) How much would it cost to pay off the loan after the 12th payment?
   d) How many payments must be made to reduce the outstanding balance to $2728.13?   24−6 ≠ 18
   e) What is the outstanding balance after 4 payments have been made?
   f) How many payments remain when the outstanding balance is $4880.32?
   g) How much would it cost to pay off the loan after the 18th payment?
   h) How many payments must be made to reduce the outstanding balance to $6526.76?

2. Determine the interest saved when the loan is paid off after the 16th payment.

3. Suppose a lump sum payment of $2000 is made after the 5th payment.
   a) What is the new outstanding balance?
   b) Assume the monthly payment remains the same. How many payments are required to pay off the loan now?

c) Determine the cost of making 19 regular payments. Then, determine the cost of making the number of payments found in part b. Determine the difference between these two costs.

d) Subtract $2000 from the amount in part c. What does this sum of money represent?

4. A car loan of $41 896 at 14.3% compounded monthly will be repaid with 60 equal monthly payments. The first payment will be made 1 month from the date the loan was taken.

a) Determine the monthly payment.

b) Calculate the outstanding balance after 10 payments have been made.

c) Determine the new outstanding balance when a lump sum of $8000 is paid after the 10th payment.

d) Calculate the number of payments that remain after the lump sum is applied. Assume the payments remain the same.

e) Calculate the interest saved by making the lump sum payment.

5. Jim bought a car. He financed $37 500 at 12.75% compounded monthly. He will repay the loan with 60 equal monthly payments.

a) Determine Jim's monthly payment.

b) After 1 year, Jim decides to increase his monthly payment by $150 a month. How many payments must he make to pay off his loan?

c) How much interest does Jim save by making the larger monthly payment?

6. Work with a partner. Investigate the effect of making lump sum payments on a loan of $10 000 at 18% compounded monthly. The loan will be repaid with equal monthly payments over 5 years.

a) Calculate the monthly payment.

b) Vary the amount of a lump sum payment and its position in the repayment schedule. Investigate the savings obtained by shortening the length of time to pay off a loan. Choose at least 6 different cases. Alternate between one person who selects the amount of the lump sum payment and the other who determines the interest saved.

c) Write a report on your findings.

In Chapter 4, you learned how a Registered Retirement Savings Plan (RRSP) can be used to save money for your retirement. Recall that an RRSP allows you to invest a percent of your earned income each year free from paying tax on these savings. An RRSP can be cashed at any time, but is subject to tax in the year in which it is cashed. Many people use an RRSP to provide an income, or pension, after they have stopped working.

You may contribute to an RRSP only if you have earned income. Once you stop working, you can no longer contribute to an RRSP. At this time, you may set up a system of regular equal withdrawals from your RRSP to provide income to replace a portion of your former income. In addition to your Canada Pension Plan (CPP) income, regular withdrawals from an RRSP fund may allow you to maintain your standard of living.

Suppose Pat retires on her 60th birthday. The amount of all investments in her RRSP is about $740 000. She decides that $650 000 of the funds in the RRSP will be invested in an annuity that pays an average rate of 8% compounded monthly for the next 20 years. What monthly pension will she receive?

The $650 000 represents the present value of the annuity.

Use the formula $PV = \dfrac{R[1 - (1 + i)^{-n}]}{i}$.

Substitute $PV = 650\ 000$, $i = \dfrac{0.08}{12}$, and $n = 12 \times 20 = 240$.

The monthly pension can be found by solving for R.

$$650\ 000 = \frac{R[1 - (1 + \frac{0.08}{12})^{-240}]}{\frac{0.08}{12}}$$

$$650\ 000 \times \frac{0.08}{12} = R[1 - (1 + \frac{0.08}{12})^{-240}]$$

$$R = \frac{650\ 000 \times \frac{0.08}{12}}{1 - (1 + \frac{0.08}{12})^{-240}}$$

$$\doteq 5436.86$$

Pat will receive a monthly pension of $5436.86.

Note that the calculation above ignores any taxes Pat would pay if she reinvests her money in an account that is not "tax sheltered."

Suppose the remaining $90 000 is invested with a financial institution and earns interest at 9% compounded annually. What will the fund amount to in 20 years?

Use the compound interest formula $A = P(1 + i)^n$.

Substitute $P = 90\ 000$, $i = 0.09$, and $n = 20$.

$A = 90\ 000(1 + 0.09)^{20}$

$\doteq 504\ 396.97$

The fund will amount to \$504 396.97 after 20 years.

The Advantages of Early Deposits into an RRSP

Consider a long-term savings plan, such as an RRSP. Does the time for which you save have much effect on the amount you have when you retire? These case studies will help you to answer this question.

If you have a company pension plan, the amount you can contribute to an RRSP will be limited. In these case studies, assume the people do not have a company pension plan.

Note that many people cannot afford to retire until they are 60 or 65 years old. All the people considered in Case Studies 1 to 4 retire at 55 to enable you to compare their savings and pensions.

Case Study 1

Gina began to contribute to her RRSP at age 21. She made monthly contributions. Her average monthly contribution, starting 1 month after her 21st birthday, was \$525. Her RRSP earned interest at an average rate of 9% compounded monthly until her 55th birthday. Gina retired on her 55th birthday and started to withdraw a monthly pension from her RRSP 1 month later.

  1. Determine the amount in Gina's RRSP on her 55th birthday.
  2. Suppose Gina decided to set aside \$20 000 of this money in the RRSP for emergencies and use the remainder to provide an annuity for her monthly income. What is the present value of her annuity?
  3. Suppose Gina was able to obtain the same average rate and chose a 25-year term for her annuity. What monthly pension could she withdraw for the next 25 years?
  4. Suppose the rate also remained the same for her \$20 000. What would it amount to in 10 years?

Case Study 2

Benji began to contribute to his RRSP at age 30. He made annual contributions. His average contribution, starting at the end of the year he was 30, was \$9000. Benji made contributions to the end of the year he was 55. His RRSP earned interest at an average rate of 9% compounded annually. Benji retired at the end of the year he was 55 and started to withdraw a monthly pension from his RRSP 1 month later.

5. Determine the amount in Benji's RRSP on the date of his last contribution.

6. Suppose Benji decided to set aside $10 000 of this money in the RRSP for emergencies and use the remainder to provide an annuity for his monthly income. What is the present value of his annuity?

7. Suppose Benji was able to obtain an average rate of 9% compounded monthly for his annuity and chose a 25-year term. What monthly pension could he withdraw for the next 25 years?

8. Suppose the rate for the $10 000 emergency fund averaged 9% compounded monthly. What would the fund amount to in 10 years?

Case Study 3

Hali began to contribute to her RRSP at age 40. She made annual contributions. Her average contribution, starting at the end of the year she was 40, was $13 500. Hali made contributions to the end of the year she was 55. Her RRSP earned interest at an average rate of 9% compounded annually. Hali retired at the end of the year she was 55 and started to withdraw a monthly pension from her RRSP 1 month later.

9. Determine the amount in Hali's RRSP on the date of her last contribution.

10. Suppose Hali decided to set aside $10 000 of this money in the RRSP for emergencies and use the remainder to provide an annuity for her monthly income. What is the present value of her annuity?

11. Suppose Hali was able to obtain an average rate of 9% compounded monthly for her annuity and chose a 25-year term. What monthly pension could she withdraw for the next 25 years?

12. Suppose the rate for the $10 000 emergency fund also averaged 9% compounded monthly. What would the fund amount to in 10 years?

Case Study 4

Germaine began to contribute to his RRSP at age 47. He made contributions monthly. His average monthly contribution, starting 1 month after his 47th birthday, was $1120. His RRSP earned interest at an average rate of 9% compounded monthly until his 55th birthday. Germaine retired on his 55th birthday and started to withdraw a monthly pension from his RRSP 1 month later.

13. Determine the amount in Germaine's RRSP on his 55th birthday.

14. Suppose Germaine decided to set aside $5000 of this money in the RRSP for emergencies and use the remainder to provide an annuity for his monthly income. What is the present value of his annuity?

15. Suppose Germaine was able to obtain the same average rate and chose a 25-year term for his annuity. What monthly pension could he withdraw for the next 25 years?

16. Suppose the rate for the $5000 emergency fund also averaged 9% compounded monthly. What would the fund amount to in 10 years?

Investigation 1

Contributions to an RRSP

Work with a partner. Use the TVM Solver on a graphing calculator. Choose different contribution amounts, times for investments, and interest rates. Determine what effects they might have on monthly retirement pensions. Research current RRSP options available. Write a report on your findings. Share your results with other members of your class or group.

Career Profile

Carpenter

For hundreds of years, wood has been an essential part of our lives—from fuel, to the furniture in a house, to the house itself. A carpenter creates, finishes or repairs wooden structures. Today's carpenter either remains an artisan, specializing in fine furniture and cabinet making, or works in the construction and housing industry.

In new construction, carpenters are involved in the building of walls, sidings, stairs, floors, roofs, and windows. There is then the finishing carpentry to be done in window frames, doors, and mouldings to give a house a finished, polished look. In renovations, carpenters have to give a lot of thought and planning to make something new fit into an existing structure.

Carpenters who are employed by a construction company, contractor, or maintenance department usually work regular hours. However, many choose to be self-employed, specializing in renovation work for houses or cabinet making. To be gainfully employed, these carpenters have to go from one project to another. A carpenter's job is physically demanding and requires strength, endurance, and excellent manual dexterity. Apprenticeship training is required for all carpenters, and certification is necessary to practise in their home province.

Where's the Math?

Basic math and skill in measurement are two essential skills. A carpenter uses ratio and proportion, trigonometry, and estimation skills regularly. Cost estimates may be key to a successful business. As the building industry still uses Imperial units, a carpenter must be able to calculate using these units.

The information you need to complete these investigations may be obtained by visiting a financial institution and reading its brochures, or by talking to its staff. If you have Internet access, you could also visit the web sites of financial institutions that issue debit and credit cards.

Investigation 1 Debit Cards

Many people use technology to do their banking. They make deposits and withdrawals through Automated Banking Machines (ABMs) or Automated Teller Machines (ATMs), pay for items through direct payment, and pay bills using the telephone or the Internet. Financial institutions provide a *debit card* to clients who wish to access their funds electronically.

With a partner, select a financial institution. Use information from this institution to complete these exercises.

1. What is the cost of a debit card?
2. List the types of transactions for which the debit card may be used.
3. What costs, if any, are associated with each transaction?
4. Research the options available to minimize the cost of using a debit card.

Write a report on your findings. Share the results with members of your class or group.

Credit Cards

Financial institutions and many businesses offer cards that allow people to make purchases or obtain cash without having the money taken directly from their account at the time of the transaction. This type of card is called a *credit card*. The card remains the property of the issuing company and may be cancelled at any time. Once the card is activated, the cardholder is responsible for all charges to the card.

With a partner, select a credit card company. Research the terms and conditions related to the credit cards your chosen company issues.

1. Determine the cards available from the company.
2. Many cards offer incentives. Determine any incentives offered by your chosen company cards. What are these incentives designed to encourage?
3. Some cards require the payment of an annual fee. Research these cards and why the fee is charged.
4. How often is a statement sent to the cardholder? What kind of statement is issued?
5. If the balance on a credit card is not paid in full by the due date, interest is charged on the outstanding balance. What rate is charged by the company you have chosen? How is the interest calculated? Is there a minimum payment that must be made?
6. Research the terms and incentives of other credit card companies.

Write a report on your findings. Include recommendations for the type of card suitable for people of different age groups and income levels. Share the results with members of your class or group.

Credit Card Costs

Jason recently received his first credit card. Here is part of the terms and conditions statement that accompanied the card.

- Interest rate 18.5%
- Minimum payment is 3% of the present balance or $10, whichever is greater.
- Interest Charges: Interest is calculated daily on all indebtedness, except that no interest will be charged on indebtedness that appears on the statement for the first time, if such indebtedness is paid in full by the due date. (This means that if you do not pay your bill in full by the due date on your monthly statement, you will be charged interest on the amount owing, from the date it was posted to your account, on your next bill.)

Jason used his card for a $180 purchase on June 19. This transaction appeared on his monthly statement, dated June 23. Part of this statement is shown below.

Last Statement	Previous Balance	Total Purchases	Cash Advances	Total Interest	Total Payments	Statement Balance
May 23/01	0.00	180.00	0.00	0.00	0.00	0.00

Transaction Date	Posting Date	Description of Transaction	Amount
June 19	June 19	Harold's Sports	180.00

This Month's Payment	+	Past Due Amount	=	Minimum Payment	Payment Due Date
10.00		0.00		10.00	July 14/01

Jason was short of money when the payment was due, so he made only the minimum payment on July 14.

$$3\% \text{ of } 180 = 0.03 \times 180$$
$$= 5.40$$

Since $10 is greater than $5.40, Jason paid $10.

This payment appeared on his July 23 statement, as shown below.

Last Statement	Previous Balance	Total Purchases	Cash Advances	Total Interest	Total Payments	Statement Balance
June 23/01	180.00	0.00	0.00	2.28	10.00	172.28

Transaction Date	Posting Date	Description of Transaction	Amount
July 23	July 23	Interest	2.28

This Month's Payment	+	Past Due Amount	=	Minimum Payment	Payment Due Date
10.00		0.00		10.00	Aug. 14/01

Although Jason made a payment of $10, the balance is not reduced by $10 because of the interest owing. The interest is calculated on the number of days from when the item is posted to the statement date, a period of 25 days.

$$I = Prt$$
$$I = 180 \times 0.185 \times \frac{25}{365}$$
$$= 2.28$$

The interest for the statement period was $2.28, as shown on the statement.

Costs of Delayed Payment

Exercises 1 and 2 refer to Jason's credit card, pages 267 to 268.

On August 14, Jason again made the minimum payment on his account. This payment appeared on his August 23 statement, as shown below.

Last Statement	Previous Balance	Total Purchases	Cash Advances	Total Interest	Total Payments	Statement Balance
July 23/01	172.28	0.00	0.00	2.71	10.00	164.99

Transaction Date	Posting Date	Description of Transaction	Amount
Aug. 23	Aug. 23	Interest	2.71

This Month's Payment	+	Past Due Amount	=	Minimum Payment	Payment Due Date
10.00		0.00		10.00	Aug. 14/01

1. The interest for this period was calculated from July 23 to August 22, inclusive, a period of 31 days. Verify that the interest is $2.71.

2. Suppose Jason continued to pay only the minimum payment each month until the balance was zero.
   a) How many months would this take?
   b) What was the total amount paid?
   c) How much interest did Jason pay?

3. With a partner, select a credit card. Determine the cost to use it when the balance is not paid on the due date. Invent various scenarios and see how the costs differ.

4. Suppose you have let the balance on your credit card grow to a point where it is impossible to pay it off in a short period of time. Suggest how you could minimize the amount of interest you pay.

MATHEMATICS TOOLKIT

Financial Tools

Annuities

> The present value of an annuity is given by $PV = \dfrac{R[1 - (1 + i)^{-n}]}{i}$.
> PV is the present value in dollars.
> R is the regular payment in dollars.
> i is the interest rate per compounding period, as a decimal.
> n is the number of payments.

The payment period is the same as the compounding period.
The payment is made at the end of each compounding period.

5.1

1. Determine the present value of each annuity. Each payment is made at the end of the compounding period.

   a) $1450 per year for 5 years at 6% compounded annually

   b) $2700 every 6 months for 8 years at 8.3% compounded semi-annually

   c) $600 per quarter for 12 years at 7% compounded quarterly

   d) $400 per month for 6 years at 9% compounded monthly

   e) $750 every 6 months for 4.5 years at 7.25% compounded semi-annually

   f) $3400 per year for 15 years at $6\frac{1}{4}$% compounded annually

   g) $1260 per month for 9.5 years at $8\frac{3}{4}$% compounded monthly

   h) $875 per quarter for 6.25 years at 7.7% compounded quarterly

2. An account pays 8% compounded monthly. How much must be deposited into the account now to provide a regular payment of $300 per month for the next 2 years? The first payment is 1 month from now.

3. Feodor will need $2000 at the end of each year for the next 4 years for tuition fees. His grandparents have purchased an annuity now to provide this money. The annuity pays 7.5% compounded annually. How much did Feodor's grandparents invest?

5.2   **4.** Determine the regular payment from each annuity. Each payment is made at the end of the compounding period.

a) Present value of $6000 at 6% compounded annually for 11 years

b) Present value of $5500 at 7% compounded semi-annually for 8 years

c) Present value of $9000 at 9% compounded quarterly for 5 years

d) Present value of $4000 at 5% compounded monthly for 3 years

e) Present value of $6750 at 8.5% compounded semi-annually for 7.5 years

f) Present value of $15 000 at $5\frac{1}{4}$% compounded monthly for 6.25 years

g) Present value of $7200 at 8.2% compounded quarterly for 3.5 years

h) Present value of $6740 at $7\frac{3}{4}$% compounded monthly for 5.75 years

5. Anne recently won $250 000 in a lottery. She has decided to invest in an annuity that will pay her $1500 a month for the next 25 years. Anne can invest her money at 9% compounded monthly. How much of her winnings must she set aside for the annuity?

6. An annuity has a present value of $25 000. Determine the regular monthly withdrawal from the annuity for 4 years at 8.4% compounded monthly.

7. Suppose the interest rate on an $8000 annuity at 5% compounded monthly for 6 years is doubled. Will the monthly withdrawal double? Write a brief explanation and include calculations to support your answer.

5.3   **8.** A portable CD player is advertised for no money down and 18 monthly payments of $17.50. The interest rate is 15% compounded monthly. Determine the equivalent cash price of the CD player.

5.4   **9.** Milan borrowed $19 785 at 12.65% compounded monthly for 48 months. His first payment is 1 month from now. Determine his monthly payment.

10. Elise has taken out a loan. She will make a monthly payment of $189.64 at the end of each month for the next 30 months. The interest rate on the loan is 10.25% compounded monthly.

a) How much did Elise borrow?

b) How much interest will Elise pay over the term of the loan?

11. Gavin has purchased a car. He financed a loan of $25 697 at 8.9% compounded monthly. He considers repaying the loan in 36 or 48 monthly payments. His first payment is 1 month from his date of purchase.

a) Determine the monthly payment for a 36-month loan.

b) Determine the monthly payment for a 48-month loan.

c) Determine the interest Gavin saves if he pays off the loan in 36 months.

d) What other factors would determine whether Gavin chooses to pay off the loan in 36 or 48 months?

12. A bank advertises car loans at 9.9% compounded monthly, with a 0.5% reduction in the rate if the loan is applied for over the Internet. The term of the loan can be from 36 to 60 months. Suppose you want to borrow $27 000. How much would you save by applying for the loan over the Internet, for each term?

a) 36 months   **b)** 48 months   **c)** 60 months

13. Trudi is buying a new boat. The boat can be purchased at Sara's Marina for $18 500. Financing is available at 12.9% compounded monthly. Donna's Discount Boats offers the same boat at $20 700 with financing at 10.8% compounded monthly. Trudi will make a down payment of $1500, and will finance the remainder over 48 months. Where should Trudi buy her boat? Write a complete explanation that includes calculations to support your opinion.

14. Halima has taken out a personal loan of $9000, which she will pay off with 60 monthly payments starting 1 month from now. The interest rate is 12.8% compounded monthly. Determine the total amount Halima will pay over the 60 months.

15. Refer to exercise 14. Suppose Halima was able to pay off her loan in 48 monthly payments. Determine the interest she would save.

16. A financial institution offers personal loans with interest rates that vary from 8.25% to 12.5% compounded monthly, depending on a person's credit rating. Two people, one with the best credit rating and the other with the worst, take out loans of $12 000 to be repaid in 30 monthly payments. How much more interest does the person with the poor credit rating pay?

1. **Knowledge/Understanding** Julia bought a new guitar. She financed $875 at 12.4% compounded monthly for 18 months. Determine Julia's monthly payment. Her first payment is 1 month after she bought the guitar.

2. How much must be deposited into an account now to provide an annuity of $1000 each quarter for the next 5 years? The account pays 8.4% compounded quarterly.

3. Determine the interest paid on a personal loan of $9500 at 13.5% compounded monthly for 48 months.

4. A large screen TV is advertised at no money down and 30 monthly payments of $219. The interest rate is 14.5% compounded monthly. Determine the cash price of the TV.

5. **Application** Josh is shopping for a new car. He can afford to make a down payment of $4500 and finance the remainder over 48 months. A monthly payment of $525 will fit into his budget. Josh can borrow money at 10.9% compounded monthly. What is the maximum price (including taxes) Josh can afford to pay for the car?

6. **Thinking/Inquiry/Problem Solving** Nancy is buying a used snowmobile for $3785. Her down payment is $550 and she will finance the remainder over 3 years. She has 2 options:

   i) The interest is 13.5% compounded monthly.

   ii) The interest is 14% compounded quarterly.

   Nancy will make each payment at the end of each compounding period. Recommend the better option for Nancy. Justify your choice with calculations.

7. A loan of $10 000 at 10.8% compounded monthly may be repaid over 48 or 60 months. How much interest would be saved by repaying the loan over 48 months?

8. **Communciation** List various ways interest may be kept to a minimum when financing is required to purchase a major item. Describe the advantages and disadvantages of each method of financing.

Being an Informed Consumer

Background

I n today's world, businesses compete for your money. They offer promotions and deals to entice you, the consumer, to buy their products and services:

> Car dealers offer low interest rates or zero interest rates near the end of a model year.

> A store offers limited hours for specials.

> A store offers "companion" specials, such as: buy a pair of pants and get a matching top half-price.

- Why do some stores offer deals between 8:00 A.M. and 10:00 A.M.?
- Suppose you purchase an item, then it goes on sale at the same store a week later. What can you do?
- Why do some credit card companies offer a one-year extension of a product's warranty when a credit card is used to buy the product?
- Stores frequently sell one or more items below their cost price. Why might the store do this? What are the advantages and disadvantages to the consumer?
- Why do some grocery stores rearrange the products from one aisle to another?
  Why do stores place popular items, such as flour, sugar, and salt, on the bottom or top shelves, leaving other shelves for new products?
  Which items are placed at eye level, or at check-out counters? Why?

Suggested Group Size: 2

Materials:

Newspapers

Flyers

Internet access

Curriculum Expectations

By the end of Explore, Research, Report, you will:

> Describe a decision involving a choice between alternatives.

> Collect relevant information related to the alternatives to be considered in making a decision.

> Summarize the advantages and disadvantages of the alternatives to a decision, using lists and organization charts.

> Compare alternatives by rating and ranking information, and by applying mathematical calculations and analysis, as appropriate, using technology.

> Explain the process used in making a decision and justify the conclusions reached.

> Identify the advantages and disadvantages to the purchaser of various types of selling and techniques of selling.

Being an Informed Consumer

1. Some stores have sales advertising "We pay the GST." In effect, a discount is given equivalent to the GST.

   a) Why can the store not deduct the GST from your bill?

   b) Suppose you buy an item for $100. Calculate the total bill including taxes.

   c) During the no GST sale, the sales clerk discounts your purchase by 7%, or $7. The price you pay for the item is $93 plus taxes. Calculate your bill for the discounted price.

   d) Look at the answer to parts b and c. Did you save an amount equal to the GST? Explain.

   e) Why do you think stores advertise these sales as "No GST" sales?

2. Suppose you have a coupon for 75¢ off on a particular brand of coffee.

   a) Copy and complete this table. Which packet size is the most economical?

Size (g)	300	369	1000
Price ($)	3.27	3.49	5.93
Price per 100 g ($)			
Coupon value ($)	0.75	0.75	0.75
Price after coupon ($)			
Price per 100 g after coupon ($)			

   b) Suppose a coupon for the same coffee is worth $1. Which packet size should you buy using this coupon? Explain.

3. A local home furnishings store offers "No payments, no interest" for 1 year, if you charge your purchase to its credit card. However, the store charges a $49.95 administration fee. Also, the administration fee, the PST, and the GST must be paid within 30 days. If the balance is not paid on time at the end of the year, interest on the full amount is added to the bill. The interest rate is 29.9% compounded annually.

   a) Suppose you buy a big screen television set, priced at $2495, plus taxes. Calculate the payment required at the end of 30 days.

b) Suppose you pay the bill after one year. Calculate the total cost.

c) Suppose you do not pay the bill after one year.

   i) Determine the interest charged.

   ii) Determine the total cost.

d) Suppose you cannot pay the bill after one year. Assume you will pay the bill with 12 equal monthly payments. As you make equal monthly payments, interest is charged on the outstanding amount. Calculate the monthly payment and the total paid in each case.

   i) Interest is charged on the full amount ($2495), excluding taxes, for 1 year. The interest rate is 29.9% compounded monthly.

   ii) You borrow money from a bank to pay the $2495. The bank charges 13.5% compounded monthly.

   iii) You obtain a cash advance from another credit card. The company charges 18.5% compounded monthly.

4. At another store, the television set from exercise 3 is on sale for $2299 plus taxes. There are no financing incentives. If you use a bank credit card, you must make a minimum monthly payment of 3% of the outstanding balance. You are charged interest at 18.5% compounded monthly.

a) Suppose only minimum payments are made. Prepare a table to show the total paid after one year and the balance owing after one year.

b) Suppose you make 12 equal monthly payments to pay off the loan. Calculate the monthly payment and the total paid.

c) Suppose you make 24 equal monthly payments to pay off the loan. Calculate the monthly payment and the total paid.

5. Compare your answers from exercises 3 and 4. List the advantages and the disadvantages of the different payment plans. Which is the best strategy for a consumer, and why?

Research

Choose one topic. Obtain information through research by reading newspapers or flyers; by interviewing family members, friends, and neighbours; by visiting businesses and examining their products; or by interviewing store managers.

You may use our web site.
www.pearsoned.ca/onmath11

Home Parties

Many products are available through home parties. Some items include kitchenware, candles, make-up, and clothing.

a) Research 3 companies. List the products they offer. Include catalogues or brochures, if possible.

b) What advantages are there to shopping at these parties? What are the disadvantages? Why do people attend these parties?

c) What enticements are there for the host or hostess to hold a party?

d) List reasons why a consumer might buy items at a party that he or she might not otherwise buy.

e) List any deals the company offers to the consumer, including the conditions of the offer. Explain the advantages to the consumer. Explain the advantages to the sales representative.

f) Companies that sell products through home parties employ multi-level marketing. In multi-level marketing, there is more than one intermediary between the producer and the consumer. In the case of home parties, each host is a retailer as well as a consumer, and, so, is an intermediary between the producer and the consumer. List reasons why a guest at a party might become a sales representative.

Telemarketing

Products or services are frequently offered through telemarketing.

a) List several items offered by telemarketing.

b) Use the list in part a. What similarities are there? Explain the type of product or service that is suitable for telemarketing.

c) Explain why you think telemarketing is successful.

d) What are the advantages to the consumer of telemarketing? What are the advantages to the company?

e) What are the disadvantages to the consumer? What are the disadvantages to the company?

Grocery Stores

Grocery stores entice consumers in different ways.

a) List the advantages and disadvantages of each of the following approaches, to both the consumer and the company.

   i) Limited quantity pricing

   ii) Special pricing for purchasing multiple quantities

    iii) "In-store" brands

    iv) Coupons for free merchandise, or for a cash discount, if a minimum amount is spent; for example, a coupon for $30 off your next bill, if you spend $250 or more

    v) Using a membership card to obtain special pricing, instead of clipping coupons

b) Visit three different grocery stores.

    i) Describe each store, and the type of consumer it appeals to.

    ii) Explain the main focus of each store. For example, it could be lowest pricing, volume discounts, great service, wide selection, or convenience.

c) Recommend a strategy for consumers to follow when they shop for groceries, so they keep their shopping bills as low as possible.

Coupon Incentives

Some stores or businesses offer coupons for use in another area of their business. For example, you buy gasoline and get a coupon for a cash discount at the company's grocery store. Businesses work together, offering coupons for one another's products. For example, a grocery store item may have a discount coupon for a theatre show.

a) Find 4 different examples of these coupon offers. Explain how the businesses or products are related.

b) Explain how the coupon offer benefits both businesses.

c) What are the advantages to the consumer of these coupons?

d) Many businesses offer coupons in a book sold by fund-raising groups.

    i) What advantages are there to the business?

    ii) What advantages are there to the consumer?

    iii) Restaurants in these books frequently offer "2 for 1" deals. Explain why restaurants make these offers.

    iv) Give two reasons why a consumer might take advantage of a "2 for 1" restaurant offer.

Retail, Catalogue, Discount Stores

Retail stores offer personal service to their customers.

a) List the advantages of shopping in a retail store over catalogue shopping.

b) List reasons why a consumer may prefer a retail store to a discount outlet.

c) Many consumers shop for some items in a retail store, and other items in a discount outlet. Suggest reasons for this. Give examples of products or occasions suitable for each type of store.

d) Visit two different retail stores.

   i) Describe the layout of each store. Include a sketch of the floor plan. Show the location of each type of merchandise.

   ii) Look at the floor plans. What are the similarities? What are the differences?

   iii) What departments must a consumer walk through to get to another department?

   iv) What departments are close to one another?

   v) Do you think the floor plans are randomly organized or strategically organized? Give reasons why the merchandise might be organized as it is.

e) During a sale, a store has deals such as "Buy one, get one free." Why does the store offer this deal instead of simply offering 50% off?

f) Retail stores are usually found in malls. What are the advantages to the consumer of having the store in a mall? What are the advantages to the store?

E-Commerce

Many companies use web sites on the Internet to expand their sales or open up new markets. Many new initiatives rely on marketing and distribution that are totally "web-based."

a) What advantages does e-commerce provide a company or consumers?

b) What are the disadvantages of e-commerce?

c) What are the costs associated with marketing products on the Internet?

d) What types of products or services are best suited to Internet sales? Explain.

e) What strategies can you suggest to improve a company's Internet sales?

f) Suppose you have a new product or service. How would you include e-commerce in your sales plan?

Other ways to shop

List advantages and disadvantages of purchasing items in each of the following ways. Support your statements with examples.

a) Television shopping

b) Purchasing from a door-to-door salesperson

c) Purchasing items in another country

d) Buying used merchandise

e) Shopping by telephone

Report

Create a bulletin board display that outlines your research. Include advertisements, pamphlets, coupons, or flyers. Show any calculations. Identify where you used the mathematics you learned in Chapters 1 to 5. Utilize spreadsheets, graphing calculators, lists, tables, and charts.

Present your results to the class. Explain how you made decisions. Justify your conclusions. Recommend strategies students can use.

Career Profile

Alarm Systems Technician

Alarm Systems Technicians install and maintain security equipment in homes, businesses, factories, farms and anywhere else where property requires protection. The technician selects the system that best meets the needs of the customer—this may range from a simple wired intrusion system, to sophisticated wireless and infra-red sensors, to closed-circuit television surveillance.

Knowledge of basic electricity, electrical standards, and electronics and how security systems and alarm equipment function are prerequisites for a career in this field. Other essentials are the ability to read and understand wiring diagrams and blueprints, and familiarity with building codes. Problem-solving and trouble-shooting skills are used constantly.

Service and installation technicians must be physically fit—they must be able to reach, stretch, bend, climb, and crawl in tight spaces to perform precise work with their hands. Although most technicians work standard hours, they have to be prepared for emergency calls at night.

Where's the Math?

Technicians are constantly working with electrical current and voltage. Math is used to calculate the correct amount of power to sensors and the relationship between wire footage and electricity. Logical math skills assist in problem solving equipment malfunctions—the technician has to test and analyse the equipment before deciding whether to replace or repair.

6 Mortgages

Chapter Project

Accommodation: Do I Rent or Buy?

The project in Section 6.6 provides an opportunity to investigate the pros and cons of renting or owning your home.

Curriculum Expectations

By the end of this chapter, you will:

> Identify the common terminology and features associated with mortgages.

> Describe the manner in which interest is usually calculated on a mortgage (that is, compounded semi-annually but calculated monthly), and compare this with the method of interest compounded monthly and calculated monthly.

> Generate an amortization table for a mortgage, using a spreadsheet or other appropriate software.

> Calculate the total amount of interest paid over the life of a mortgage, using a spreadsheet or other appropriate software, and compare the amount with the original principal of the mortgage or value of the property.

> Compare the effects of various payment periods, payment amounts, and interest

rates on the length of time needed to pay off a mortgage.

> Demonstrate, through calculations, using technology, the effect on interest paid of retiring a loan before it is due.

> Collect, organize, and analyse data involving the costs of various kinds of accommodation in the community.

> Compare the costs of maintaining an apartment with the costs of maintaining a house.

> Compare the advantages and disadvantages of renting accommodation with the advantages and disadvantages of buying accommodation.

> Summarize the findings of investigations in effective presentations, blending written and visual forms.

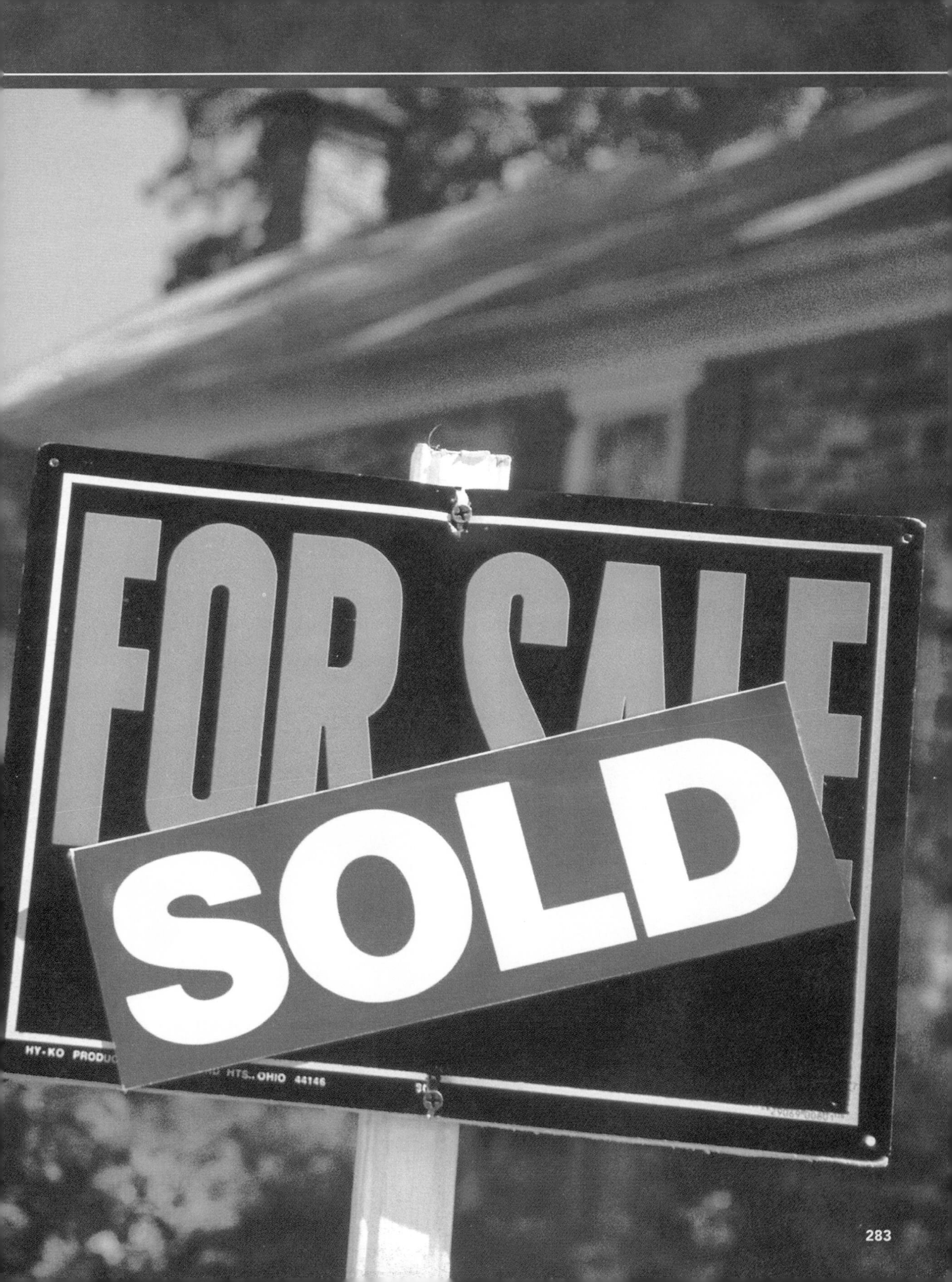
FOR
SOLD
HTS., OHIO 44146

1 Review: Using a Scientific Calculator to Evaluate Numerical Expressions

A calculator uses the order of operations rules when it performs a calculation. However, it does not recognize the convention of a fraction bar as a grouping symbol. This means that brackets must be inserted to ensure the numerator and denominator of a fraction are evaluated before dividing.

Example 1

Calculate $\frac{0.0825 \times 6995}{1.0825^{24} - 1}$. Give the answer to 3 decimal places.

Solution

$$\frac{0.0825 \times 6995}{1.0825^{24} - 1}$$

Use a calculator.

The denominator of the fraction requires the subtraction of terms, so insert brackets.

$$\frac{0.0825 \times 6995}{(1.0825^{24} - 1)}$$

Key in: 0.0825 $\boxed{\times}$ 6995 $\boxed{\div}$ $\boxed{(}$ 1.0825 $\boxed{\wedge}$ 24 $\boxed{-}$ 1 $\boxed{)}$ $\boxed{\text{ENTER} =}$

$$\frac{0.0825 \times 6995}{1.0825^{24} - 1} \doteq 101.190\ 025\ 8$$

$$\doteq 101.190 \text{ to 3 decimal places}$$

Exercises

1. Calculate. Give the answers to 3 decimal places.

a) $\left(1 + \frac{0.08}{12}\right)^3$

b) $\left(1 - \frac{0.065}{4}\right)^{-24}$

c) $\frac{0.096 \times 125\ 000}{1 - (1 + 0.096)^{-12}}$

d) $\frac{245[(1 + 0.056)^{36} - 1]}{0.056}$

2 Review: Rational Exponents

In Chapter 3, you learned about rational exponents, such as $\frac{1}{2}$.

Recall that the Exponents Laws are true for all rational exponents.

Example 1

Evaluate.

a) $16^{\frac{3}{2}}$ **b)** $8^{-\frac{1}{3}}$ **c)** $1.006^{\frac{1}{6}}$

Solution

a) $16^{\frac{3}{2}}$

Write the base as a power. $16 = 2^4$

So, $16^{\frac{3}{2}} = (2^4)^{\frac{3}{2}}$ Use the power of a power law.

$16^{\frac{3}{2}} = 2^{4 \times \frac{3}{2}}$

$= 2^6$

$= 64$

b) $8^{-\frac{1}{3}}$

Write the base as a power of 2. $8 = 2^3$

So, $8^{-\frac{1}{3}} = (2^3)^{-\frac{1}{3}}$ Use the power of a power law.

$= 2^{-1}$

$= \frac{1}{2}$

c) $1.006^{\frac{1}{6}}$

1.006 cannot be written as the power of an integer, so use a calculator.

Key in: 1.006 $\boxed{\wedge}$ $\boxed{(}$ 1 $\boxed{\div}$ 6 $\boxed{)}$ $\boxed{\text{ENTER} \atop =}$

$1.006^{\frac{1}{6}} \doteq 1.000\ 997\ 509$

Exercises

1. Evaluate.

a) $32^{\frac{3}{5}}$ **b)** $36^{\frac{5}{2}}$ **c)** $49^{-\frac{3}{2}}$ **d)** $1.085^{-0.5}$ **e)** $1.095^{\frac{1}{6}}$ **f)** $1.0625^{-\frac{1}{6}}$

Most people do not have the cash to buy a home outright. They finance the home by obtaining a *mortgage*. A mortgage is a loan to buy property, with the property as security. If the buyer, or *mortgagor*, fails to make the payments, the lending institution, or *mortgagee*, can sell the property and use the money to pay off the mortgage.

The home buyer is required to have a percent of the house price in cash as a *down payment*. The remainder is obtained through a mortgage. The buyer agrees to pay back the mortgage over a specified period of time with a series of equal regular payments. A mortgage, therefore, is an annuity.

Mortgage payments are usually made monthly. Since a large sum of money is involved, the time taken to repay a mortgage usually ranges from 10 to 30 years.

Mortgages in Canada cannot legally be compounded more frequently than semi-annually. In the work on annuities that you have done so far, the compounding frequency has been the same as the payment interval. For this to be the case with a Canadian mortgage, an adjustment is made to the interest rate used. You will learn more of this in Section 6.4. For simplicity, we will consider both monthly compounding and monthly payments until stated otherwise.

Example 1

A mortgage of $190 000 is required to purchase a house. The mortgage will be repaid with equal monthly payments over 25 years at 8% compounded monthly.

a) What is the monthly payment?

b) What is the total interest paid over the 25 years?

Solution

a) A mortgage is an annuity.

The amount of the mortgage is the present value of the annuity.

Use the formula $PV = \frac{R[1 - (1 + i)^{-n}]}{i}$.

Substitute $PV = 190\ 000$, $n = 25 \times 12 = 300$, and $i = \frac{0.08}{12}$.

$$190\ 000 = \frac{R[1 - (1 + \frac{0.08}{12})^{-300}]}{\frac{0.08}{12}}$$

$$190\ 000 \times \frac{0.08}{12} = R[1 - (1 + \frac{0.08}{12})^{-300}]$$

$$\frac{190\ 000 \times \frac{0.08}{12}}{1 - (1 + \frac{0.08}{12})^{-300}} = R$$

$$R \doteq 1466.45$$

The monthly payment is $1466.45.

b) To repay the mortgage, 300 payments of $1466.45 are made.

So, the total amount paid is $300 \times \$1466.45 = \$439\ 935$.

The amount of the mortgage is $190 000.

The total interest paid over the 25 years is
$439 935 − $190 000 = $249 935.

Discuss

- How does the total amount paid compare with the amount of the mortgage?
- What percent of the total amount paid is interest?

When both the principal and interest on a mortgage are repaid with a series of equal regular payments, we say the mortgage is *amortized*. The mortgage in *Example 1* was amortized by making monthly payments of $1466.45 for 25 years.

The length of time for which a mortgage is repaid is called the *amortization period*. Since interest rates change frequently, mortgage rates are rarely fixed for the entire amortization period. Instead, the interest rate is set for a length of time called the *term* of the mortgage. The term normally ranges from 6 months to 10 years. At the end of the term, the mortgage must be paid off or renewed at the current rate of interest.

Example 2 Suppose the mortgage in *Example 1* has an initial term of 5 years. The mortgage is renewed for another 5-year term at 6% compounded monthly.

a) Calculate the outstanding principal when the mortgage is renewed.

b) What is the new monthly payment?

Solution

a) 300 payments are required to pay off the mortgage.

In 5 years, 5×12, or 60 payments are made.

There are $300 - 60$, or 240 payments remaining.

The outstanding principal is the present value of the remaining 240 payments.

Use the formula $PV = \frac{R[1 - (1 + i)^{-n}]}{i}$.

Substitute $R = 1466.45$, $i = \frac{0.08}{12}$, and $n = 240$.

$$PV = \frac{1466.45[1 - (1 + \frac{0.08}{12})^{-240}]}{\frac{0.08}{12}}$$

$$\doteq 175\ 320.39$$

The outstanding principal is $175 320.39.

b) We need to determine the monthly payment for a mortgage of $175 320.39 at 6% compounded monthly for 20 years.

Use the formula $PV = \frac{R[1 - (1 + i)^{-n}]}{i}$.

Substitute $PV = 175\ 320.39$, $i = \frac{0.06}{12} = 0.005$, and $n = 240$.

$$175\ 320.39 = \frac{R[1 - (1 + 0.005)^{-240}]}{0.005}$$

$$175\ 320.39 \times 0.005 = R[1 - 1.005^{-240}]$$

$$\frac{175\ 320.39 \times 0.005}{1 - 1.005^{-240}} = R$$

$$R \doteq 1256.05$$

The new monthly payment is $1256.05.

The monthly payment could change several more times over the amortization period, depending on the length of the terms negotiated.

A

1. Determine the monthly payment for each mortgage. The interest is compounded monthly.

	Mortgage amount	Amortization period	Interest rate
a)	$140 000	25 years	6%
b)	$140 000	20 years	6%
c)	$140 000	30 years	6%
d)	$200 000	25 years	5.25%
e)	$200 000	25 years	7%
f)	$200 000	25 years	8.5%
g)	$100 000	15 years	6.5%
h)	$250 000	30 years	5.75%

2. Determine the total amount paid and the total interest paid during the lifetime of each mortgage in exercise 1. Assume the interest rate remains the same over the amortization period.

B

3. Until the 1970s, it was possible to get a mortgage at a fixed rate of interest for the entire amortization period. Suggest reasons why lenders stopped this practice.

4. **Communication** Explain the difference between the amortization period and the term of a mortgage.

5. **Knowledge/Understanding** Anita applies for a mortgage of $72 000 amortized over 20 years. The bank currently offers the following mortgage rates, compounded monthly.

ABC Bank	
Mortgage Rates	
1-year term	7.40%
2-year term	7.45%
3-year term	7.55%
4-year term	7.65%
5-year term	7.75%

a) Calculate the monthly payment for each term.

    i) 1 year   **ii)** 3 years   **iii)** 5 years

b) Suggest some reasons to choose a 5-year term instead of a 1-year term.

6. A mortgage of $147 500 at 7.5% compounded monthly is amortized over 25 years. After the original 7-year term, the mortgage is renewed at 8.25% compounded monthly. Calculate the new monthly payment.

7. The Samuels have a mortgage of $123 000 amortized over 25 years at 7.25% compounded monthly. After the original 4-year term, the mortgage is renewed at 6.5% compounded monthly. Calculate the new monthly payment.

8. Thinking/Inquiry/Problem Solving Jai took out a mortgage of $100 000 at 8% compounded monthly and an amortization period of 20 years. Genevieve took out a mortgage of $100 000 at 8% compounded monthly and an amortization period of 10 years. Does halving the amortization period double the monthly payment? Include all necessary calculations to support your answer.

9. In a conventional mortgage, the purchaser can borrow up to 75% of the purchase price of a property. The Murphys plan to obtain a mortgage on a house with a purchase price of $249 000. The mortgage will be amortized over 25 years at 6.5% compounded monthly. Assume the Murphys qualify for the maximum mortgage.

a) What is the maximum conventional mortgage the Murphys can obtain?

b) What will be the monthly payment on the maximum conventional mortgage?

10. Application Kiya purchased a house for $210 000. She made a down payment of 25% of the purchase price and took out a mortgage for the rest. The mortgage has an interest rate of 7.25% compounded monthly, an amortization period of 30 years, and a 3-year term. Calculate Kiya's monthly payment.

11. A bank advertises "3% cash back up to $3000" on a mortgage transferred from another financial institution. John has a mortgage of $150 000 at 6.5% compounded monthly with a 25-year amortization period. There are 20 years remaining on the amortization. He decides to make the transfer and apply the cash back to reduce the principal on the mortgage.

a) What is the present value of John's mortgage?

b) What is the amount of the "cash back"?

c) What is the outstanding principal after John transfers the mortgage?

12. A $100 000 mortgage is obtained at 7.2% compounded monthly.

a) Copy and complete this table.

Amortization period	Monthly payment	Total payments	Total interest paid	Interest saved
10 years				
15 years				
20 years				
25 years				—

b) How does the monthly payment change as the amortization period increases?

c) How does the total interest paid change as the amortization period increases?

13. A bank charges 7.75% compounded monthly on a mortgage. The Petersons have an excellent credit rating. They negotiated a rate of 7% compounded monthly on a mortgage of $230 000 amortized over 25 years. By how much did the Petersons reduce their monthly payment by negotiating the lower rate of interest?

 14. In the late 1970s and early 1980s, mortgage rates increased dramatically over a short period of time. The Khans initially took out a mortgage of $125 000 with a 25-year amortization period and a 3-year term. The interest rate was 6.75% compounded monthly. When they renewed the mortgage, the interest rate had risen to 18.75% compounded monthly. By how much did the Khans' monthly payment increase?

15. The Leungs purchased a home for $300 000. They put 40% down and took out a mortgage for the rest. The mortgage had an interest rate of 7.75% compounded monthly, a 15-year amortization period, and a term of 7 years. At the end of the term, the Leungs renewed their mortgage at 6.5% compounded monthly for the remaining 8 years.

a) What was the monthly payment during the 7-year term?

b) What was the monthly payment during the 8-year term?

c) How much interest did the Leungs pay over the 15 years?

16. Determine the difference in the interest paid over a 5-year term on a $250 000 mortgage at 8.75% compounded monthly compared to 17.5% compounded monthly. Assume the mortgage is amortized over 25 years.

Tina and Diego have just purchased their first home. They will make monthly mortgage payments of $694.63 on a $90 000 mortgage with an interest rate of 8% compounded monthly. The amortization period for the mortgage is 25 years. The term is 1 year.

When Tina and Diego obtained their mortgage, their bank provided them with an *amortization schedule*. It shows in detail how the mortgage is to be repaid during the 1-year term. It lists each payment, how much of each payment is interest, how much of each payment goes to reduce the principal, and the outstanding principal after each payment. Since the mortgage is amortized for 25 years, only a small portion of the outstanding principal will be paid off in 1 year.

Amortization Schedule

Mortgage amount: $90 000.00
Annual interest rate: 8%
Monthly payment: $694.63

Payment number	Monthly payment	Interest paid	Principal paid	Outstanding principal
0	–	–	–	$90 000.00
1	$694.63	$600.00	$94.63	$89 905.37
2	$694.63	$599.37	$95.26	$89 810.11
3	$694.63	$598.73	$95.90	$89 714.21
4	$694.63	$598.09	$96.54	$89 617.67
5	$694.63	$597.45	$97.18	$89 520.49
6	$694.63	$596.80	$97.83	$89 422.66
7	$694.63	$596.15	$98.48	$89 324.18
8	$694.63	$595.49	$99.14	$89 225.04
9	$694.63	$594.83	$99.80	$89 125.24
10	$694.63	$594.17	$100.46	$89 024.78
11	$694.63	$593.50	$101.13	$88 923.65
12	$694.63	$592.82	$101.81	$88 821.84

In Section 5.5, you learned to create repayment schedules for loans. The same process is used to create an amortization schedule. Recall how the numbers in the amortization schedule are generated.

Payment 1

When payment 1 is made, 1 month or $\frac{1}{12}$ of a year has passed.

1 month's interest is owed on $90 000.

The interest is $90 000 $\times$ 0.08 $\times \frac{1}{12}$ = $600.

The monthly payment is $694.63.

Of the monthly payment, $600 is interest.

The remainder of the payment, $694.63 − $600 = $94.63, goes toward reducing the principal.

So, the outstanding principal is $90 000 − $94.63 = $89 905.37.

Payment 2

When payment 2 is made, 1 month's interest is due on the outstanding principal, $89 905.37.

The interest is $89 905.37 $\times$ 0.08 $\times \frac{1}{12}$ = $599.37.

The principal is reduced by $694.63 − $599.37 = $95.26.

The outstanding principal is $89 905.37 − $95.26 = $89 810.11.

The remaining payments are calculated in a similar way.

An amortization schedule can be created quickly and efficiently using a spreadsheet. If you need to review creating and working with a spreadsheet, *Utilities 4* to *6* in the appendix provide a review. You could also consult the Help menu of the spreadsheet program or the User's Guide that came with the program.

In the following investigation, you will create a template to generate any amortization schedule. You can then use the template to generate a specific amortization schedule. The instructions are for Microsoft® Excel. If you have a different spreadsheet program, you may need to modify some of the instructions or formulas. Use the Help menu, or the User's Guide.

Investigation 1   **Using a Spreadsheet to Create an Amortization Schedule**

1. Open a new spreadsheet.

2. Copy the cells on the next page in the spreadsheet. Format the spreadsheet appropriately (see Utility 6).

	A	B	C	D	E
1	Amortization Schedule				
2					
3	Principal:				
4	Annual interest rate:				
5	Amortization period (years):				
6	Monthly payment:				
7					
8	Payment	Monthly	Interest	Principal	Outstanding
9	Number	Payment	Paid	Paid	Principal
10	0				=B3
11	=A10+1	=$B$6			

3. You will create the amortization schedule on page 292. Enter appropriate values in cells B3 to B6.

4. Enter these formulas:

- In Cell B6: $=\text{round}(B3*B4/12/(1-(1+B4/12)^{\wedge}(-B5*12)), 2)$
- In Cell C11: $=\text{round}(E10*\$B\$4/12, 2)$
- In Cell D11: $=B11-C11$
- In Cell E11: $=E10-D11$

5. Look at the formula in cell B6. What is being calculated? Explain.

6. Look at the formula in cell C11.

a) Which part of the formula changes? Which part stays the same?

b) Explain why you divide by 12.

7. Look at the formulas in cells D11 and E11. What is being calculated? Explain.

8. Save the spreadsheet.

9. Create the amortization schedule on page 292.
Select cells A11 through E11. Use Fill Down to extend the schedule for 12 payments. Use this schedule to answer exercises 10 to 13.

10. Each mortgage payment includes the interest due and a portion of the outstanding principal.

a) How much of the 4th payment is interest?

b) How much of the 2nd payment is used to reduce the principal?

c) What is the outstanding principal after the 12th payment?

d) Why does the interest paid decrease with each payment?

e) Why does the principal paid increase with each payment?

11. a) Use the SUM function in cells B23, C23, and D23 to find the total amount paid, the total interest paid, and the total principal repaid in the first 12 payments.

b) Are you surprised by how little principal is paid down in 1 year? Explain.

12. Select cells A22 through E22. Use Fill Down to extend the schedule to show the monthly payments over the 25-year amortization period.

   a) What assumptions were made when the schedule was extended for the entire amortization period?

   b) How much of the 1st payment is interest? How much of the 300th payment is interest?

   c) What is the total interest paid in the 1st year? What is the total interest paid in the 25th year?

   d) How much is the principal reduced in the 1st year? How much is the principal reduced in the 25th year?

   e) At the beginning, more money goes toward paying interest than toward reducing the principal. Explain.

13. Determine the total amount paid and the total interest paid over the lifetime of the mortgage. How do these amounts compare with the original principal of the mortgage?

Real Estate Agent

A real estate agent helps people buy and sell residential and commercial property. The agent markets the property by showing it to prospective buyers, negotiates the sale, closes the deal, and prepares the paperwork. To do the job well, a real estate agent must be knowledgeable in tax laws, mortgages, and interest rates. Most importantly, the agent must be a skilled salesperson who understands how to effectively list, show, sell, and close the deal on a variety of properties. Excellent communication and people skills are prerequisites for success in this competitive field.

When an offer to purchase a property is made, the agent is the mediator between the buyer and seller. An agent will strive to get the best possible price and conditions of sale for the client. When these are agreed upon, a responsible agent will clearly explain the implications of the contract to the client as the offer to purchase is a legally binding document.

Real estate agents earn commission. Most work with an agency to which they pay a fee for office space, advertising and promotion, and other costs for the properties and clients they represent. There is no set work week for real estate agents—they are on call whenever there is a sale to be made. To be a licensed real estate agent in Canada involves coursework and a final exam.

Where's the Math?

Many homeowners require a mortgage to purchase property. A real estate agent must be able to determine a client's affordable price range, understand the details of amortization tables, and property taxes. A clear understanding of the math of finance is essential.

Marjorie and Kevin have just bought their first home. They will make monthly payments of $1340.37 on a $170 000 mortgage with an interest rate of 8.25% compounded monthly. The mortgage is amortized over 25 years. However, as a special introductory offer, the bank will charge only 2.5% interest compounded monthly on their mortgage for the first 6 months. Because the payments are constant, more of each payment reduces the principal. How does this affect the payments against the principal in the 6 months?

An amortization schedule lists how much of a payment is interest, and how much goes to reduce the principal. Since only 6 payments are involved, the schedule can be created using a calculator. If you have access to a computer with a spreadsheet program, you may use the spreadsheet you created in Section 6.2 to generate the schedule.

Each month, a payment of $1340.37 is made.
During the introductory offer, an interest rate of 2.5% is charged.

Payment 1
When payment 1 is made, 1 month's interest is owed on $170 000.
The interest is $170\ 000 \times 0.025 \times \frac{1}{12} = \$354.17$.
Of the monthly payment, $354.17 is interest.
The remainder of the payment, $1340.37 − $354.17 = $986.20, goes toward reducing the principal.
So, the outstanding principal is $170 000 − $986.20 = $169 013.80.

Payment 2
When payment 2 is made, 1 month's interest is owed on $169 013.80.
The interest is $169\ 013.80 \times 0.025 \times \frac{1}{12} = \$352.11$.
The principal is reduced by $1340.37 − $352.11 = $988.26.
The outstanding principal is $169 013.80 − $988.26 = $168 025.54.

The remaining payments are calculated in a similar way.

Amortization Schedule

Mortgage amount: $170 000.00
Annual interest rate: 2.5%
Monthly payment: $1340.37

Payment number	Monthly payment	Interest paid	Principal paid	Outstanding principal
0	–	–	–	$170 000.00
1	$1340.37	$354.17	$986.20	$169 013.80
2	$1340.37	$352.11	$988.26	$168 025.54
3	$1340.37	$350.05	$990.32	$167 035.22
4	$1340.37	$347.99	$992.38	$166 042.84
5	$1340.37	$345.92	$994.45	$165 048.39
6	$1340.37	$343.85	$996.52	$164 051.87
Total		$2094.09	$5948.13	

Thus, the principal paid in the first 6 months, at 2.5%, is $5948.13.

How does this amount compare to the amount by which the principal would have been reduced without the special offer?

One way to determine the amount is to create another amortization schedule with the interest rate changed to 8.25%.

A second way uses our knowledge of the present value of an annuity. The outstanding principal after 6 months is the present value of the remaining 294 payments.

To calculate the present value of the remaining payments, use the formula $PV = \frac{R[1 - (1 + i)^{-n}]}{i}$.
Substitute $R = 1340.37$, $i = \frac{0.0825}{12}$, and $n = 294$.

$$PV = \frac{1340.37[1 - (1 + \frac{0.0825}{12})^{-294}]}{\frac{0.0825}{12}}$$

$\doteq 168\ 953.05$

After 6 payments have been made, the outstanding principal is $168 953.05. Thus, the principal paid in the first 6 months, at 8.25%, is
$170 000 − $168 953.05 = $1046.95.

Marjorie and Ken saved an extra $5948.13 − $1046.95 = $4901.18 with the introductory offer.

Since mortgages involve large sums of money, lending institutions frequently offer special promotions to entice new customers. An amortization schedule can help give a customer a clearer picture of her or his particular situation.

In the following exercises, you may use a calculator or appropriate software to create the amortization schedules.

1. A mortgage of $210 000 is amortized over 25 years at 9% compounded monthly with a 5-year term.

   a) Determine the monthly payment.

   b) Create an amortization schedule for the first 6 payments.

2. Use the amortization schedule from exercise 1.

   a) How much of the 1st payment is interest?

   b) How much of the 3rd payment is used to reduce the principal?

   c) What is the total interest paid in the first 6 payments?

   d) What is the outstanding principal after 6 payments?

3. For each mortgage, determine the monthly payment then make an amortization schedule for the first 6 payments. Assume the interest is compounded monthly.

	Mortgage amount	Annual interest rate	Amortization period
a)	$150 000	7.75%	20 years
b)	$90 000	6%	25 years
c)	$275 000	8.65%	30 years
d)	$300 000	9.3%	25 years
e)	$129 000	7.25%	15 years

4. **Knowledge/Understanding** A bank offers mortgages with a 1-year term at a rate of 8.75% compounded monthly. However, customers who obtain a mortgage this week receive a special introductory rate of 2% compounded monthly for the first 6 months. Suppose you obtain a $240 000 mortgage this week. Create an amortization schedule for the first year of the mortgage. The mortgage is amortized over 25 years.

5. Make an amortization schedule for 1 year for the mortgage in exercise 4, without the introductory offer. How much interest is saved in the first year with the introductory offer?

6. Communication Refer to exercise 5. One bank customer who obtained a mortgage this week thought that he should make reduced payments during the first 6 months. Write a short report for the customer to explain why it would benefit him to make the regular payments for the first 6 months. Use calculations, where appropriate, in your explanation.

7. Application The Dixons purchased a cottage for $39 000. The person from whom they bought the cottage holds the mortgage. They paid $4000 down, and agreed to make equal payments at the end of every 3 months for 15 years. The annual interest rate was 14% compounded quarterly.

a) What is the quarterly payment?

b) How much will the Dixons owe after 10 years?

c) How much will they have paid in total after 15 years?

8. Thinking/Inquiry/Problem Solving A *sinking fund* is an interest-bearing fund into which payments are made at regular intervals to provide a desired amount of money at a specified time in the future. By law, condominium corporations must set up sinking funds, called *reserve funds*, to save for major repairs and replacements to the property. A condominium corporation estimates that it must replace boilers 2 years from now at an estimated cost of $60 000. The corporation has a reserve fund account into which it will make equal payments at the end of every quarter for the next 2 years. The account earns 6.5% interest compounded quarterly. Create a reserve fund schedule. The schedule should show the payment number, the amount of the payment, the interest earned, the increase in the fund, and the balance of the fund at the end of each payment period.

As mentioned in Section 6.1, Canadian law requires that the interest charged on a mortgage be compounded no more frequently than semi-annually. However, mortgage payments are usually made monthly. The monthly payment is calculated using the formula for the present value of an annuity. Recall that this formula is only valid when the payment period is the same as the compounding period. One way to get around this difficulty is to convert the semi-annual rate to its equivalent monthly rate.

Two rates of interest with different compounding periods are *equivalent* if, for a given principal, each produces the same interest after 1 year.

For example, consider two $100 investments.
Suppose one investment earns 12% compounded semi-annually, while the other earns 11.71% compounded monthly.
The amount after 1 year can be calculated using the formula $A = P(1 + i)^n$.

12% compounded semi-annually   11.71% compounded monthly

$$A = 100\left(1 + \frac{0.12}{2}\right)^2 \qquad\qquad A = 100\left(1 + \frac{0.1171}{12}\right)^{12}$$
$$\doteq 112.36 \qquad\qquad\qquad\qquad\qquad \doteq 112.36$$

Both investments earn $112.36 − $100 = $12.36 interest in 1 year.
Thus, 11.71% compounded monthly is equivalent to 12% compounded semi-annually.

Here is the formula that can be used to convert an annual rate, s, compounded semi-annually, to an equivalent annual rate, M, compounded monthly.

TAKE NOTE

Equivalent Annual Rate

The formula to convert an interest rate compounded semi-annually to the equivalent rate compounded monthly is:
$$M = 12\left[\left(1 + \tfrac{s}{2}\right)^{\frac{1}{6}} - 1\right]$$

M is the equivalent annual rate compounded monthly, expressed as a decimal.
s is the annual rate compounded semi-annually, expressed as a decimal.

Example 1

Determine the interest rate compounded monthly that is equivalent to 7.5% compounded semi-annually.

Solution

Use the formula $M = 12[(1 + \frac{s}{2})^{\frac{1}{6}} - 1]$.

Substitute $s = 0.075$.

$M = 12[(1 + \frac{0.075}{2})^{\frac{1}{6}} - 1]$
$\doteq 0.073\ 854\ 287$
$\doteq 0.0739$

An interest rate of approximately 7.39% compounded monthly is equivalent to 7.5% compounded semi-annually.

Example 2

Determine the monthly payment on a mortgage of $160 000 amortized over 25 years at 6.4% compounded semi-annually.

Solution

The compounding period and the payment period must be the same.

Change the interest rate compounded semi-annually to the equivalent rate compounded monthly.

Use the formula $M = 12[(1 + \frac{s}{2})^{\frac{1}{6}} - 1]$.

Substitute $s = 0.064$.

$M = 12[(1 + \frac{0.064}{2})^{\frac{1}{6}} - 1]$
$\doteq 0.063\ 162\ 985$

To determine the monthly payment, use the formula $PV = \frac{R[1 - (1 + i)^{-n}]}{i}$.

The interest rate compounded monthly is $\frac{0.063\ 162\ 985}{12} \doteq 0.005\ 263\ 582$.

The number of payments is $25 \times 12 = 300$.

Substitute $PV = 160\ 000$, $i = 0.005\ 263\ 582$, and $n = 300$.

$160\ 000 = \frac{R[1 - (1 + 0.005\ 263\ 582)^{-300}]}{0.005\ 263\ 582}$

$R = \frac{160\ 000 \times 0.005\ 263\ 582}{1 - 1.005\ 263\ 582^{-300}}$

$\doteq 1062.04$

The monthly payment is $1062.04.

Discuss

In *Example 2*:

- Why is the value of M not rounded before it is used to calculate the monthly payment?
- How can you use the store and recall features of your calculator to simplify the calculation for the monthly payment?

Although the interest charged on mortgages is usually compounded semi-annually in Canada, the situation is different in other countries. In the United States, for example, the interest charged on mortgages can be compounded monthly.

In *Example 2*, we determined that the monthly payment on a mortgage of $160\ 000 amortized over 25 years at 6.4% compounded semi-annually is $1062.04. What is the monthly payment on this mortgage when the same rate of interest is compounded monthly instead of semi-annually?

To determine the monthly payment, use the formula $PV = \frac{R[1 - (1 + i)^{-n}]}{i}$.

Substitute $PV = 160\ 000$, $n = 300$, and $i = \frac{0.064}{12}$.

$$160\ 000 = \frac{R[1 - (1 + \frac{0.064}{12})^{-300}]}{\frac{0.064}{12}}$$

$$R = \frac{160\ 000 \times \frac{0.064}{12}}{1 - (1 + \frac{0.064}{12})^{-300}}$$

$$\doteq 1070.36$$

The monthly payment is $1070.36.

The monthly payment is greater when mortgage interest is compounded monthly instead of semi-annually. This is to be expected since interest grows more rapidly as the frequency of compounding increases. With semi-annual compounding instead of monthly compounding, the mortgagor saves $1070.36 − $1062.04 = $8.32 per month. If the mortgage is held at the same rate for the entire 25-year amortization period, the mortgagor saves $8.32 × 300 = $2496 over the lifetime of the mortgage.

A

1. Use a calculator to evaluate each expression. Give each answer to 9 decimal places.

   a) $12[(1 + \frac{0.085}{2})^{\frac{1}{6}} - 1]$

   b) $12[(1 + \frac{0.12}{2})^{\frac{1}{6}} - 1]$

   c) $12[(1 + \frac{0.05}{2})^{\frac{1}{6}} - 1]$

   d) $12[(1 + \frac{0.115}{2})^{\frac{1}{6}} - 1]$

   e) $12[(1 + \frac{0.078}{2})^{\frac{1}{6}} - 1]$

   f) $12[(1 + \frac{0.095}{2})^{\frac{1}{6}} - 1]$

2. Determine the interest rate compounded monthly that is equivalent to each rate compounded semi-annually. Give each answer to 2 decimal places.

   a) 8.46%

   b) 6.25%

   c) 5.5%

   d) 10.4%

   e) 9.75%

   f) 12.17%

B

3. **Communication** Explain why it is to the mortgagor's benefit to have interest on mortgages compounded semi-annually instead of monthly.

4. Determine the monthly payment for each mortgage.

   a) $150 000 amortized over 25 years at 6% compounded semi-annually

   b) $225 000 amortized over 20 years at 7.25% compounded semi-annually

   c) $190 000 amortized over 30 years at 8.6% compounded semi-annually

   d) $200 000 amortized over 25 years at 5.25% compounded semi-annually

   e) $187 000 amortized over 25 years at 9% compounded semi-annually

   f) $95 000 amortized over 20 years at 8.5% compounded semi-annually

5. Determine the total interest paid over the lifetime of each mortgage. Assume the interest rate remains the same for the entire amortization period.

   a) $140 000 amortized over 25 years at 7.25% compounded semi-annually

   b) $165 000 amortized over 20 years at 8% compounded semi-annually

   c) $120 000 amortized over 30 years at 9.5% compounded semi-annually

   d) $80 000 amortized over 25 years at 8.25% compounded semi-annually

   e) $235 000 amortized over 25 years at 5.75% compounded semi-annually

   f) $295 000 amortized over 25 years at 7.5% compounded semi-annually

6. **Knowledge/Understanding** Cheung has a $225 000 mortgage with an interest rate of 7.5% compounded semi-annually. The mortgage is amortized over 25 years and has a 5-year term. Determine the monthly payment.

7. Alexander purchased a home for $210 000. He put 30% down and took out a mortgage for the rest. The mortgage has an interest rate of 6.5% compounded semi-annually and a 30-year amortization period. Determine the monthly payment.

8. Victoria has an $80 000 mortgage with an amortization period of 20 years and an interest rate of 8% compounded semi-annually.

   a) Determine the monthly payment.

   b) Make an amortization schedule for the first 6 payments.

9. A mortgage of $200 000 is amortized over 25 years. Determine the total interest paid over the lifetime of the mortgage at each interest rate. Assume the interest rate is the same for the entire amortization period.

   a) 9% compounded semi-annually

   b) 9% compounded monthly

10. **Thinking/Inquiry/Problem Solving** In the United States, mortgage interest can be compounded monthly. Sami has a $90 000 mortgage with an interest rate of 7.5% compounded semi-annually for 25 years. The term of the mortgage is 3 years. The mortgage is renewed at the same interest rate, but now the interest is compounded monthly. By how much will the monthly payment increase?

11. **Application** A bank advertises "3% cash back" on mortgages transferred from another financial institution. Farida has a mortgage of $310 000 at 8.5% compounded semi-annually with a 30-year amortization period. There are 25 years remaining on the amortization. She decides to make the transfer and apply the cash back to reduce the principal on the mortgage.

   a) What is the present value of Farida's mortgage?

   b) What is the outstanding principal after Farida transfers the mortgage?

1. Determine the monthly payment for each mortgage.

   a) $90 000 amortized over 15 years at 9% compounded monthly

   b) $320 000 amortized over 25 years at 7.5% compounded monthly

2. Determine the total interest paid over the lifetime of each mortgage. Assume the interest rate remains the same for the entire amortization period.

   a) $150 000 amortized over 25 years at 7.5% compounded monthly

   b) $150 000 amortized over 20 years at 7.5% compounded monthly

3. The Murphys have a mortgage of $167 000 amortized over 25 years at 8.3% compounded monthly with a 5-year term. The mortgage is renewed for another 5-year term at 7.6% compounded monthly. Determine the new monthly payment.

4. Determine the difference in the interest paid over a 7-year term on a $195 000 mortgage amortized over 25 years at 6.5% compounded monthly compared to one at 14.75% compounded monthly.

5. A mortgage of $160 000 is amortized over 25 years at 7% compounded monthly with a 5-year term.

   a) Determine the monthly payment.

   b) Make an amortization schedule for the first 6 payments.

6. Use the amortization schedule from exercise 5.

   a) How much of the 1st payment is interest?

   b) How much is the principal reduced with the 3rd payment?

   c) What is the outstanding principal after the first 6 payments?

   d) How much interest is paid in the first 6 months?

7. Determine the interest rate compounded monthly that is equivalent to each rate compounded semi-annually.

   a) 7%   b) 8.3%   c) 6.75%   d) 10.1%

8. Determine the monthly payment for each mortgage.

   a) $170 000 amortized over 25 years at 8% compounded semi-annually

   b) $129 000 amortized over 30 years at 6.6% compounded semi-annually

9. Determine the difference in the interest paid over a 25-year period on a $259 000 mortgage at 7.5% compounded monthly and at 7.5% compounded semi-annually.

6.5 Using a Graphing Calculator to Investigate Methods for Saving Interest

In this section, you will investigate methods for saving interest on a mortgage. The mortgage calculations can be simplified by using the TVM Solver application on the TI-83 Plus calculator. For more information on the TVM Solver, refer to *Utility 3*.

The instructions in this section are for the TI-83 Plus calculator. If you use a different calculator, refer to its User's Guide.

To access the TVM Solver, press [APPS] **1 1**. The screen below appears.

The variables represent the following quantities.

N: total number of payments
I%: annual interest rate as a percent
PV: present value
PMT: payment each period
FV: future value, or amount
P/Y: number of payments per year
C/Y: number of compounding periods per year
PMT: indicates whether the payments are due at the end or the beginning of each period.

It is not necessary to calculate an equivalent rate when you work with the TVM Solver; it calculates the rate. To indicate that the mortgage interest is compounded semi-annually, but the payments are made monthly, use P/Y = 12 and C/Y = 2.

Example 1

A mortgage of $150 000 is amortized over 25 years with an interest rate of 8% compounded semi-annually.

  a) What is the monthly payment?

  b) Suppose you choose to make weekly payments instead of monthly payments. What is the weekly payment?

  c) Calculate the total interest paid with the weekly payments.

Solution

a) Monthly payments are made for 25 years.

So, the total number of payments made is $12 \times 25 = 300$.

In the TVM Solver, enter the values shown below left.

 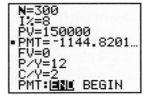

Use the arrow keys to move the cursor to PMT.

Press ALPHA ENTER to obtain the screen above right.

The monthly payment is $1144.82. The negative sign on the screen indicates the payment is made against a loan.

b) When weekly payments are made for 25 years, the total number of payments is $25 \times 52 = 1300$. Thus, N = 1300 and P/Y = 52

Enter the values shown in the screen below left.

 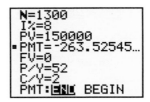

Use the arrow keys to move the cursor to PMT.

Press ALPHA ENTER to obtain the screen above right.

The weekly payment is $263.53.

c) Use the screen and data from part b.

Press 2nd MODE for QUIT.

Press APPS 1 ALPHA MATH to show ΣInt(.

Input 1 , 1300) .

This calculates the interest from payment 1 to payment 1300.

Press ENTER to display −192583.0875.

The number is negative because the interest is paid on a loan.

The total interest paid with the weekly payments is $192 583.09.

If you can afford it and when it is allowed, usually at the end of a term, it is a good idea to pay down some of the outstanding principal on a mortgage.

Example 2

Refer to the mortgage in *Example 1*. Suppose the mortgage had an initial term of 5 years. When the mortgage is renewed, a lump sum payment of $15 000 is applied to the principal. Determine the number of monthly payments remaining.

Solution

Calculate the monthly payment on the mortgage. This repeats the calculation in *Example 1a*.

Use the TVM Solver.

Enter the values shown in the first screen in *Example 1a*.

Use the arrow keys to move the cursor to PMT.

Press ⎡ALPHA⎤ ⎡ENTER⎤ to obtain the second screen in *Example 1a*. This screen is shown below left.

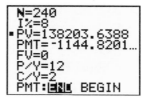

In 5 years, 5×12, or 60 payments were made.

There are $300 - 60$, or 240 payments remaining.

To calculate the present value of the remaining payments; that is, the outstanding principal, change N to 240.

Move to the row for PV.

Press ⎡ALPHA⎤ ⎡ENTER⎤ to obtain the screen above right.

The outstanding principal after 5 years is $138 203.64.

Apply the payment of $15 000.

Now, the outstanding principal is $138 203.64 − $15 000 = $123 203.64.

To calculate the number of payments remaining, change PV to 123 203.64.

Move the cursor to N.

Press ⎡ALPHA⎤ ⎡ENTER⎤ to obtain the screen below left.

```
▪N=187.1615714          N=187
 I%=8                   I%=8
 PV=123203.64          ▪PV=123149.3675
 PMT=-1144.8201…        PMT=-1144.8201…
 FV=0                   FV=0
 P/Y=12                 P/Y=12
 C/Y=2                  C/Y=2
 PMT:ENM BEGIN          PMT:ENM BEGIN
```

Instead of 240 payments, there are only 187.16 payments remaining.

The lump sum payment is adjusted to make the number of payments remaining a whole number; that is, 187.

To calculate the additional principal required, change N to 187.

Move to the row for PV.

Press [ALPHA] [ENTER] to obtain the last screen on page 308.

To have 187 payments remaining, the principal must be paid down to $123 149.37.

An additional $123 203.64 − $123 149.37 = $54.27 must be paid.

The adjusted lump sum payment is $15 000 + $54.27 = $15 054.27.

There are 187 payments remaining when a lump sum payment of $15 054.27 is made at the end of 5 years.

In previous sections in this chapter, you calculated the total interest paid over the lifetime of a mortgage. It is a considerable sum of money, usually in the tens of thousands of dollars. In the following investigations, you will examine ways to repay a mortgage more quickly, thereby reducing the interest paid over the lifetime of the mortgage.

The following assumptions are made for each *Investigation*.

- The original mortgage is $215 000 amortized over 25 years at 8.25% compounded semi-annually.
- Unless otherwise indicated, assume monthly payments are made.
- Unless otherwise indicated, assume the interest rate remains constant during the amortization period.

Investigation 1

Shortening the Payment Period

Most lending institutions allow mortgage payments to be made weekly, bi-weekly (every 2 weeks), bi-monthly (twice a month), or monthly.

1. a) Copy and complete this table.

Payment frequency	P/Y	N	PMT	Total amount paid	Total interest paid	Interest saved
Monthly						—
Bi-monthly						
Bi-weekly						
Weekly						

b) Is the interest saved significant when payments are made more often? Explain.

c) Why would a homeowner choose to make weekly, bi-weekly, or bi-monthly payments instead of monthly payments?

2. Most financial institutions allow "accelerated" weekly mortgage payments. With this option, the weekly payment is calculated as a monthly payment divided by 4.

a) Use the monthly payment calculated in exercise 1. Calculate the accelerated weekly payment.

b) Calculate the number of weeks required to pay off the mortgage when accelerated weekly payments are made.

c) Enter the information from parts a and b in the following table. Then, complete the remaining columns in the table. The numbers for the first 2 rows of the table can be obtained from *Investigation 1*, exercise 1.

Payment frequency	P/Y	PMT	N	Total amount paid	Total interest paid	Interest saved
Monthly						—
Weekly						
Accelerated weekly						

d) Is the interest saved significant when accelerated weekly payments are made? Explain.

3. Explain why the interest savings are much greater with accelerated weekly payments than with monthly payments or regular weekly payments.

 Investigation 2   **Shortening the Amortization Period**

1. Most homeowners choose an amortization period of 25 years. However, it is possible to obtain shorter amortization periods.

a) Copy and complete this table. The numbers for the first row can be obtained from *Investigation 1*, exercise 1a.

Amortization period	N	PMT	Total amount paid	Total interest paid	Interest saved
25 years					—
20 years					
15 years					

b) How does the monthly payment change as the amortization period decreases?

c) How does the total interest paid change as the amortization period increases?

d) Why does reducing the amortization period reduce the interest paid?

e) What factors influence a homeowner's choice of amortization period?

2. Once a year, over the term of a mortgage, some financial institutions will allow an increase in the monthly payment. In *Investigation 1* exercise 1a, you calculated the monthly payment on the mortgage amortized over 25 years.

a) Suppose the monthly payment is increased by $100.

    i) How many payments are needed to pay off the mortgage?

    ii) Determine the total amount paid over the lifetime of the mortgage.

    iii) Determine the total interest paid over the lifetime of the mortgage.

    iv) Determine the interest saved by increasing the monthly payment.

b) Repeat part a, this time with a $200 increase in the monthly payment. When the amount added to the monthly payment is doubled, is the interest saved also doubled? Explain.

c) Why does increasing the monthly payment reduce the amortization period?

3. Recall that the original mortgage was $215 000 over 25 years at 8.25% compounded semi-annually. After 5 years, the mortgage was renewed for a 10-year term at 6.5% compounded semi-annually. Then, the mortgage was renewed for a final 10-year term at 8.75% compounded semi-annually.

a) Copy and complete this table.

	PV at beginning of term	PMT	Total amount paid during the term
Term 1 (5 years)			
Term 2 (10 years)			
Term 3 (10 years)			

b) Determine the total amount paid over the lifetime of the mortgage.

c) What is the total interest paid over the lifetime of the mortgage?

4. Consider the mortgage of $215 000 at 8.25% compounded semi-annually. The initial term was 5 years.

a) After 5 years, the mortgage was renewed for a further 10 years at 6.5% compounded semi-annually. The mortgagor decided not to change the monthly payment. Determine the number of monthly payments required to pay off the mortgage.

b) Determine the outstanding principal at the end of the 10-year term.

c) At the end of the 10-year term, the mortgage is renewed at 8.75% compounded semi-annually for the final term of the mortgage. Use the result of part a. Determine the new monthly payment.

d) Determine the total amount paid over the lifetime of the mortgage.

e) How much interest did the mortgagor save by making the larger payment for 10 years?

5. A mortgage company offers first-time buyers a special rate that is 0.75% less than the regular rate. The term of the mortgage is 7 years.

a) Copy and complete this table. The outstanding principal, total amount paid, and total interest paid are to be calculated for the 7-year term. The principal repaid is calculated using

Principal repaid = Original mortgage − Outstanding principal.

Interest rate	I	PMT	Outstanding principal	Principal repaid	Total amount paid	Total interest paid	Interest saved
Regular rate							—
First-time buyer rate							

b) Suppose a first-time buyer accepted the introductory offer but kept the monthly payment the same as for the regular rate. Determine the outstanding principal at the end of the 7-year term.

Making a Lump Sum Payment

1. Remember the mortgage of $215 000 at 8.25% compounded semi-annually. Suppose a lump sum payment of $13 800 was made at the end of the 5-year term (the 1st term).

a) Determine the outstanding principal on the mortgage after the lump sum payment.

b) Determine the number of monthly payments required to pay off the mortgage.

c) What is the outstanding principal on the mortgage after the lump sum payment has been adjusted to make the number of payments remaining a whole number?

d) When the mortgage is renewed after the 1st term, what is the new monthly payment?

e) Calculate the outstanding principal at the end of the 2nd term.

f) How many more payments are required to pay off the mortgage?

g) Calculate the monthly payment during the final term of the mortgage.

h) Calculate the total amount paid during the lifetime of the mortgage.

i) How much interest was saved by making the lump sum payment?

Briefly summarize the major ideas from each *Investigation*.

Career Profile

Graphic Designer

"Graphic design production is an interdisciplinary, problem-solving activity which combines visual sensitivity with skill and knowledge in the area of communication, technology, and business." (Graphic Design Production Program Standards, Ontario Ministry of Colleges and Universities).

The job of graphic designers is to present information visually to aid communication and orientation. An integral part of the training in this field includes principles of design, colour theory, perspective, typography, composition, and layout.

The work of graphic designers is reflected everywhere —on billboards, posters, packaging, books and magazines, cards, web sites, and CD-ROMs. One of the keys to success in this career is a solid background in computers. Computer technology, more specifically the creation of various software programs, has over the last decade helped graphic designers in their work. However, graphic designers must possess excellent skills in "communicating ideas, concepts, and functions to specific audiences—age groups, income levels, and gender." They work directly with clients to understand the purpose and nature of the project and its audience.

Designers may choose to work regular hours in an office environment, or operate their own business. They may specialize in one or more aspects of the media: electronic, audiovisual, multimedia, print, packaging, signage, and display. Career choices in this profession are varied, such as advertising, desktop publishing, art direction, quality control, project management, and research.

Where's the Math?

Basic math skills are required to calculate aspect ratios and proportion. A project may require budgeting and making cost estimates that will use estimation and problem solving skills.

In this chapter, you have worked with concepts and calculations related to mortgages. The skills you have developed will help you to complete the investigations that follow. When completing the investigations, keep in mind that for many exercises there is no single correct answer. Whether to rent or to buy is an individual or family decision, based on personal preference and lifestyle. When you conduct your research, consult a variety of sources, such as your parents or guardians, newspapers, the Internet, older brothers and sisters, real estate brokers, rental agents, insurance agents, service businesses, financial institutions, and friends who live alone.

Investigation 1 **Initial Costs**

Whether you buy or rent accommodation, there are initial costs that require a considerable amount of money. Depending on the situation, these costs can include first and last months' rent, a down payment, utility deposits, and new furnishings and appliances.

1. Research the initial costs involved in:

   a) Buying a first house

   b) Buying a first condominium

   c) Renting a first apartment

   d) Renting a first house

2. Organize the information in a chart to illustrate the costs that are common to all types of accommodation and those that are different. You do not have to include dollar amounts in this chart.

3. With a partner, research real estate and rental property in your community. Select a first house or condominium you might buy, and a first apartment you might rent. Create a chart that lists the specific initial costs for each type of accommodation. Include estimated dollar amounts in this chart.

4. Compare the initial startup costs. Which accommodation requires the greater initial outlay? Which accommodation do you think most people will choose? Explain.

5. Save your research and charts.

Monthly Costs

Whether you rent or buy accommodation, there are costs associated with everyday living. Depending on the situation, these costs can include mortgage payments, rent, heat, electricity, water, gas, maintenance, repairs, and insurance.

1. Research the everyday living costs for maintaining a rented apartment or house, and those for maintaining a house that you own.

2. Organize the information in a chart to show the costs that are common and those that are different. You do not have to include dollar amounts in this chart.

3. Use the results of your real estate and rental research from *Investigation 1*. With a partner, select a house to buy that would be suitable for a family of four with two young children, and a suitable apartment or house to rent by the same family.

4. Compare the everyday costs for each type of accommodation.
   a) Estimate the cost of each item you identified in exercise 1 for 1 year.
   b) Calculate the estimated total annual costs.
   c) Divide by 12 to obtain the average monthly costs.
   d) Estimate the average monthly costs for each type of accommodation.

Factors other than initial and everyday costs affect the decision to rent or to buy. These can include preferred lifestyle, health, and type of employment.

5. Consider these factors, then list the advantages and disadvantages of owning your own house.

6. Make a similar list for renting an apartment or house.

7. Save your research, charts, and lists.

You will probably be faced with the decision whether to rent or to buy in the future. The following Investigation will provide you with the tools to make an informed decision when that time comes.

Estimating the Long-Term Costs of Buying Versus Renting

You will estimate the cost to own a home and the cost to rent a home suitable for a family of four over the next 25 years. You should assume:

- The family has sufficient startup funds for either a house or an apartment.
- The family can afford the everyday costs for either the house or the apartment.

Base your calculations on the house and apartment you chose in *Investigation 2* for the family of 4. Alternatively, you may choose different accommodation.

1. Estimate the costs for each type of accommodation over the next 25 years. This list suggests costs to include. Choose the items you think are important.

   - What is the monthly mortgage payment? Will it increase or decrease over the 25 years?
   - What is the monthly rent for the apartment? Will it increase or decrease over the 25 years?
   - What are the regular monthly costs?
   - What are the maintenance costs?
   - What unexpected costs could arise?
   - What effect will inflation have?
   - Are any costs the same for both types of accommodation?
   - What is the difference in the down payment for a house and the first and last months' rent for an apartment?
   - Suppose there is extra money. Should the mortgage be paid down or should the money be invested?

3. Organize the data using charts, graphs, and spreadsheets.

Use the results of *Investigations 1*, *2*, and *3*. Write a report that discusses the advantages and disadvantages of buying or renting accommodation. Which choice will be better for the lifestyle you plan to have in the future?

Review Exercises

MATHEMATICS TOOLKIT

Mortgage Tools

> To determine the monthly mortgage payment, use the formula for the present value of an annuity:

$$PV = \frac{R[1 - (1 + i)^{-n}]}{i}$$

 PV is the amount of the mortgage in dollars.
 R is the monthly payment in dollars.
 i is the interest rate per month, as a decimal.
 n is the number of monthly payments.

> To change a rate compounded semi-annually to the equivalent rate compounded monthly, use this formula:

$$M = 12[(1 + \tfrac{s}{2})^{\frac{1}{6}} - 1]$$

 M is the equivalent annual rate compounded monthly, as a decimal.
 s is the annual rate compounded semi-annually, as a decimal.

6.1

1. Determine the monthly payment for each mortgage.
    a) $110 000 amortized over 25 years at 6.7% compounded monthly
    b) $162 000 amortized over 20 years at 8.4% compounded monthly
    c) $240 000 amortized over 30 years at 9.3% compounded monthly
    d) $275 000 amortized over 25 years at 7.25% compounded monthly
    e) $75 000 amortized over 15 years at 5.5% compounded monthly
    f) $258 000 amortized over 30 years at 9.75% compounded monthly

2. Determine the total interest paid for each mortgage. Assume the interest rate remains the same for the amortization period.
    a) $165 000 amortized over 25 years at 5% compounded monthly
    b) $139 000 amortized over 20 years at 8.45% compounded monthly
    c) $264 000 amortized over 30 years at 7.12% compounded monthly
    d) $248 000 amortized over 25 years at 6.55% compounded monthly
    e) $140 000 amortized over 25 years at 8.75% compounded monthly
    f) $290 000 amortized over 15 years at 9.6% compounded monthly

3. A mortgage of $240 000 is to be amortized over 25 years with a 5-year term. Institution A offers a rate of 8.25% compounded monthly, while Institution B offers a rate of 7.8% compounded monthly. Determine the amount of interest saved over the 5-year term by a person who selects Institution B over Institution A.

4. A bank advertises 3% cash back on all new mortgages. A person shopping for a mortgage of $215 000 decides to take advantage of this offer and apply the cash back to the principal. The mortgage is amortized over 25 years at 7.45% compounded monthly with a 25-year term.

a) Determine the monthly payment using the original principal.

b) Determine the monthly payment after the cash back has been applied to the principal.

c) Determine the interest saved by applying the cash back to the principal.

d) How could a person save a greater amount of interest?

6.3 **5.** A mortgage of $187 000 is amortized over 25 years at 8.5% compounded monthly with a 5-year term. Determine the monthly payment, then make an amortization schedule for the first 8 payments.

6. Use the amortization schedule from exercise 5.

a) How much interest is due at the end of the 1st month?

b) How much was the principal reduced with the 4th payment?

c) How much is the principal reduced with the first 8 payments?

d) How much interest is paid in the first 8 months?

7. A mortgage of $264 000 is amortized over 25 years at 7.35% compounded semi-annually with a 7-year term. Determine the monthly payment, then make an amortization schedule for the first 6 payments.

8. Use the amortization schedule from exercise 7.

a) How much interest is due at the end of the 2nd month?

b) How much was the principal reduced with the 5th payment?

c) How much is the principal reduced with the first 6 payments?

d) How much interest is paid in the first 5 months?

6.4 **9.** Use a calculator to evaluate each expression.

a) $12[(1 + \frac{0.09}{2})^{\frac{1}{6}} - 1]$

b) $12[(1 + \frac{0.078}{2})^{\frac{1}{6}} - 1]$

c) $12[(1 + \frac{0.095}{2})^{\frac{1}{6}} - 1]$

d) $12[(1 + \frac{0.135}{2})^{\frac{1}{6}} - 1]$

e) $12[(1 + \frac{0.065}{2})^{\frac{1}{6}} - 1]$

f) $12[(1 + \frac{0.1375}{2})^{\frac{1}{6}} - 1]$

10. Determine the interest rate compounded monthly that is equivalent to each rate.

  a) 7.41% compounded semi-annually

  b) $5\frac{1}{2}$% compounded semi-annually

  c) 6.8% compounded semi-annually

  d) $10\frac{3}{4}$% compounded semi-annually

  e) 8.64% compounded semi-annually

  f) 9.43% compounded semi-annually

11. Determine the monthly payment for each mortgage.

  a) $149 000 amortized over 25 years at 8% compounded semi-annually

  b) $135 000 amortized over 20 years at 7.14% compounded semi-annually

  c) $260 000 amortized over 30 years at 6.37% compounded semi-annually

  d) $199 000 amortized over 25 years at 8.25% compounded semi-annually

  e) $211 000 amortized over 25 years at 10.25% compounded semi-annually

  f) $200 000 amortized over 25 years at 5.86% compounded semi-annually

  g) $276 000 amortized over 30 years at 11.75% compounded semi-annually

12. Determine the total interest paid for each mortgage. Assume the interest rate remains the same for the amortization period.

  a) $132 000 amortized over 25 years at 8.25% compounded semi-annually

  b) $145 000 amortized over 20 years at 6% compounded semi-annually

  c) $179 000 amortized over 25 years at 6.5% compounded semi-annually

  d) $247 000 amortized over 25 years at 8.95% compounded semi-annually

  e) $268 000 amortized over 25 years at $7\frac{1}{2}$% compounded semi-annually

13. A mortgage of $145 000 at 7.45% compounded semi-annually and amortized over 25 years is renegotiated after a 7-year term. The new rate is 9.1% compounded semi-annually. Determine the new monthly payment.

Use a calculator with a TVM Solver, a spreadsheet, or other appropriate technology for exercises 14 and 15.

6.5 **14.** A $235 000 mortgage is amortized over 25 years at 9.25% compounded semi-annually. Assume this rate remains the same for the lifetime of the mortgage.

a) Determine the monthly payment for the mortgage.

b) Determine the total amount paid over the lifetime of the mortgage.

c) Determine the interest paid over the lifetime of the mortgage.

d) Suppose the mortgagor increases the monthly payment by $150. How many payments would it take to pay off the mortgage?

e) Determine the total amount paid over the lifetime of the mortgage at the increased monthly payment.

f) Determine the interest paid over the lifetime of the mortgage at the increased monthly payment.

g) Determine the interest saved by increasing the payment by $150 per month.

15. Remember that, with "weekly accelerated" mortgage payments, the weekly payment is calculated by dividing the monthly payment by 4. A $185 000 mortgage is amortized over 25 years at 8.5% compounded semi-annually. Assume this rate remains the same over the lifetime of the mortgage.

a) Determine the monthly payment.

b) Determine the total amount paid and the interest paid over the lifetime of the mortgage.

c) Calculate the weekly accelerated payment, and the number of weeks needed to pay off the mortgage.

d) Determine the total amount paid and the interest paid over the lifetime of the mortgage using the weekly accelerated payment.

e) How much interest is saved over the lifetime of the mortgage using the weekly accelerated method?

1. Determine the monthly payment for each mortgage.
   a) $87 000 amortized over 25 years at 9% compounded monthly
   b) $271 000 amortized over 30 years at $7\frac{1}{2}$% compounded monthly

2. **Knowledge/Understanding** Determine the amount of interest paid for each mortgage. Assume the interest rate remains the same for the amortization period, and the mortgage is not paid off early.
   a) $148 000 amortized over 25 years at 8.1% compounded monthly
   b) $129 000 amortized over 20 years at 7.3% compounded monthly

3. A $185 000 mortgage is amortized over 25 years at 8.5% compounded monthly with a 5-year term.
   a) Determine the monthly payment.
   b) Make an amortization table for the first 5 payments.

4. Determine the rate compounded monthly that is equivalent to 7.4% compounded semi-annually.

5. a) Determine the monthly payment for a mortgage of $165 000 amortized over 25 years at 9% compounded semi-annually.
   b) Determine the accelerated weekly payment for a mortgage of $216 000 amortized over 20 years at 7.6% compounded semi-annually.

6. **Application** A $215 000 mortgage is amortized over 25 years at 7.5% compounded semi-annually with a 5-year term. At the end of the 5-year term, the mortgage is renegotiated. The new rate is 6.84% compounded semi-annually for a second 5-year term. Determine the monthly payment for this second term.

7. Determine the difference in the interest paid over a 5-year term on a $159 000 mortgage amortized over 25 years: at 8% compounded semi-annually; and at 16.25% compounded semi-annually.

8. **Thinking/Inquiry/Problem Solving** A customer of a US bank is offered the choice of two mortgages, each for $225 000 with a 25-year term. Option A charges interest at 7.4% compounded monthly. Option B charges interest at 7.5% compounded semi-annually. Which option costs the mortgagor less? How much will be saved by choosing this option?

9. **Communication** Explain how weekly accelerated payments on a mortgage save money compared to monthly payments.

Planning for the Future

Chapter Project

Investment Options

Throughout this book, you have calculated the interest earned when you invest money. The project in Section 7.7 provides the opportunity to research various kinds of investments.

Curriculum Expectations

By the end of this chapter, you will:

> Determine, through investigation, the properties of a variety of investment alternatives, and compare the alternatives from the point of view of risk versus return.

> Design an effective financial plan to facilitate the achievement of a long-term goal.

> Identify the procedures, costs, advantages, and disadvantages involved in buying a new vehicle and a used vehicle.

> Compare the costs involved in buying versus leasing the same vehicle.

> Calculate the fixed and variable costs involved in owning and operating a vehicle.

> Determine, through investigation, the cost of purchasing or leasing a chosen new vehicle or purchasing a chosen used vehicle, including financing.

> Describe and estimate the living costs involved for different family groupings.

> Design a budget suitable for a family described in a given case study, reflecting the current costs of common items, using technology.

> Explain and justify budgets, using appropriate mathematical forms.

> Determine the effect on an overall budget of changing one component, using a spreadsheet or budgeting software.

1 Review: The Present Value of an Annuity

Recall the formula for the present value of an annuity:

$$PV = \frac{R[1 - (1 + i)^{-n}]}{i}$$

PV is the present value in dollars.
R is the regular payment in dollars.
i is the interest rate per compounding period, as a decimal.
n is the number of payments.

In this chapter, we shall use the formula for the present value of an annuity to determine the monthly payment for a loan. Instead of rearranging the formula to solve for R each time, we rearrange the formula here, and use that to calculate R.

Use $PV = \frac{R[1 - (1 + i)^{-n}]}{i}$. Multiply each side by i.

$(PV)(i) = R[1 - (1 + i)^{-n}]$ Divide each side by $1 - (1 + i)^{-n}$.

$\frac{(PV)(i)}{1 - (1 + i)^{-n}} = R$, or $R = \frac{(PV)(i)}{1 - (1 + i)^{-n}}$

Example 1

The loan for a new car is $23 476. The loan is financed at 7.9% compounded monthly for 48 months. Calculate the monthly payment.

Solution

Use the formula $R = \frac{(PV)(i)}{1 - (1 + i)^{-n}}$. Substitute $PV = 23\ 476$, $i = \frac{0.079}{12}$, $n = 48$.

$$R = \frac{23\ 476 \times \frac{0.079}{12}}{1 - \left(1 + \frac{0.079}{12}\right)^{-48}}$$

$$\doteq 572.02$$

The monthly payment is $572.02.

Exercises

1. Use the formula above to calculate R for each set of values.

   a) $PV = \$21\ 382$, $i = \frac{0.08}{12}$, $n = 36$

   b) $PV = \$9356$, $i = \frac{0.05}{12}$, $n = 24$

Next to buying a home, a vehicle is one of the most expensive purchases you will make. You will probably buy several vehicles in your lifetime. Personal preference and lifestyle will influence the type of vehicle you buy. However, there are financial considerations as well. The skills you develop in this chapter can help you make an informed decision when you buy a vehicle.

Regardless of whether you buy a new or used vehicle, you will likely finance the purchase. Vehicle loans are available through financial institutions or through the vehicle dealership. Before you shop for a vehicle, you need to know what loan you can afford.

Example 1

Jorge is ready to buy his first car. He has saved $4000 for a down payment, and will finance the rest. The maximum monthly car payment Jorge can afford is $450. The interest rate on a 48-month car loan is 4.9% compounded monthly.

a) How large a car loan can Jorge afford?

b) What is the maximum price of the car, including taxes, that Jorge can afford?

Solution

a) The amount of the loan is the present value of an annuity with payments of $450 a month for 48 months at 4.9% interest compounded monthly.

Use the formula $PV = \dfrac{R[1 - (1 + i)^{-n}]}{i}$.

Substitute $R = 450$, $i = \dfrac{0.049}{12}$, and $n = 48$.

$$PV = \dfrac{450[1 - (1 + \frac{0.049}{12})^{-48}]}{\frac{0.049}{12}}$$

$$\doteq 19\ 578.82$$

Jorge can afford a car loan of approximately $19 600.

b) Jorge will make a down payment of $4000.

He can afford a car loan of approximately $19 600.

Thus, the maximum price car that Jorge can afford is $4000 + \$19\ 600 = \$23\ 600$.

This price has to cover all taxes and fees.

Buying a New Vehicle

When you buy a new vehicle, the starting point for the price you will eventually pay is the *Manufacturer's Suggested Retail Price (MSRP)*. Since the MSRP is a suggested price, it is subject to negotiation. Once you and the salesperson agree on a purchase price for the vehicle, other costs are added to obtain the actual amount you will pay for the vehicle.

The additional costs vary depending on the vehicle and the dealership. Some of these costs are freight charge, tire/air tax, gas tax, administration fee, licence plate fee, gas fee, lien payout, GST, and PST. The additional costs are added to the agreed upon purchase price to obtain the delivery price of the vehicle.

Most people pay for a vehicle by making a down payment and financing the rest. Suppose Jorge, in *Example 1*, purchases a compact car with an MSRP of $19 721. He negotiates a discount of $1045. The delivery price includes the following additional costs: a $670 freight charge, a $100 tire/air tax, a $75 gas tax, an $85 administration fee, a $74 licence plate fee, and a $20 gas fee. Jorge makes a down payment of $4000, and finances the rest through the dealership at 4.9% compounded monthly for 48 months. He pays a $54 fee to arrange the financing.

The dealership provides Jorge with a computer printout, called a *deal review*. This itemizes the costs and financial arrangements involved in purchasing the car. Since Jorge will finance the car through the dealership, the deal review also includes the finance charges and Jorge's monthly payment.

	DEAL REVIEW				
1	MSRP	19 721.00	1	Gas Fee	20.00
1	Discount	1045.00	1	Lien Payout	0.00
2	Purchase Price	18 676.00	6	Delivery Price	22 640.90
1	Freight	670.00	1	MFG Rebate	0.00
1	Tire/Air Tax	100.00	1	Down Payment	4000.00
1	Gas Tax	75.00	1	Finance Fee	54.00
1	Administration Fee	85.00	7	Amount Financed	18 694.90
3	Taxable Subtotal	19 606.00	1	Interest Rate	4.9%
1	Trade-in Allowance	0.00	1	Loan Term	48 months
4	Taxable Total	19 606.00	8	Monthly Payment	429.68
5	PST	1568.48	9	Interest Due at 4.9%	1929.74
5	GST	1372.42	10	Balance Due	20 624.64
1	Licence Plate Fee	74.00			

The numbers in blue to the left of the items on page 326 refer to the steps below.

1 The costs, fees, and discounts associated with the purchase of the vehicle are entered in the deal review.

This is Jorge's first car. He does not have a car to trade in (Trade-in Allowance).

He does not owe any money on the trade-in (Lien Payout).

The car he is buying is not eligible for a discount called a manufacturer's rebate (MFG Rebate), which is sometimes available to new-car buyers.

Thus, zero is entered for each of these 3 items.

2 The purchase price is the difference between the MSRP and the negotiated discount.

$$\begin{aligned} \text{Purchase Price} &= \text{MSRP} - \text{Discount} \\ &= \$19\ 721 - \$1045 \\ &= \$18\ 676 \end{aligned}$$

3 The taxable subtotal is the sum of the purchase price, freight charge, tire/air tax, gas tax, and administration fee.

$$\begin{aligned} \text{Taxable Subtotal} &= \text{Purchase Price} + \text{Freight Charge} + \text{Tire/Air Tax} + \\ &\quad \text{Gas Tax} + \text{Administration Fee} \\ &= \$18\ 676 + \$670 + \$100 + \$75 + \$85 \\ &= \$19\ 606 \end{aligned}$$

4 The taxable total accommodates the trade-in allowance for a previous car.

$$\begin{aligned} \text{Taxable Total} &= \text{Taxable Subtotal} - \text{Trade-in Allowance} \\ &= \$19\ 606 - \$0 \\ &= \$19\ 606 \end{aligned}$$

5 The PST is 8% of the taxable total, and the GST is 7% of the taxable total.

$$\begin{aligned} \text{PST} &= 0.08 \times \text{Taxable Total} \\ &= 0.08 \times \$19\ 606 \\ &= \$1568.48 \end{aligned} \qquad \begin{aligned} \text{GST} &= 0.07 \times \text{Taxable Total} \\ &= 0.07 \times \$19\ 606 \\ &= \$1372.42 \end{aligned}$$

6 The delivery price is the sum of the taxable total, PST, GST, licence plate fee, gas fee, and lien payout.

$$\begin{aligned} \text{Delivery Price} &= \text{Taxable Total} + \text{PST} + \text{GST} + \text{Licence Plate Fee} + \\ &\quad \text{Gas Fee} + \text{Lien Payout} \\ &= \$19\ 606 + \$1568.48 + \$1372.42 + \$74 + \$20 + \$0 \\ &= \$22\ 640.90 \end{aligned}$$

7 The amount financed is calculated as follows.

Amount Financed = Delivery Price − Down Payment − MFG Rebate
+ Finance Fee

$$= \$22\ 640.90 - \$4000 - \$0 + \$54$$
$$= \$18\ 694.90$$

8 The monthly payment is calculated using the formula

$$R = \frac{(PV)(i)}{1 - (1 + i)^{-n}}.$$

Substitute $PV = 18\ 694.90$, $i = \frac{0.049}{12}$, and $n = 48$.

$$R = \frac{18\ 694.90 \times \frac{0.049}{12}}{1 - (1 + \frac{0.049}{12})^{-48}}$$

$$\doteq 429.68$$

The monthly payment is $429.68.

9 The interest due is the difference between the total monthly payments and the amount financed.

Interest Due = Total monthly payments − Amount financed

$$= \$429.68 \times 48 - \$18\ 694.90$$
$$= \$1929.74$$

10 The balance due is the sum of the amount financed and the interest due.

Balance Due = Amount Financed + Interest Due

$$= \$18\ 694.90 + \$1929.74$$
$$= \$20\ 624.64$$

If Jorge accepts the deal review and buys the car, he signs a contract and makes the down payment. After the dealership prepares the vehicle for delivery by cleaning and servicing it, Jorge can drive it away.

Buying a Used Vehicle

Unlike a home, which increases in value over time, the value of a vehicle generally decreases or *depreciates* as it ages. On average, a new vehicle depreciates between 20% and 30% during the first year. It can make financial sense to buy a used vehicle in good mechanical condition instead of a new vehicle.

The process to buy a used vehicle at a car dealership is similar to the process to buy a new vehicle.

Example 2

Melissa buys a used sports car with a list price (asking price) of $22 625. She negotiates a discount of $1080 off the list price. Melissa does not have a down payment. However, she will receive a $5780 trade-in on her old car on which she still owes $850. She will finance the sports car through the car dealership at 9.9% compounded monthly for 48 months.

Copy and complete the deal review for this transaction. The fees charged by the dealership have already been entered.

	DEAL REVIEW					
1	List Price		1	Gas Fee	20.00
1	Discount		1	Lien Payout	
2	Purchase Price		6	Delivery Price	
1	Freight	0.00	1	MFG Rebate	
1	Tire/Air Tax	0.00	1	Down Payment	
1	Gas Tax	0.00	1	Finance Fee	54.00
1	Administration Fee	85.00	7	Amount Financed	
3	Taxable Subtotal		1	Interest Rate	
1	Trade-in Allowance		1	Loan Term	
4	Taxable Total		8	Monthly Payment	
5	PST		9	Interest Due at 9.9%	
5	GST		10	Balance Due	
1	Licence Plate Fee	74.00			

Solution

1 Enter the costs and discounts associated with the purchase.

2 Purchase Price = $22 625 − $1080 = $21 545

3 Taxable Subtotal = $21 545 + $85 = $21 630

4 Taxable Total = $21 630 − $5780 = $15 850

5 PST = 0.08 × $15 850 = $1268
GST = 0.07 × $15 850 = $1109.50

6 Delivery Price = $15 850 + $1268 + $1109.50 + $74 + $20 + $850
= $19 171.50

7 Amount Financed = $19 171.50 + $54 = $19 225.50

8 For the monthly payment, use

$$R = \frac{(PV)(i)}{1 - (1 + i)^{-n}}$$

$$R = \frac{19\ 225.50 \times \frac{0.099}{12}}{1 - (1 + \frac{0.099}{12})^{-48}}$$

$$\doteq 486.69$$

The monthly payment is $486.69.

9 Interest Due = $486.69 \times 48 - \$19\ 225.50 = \$4135.62$

10 Balance Due = $19\ 225.50 + \$4135.62 = \$23\ 361.12$

	DEAL REVIEW				
1	List Price	22 625.00	1	Gas Fee	20.00
1	Discount	1080.00	1	Lien Payout	850.00
2	Purchase Price	21 545.00	6	Delivery Price	19 171.50
1	Freight	0.00	1	MFG Rebate	0.00
1	Tire/Air Tax	0.00	1	Down Payment	0.00
1	Gas Tax	0.00	1	Finance Fee	54.00
1	Administration Fee	85.00	7	Amount Financed	19 225.50
3	Taxable Subtotal	21 630.00	1	Interest Rate	9.9%
1	Trade-in Allowance	5780.00	1	Loan Term	48 months
4	Taxable Total	15 850.00	8	Monthly Payment	486.69
5	PST	1268.00	9	Interest Due at 9.9%	4135.62
5	GST	1109.50	10	Balance Due	23 361.12
1	Licence Plate Fee	74.00			

Discuss

Which charges must you pay to buy a new car but not a used car?

When you buy a used vehicle or trade in a vehicle, the price you pay or receive for the vehicle is called its *resale value*. This value is based on the estimated depreciation of the vehicle. The amount of depreciation depends on the vehicle because some vehicles retain their values better than others.

For example, suppose a car with an initial MSRP of $35 769 depreciates by 22% per year.
Each year, the value of the car decreases, on average, by 22%.
It is worth 100% − 22% = 78%, or 0.78 of its value the preceding year.
Thus, the value of the car can be expressed as a power of 0.78.

After 1 year: Resale value = \$35 769 × 0.78 = \$27 899.82

After 2 years: Resale value = \$35 769 × $(0.78)^2 \doteq$ \$21 761.86

After 3 years: Resale value = \$35 769 × $(0.78)^3 \doteq$ \$16 794.25

After 4 years: Resale value = \$35 769 × $(0.78)^4 \doteq$ \$13 239.92

$\vdots$

After n years: Resale value = \$35 769 × $(0.78)^n$, or \$35 769$(1 - 0.22)^n$

Discuss

What type of sequence do the resale values form? Explain.

In general, the resale value, V dollars, of a vehicle n years old with an MSRP of P dollars that is depreciating by r percent per year can be obtained as follows.

TAKE NOTE
Resale Value of a Vehicle
$V = P(1 - r)^n$ V is the resale value in dollars. P is the MSRP in dollars. r is the annual depreciation rate, expressed as a decimal. n is the age of the car in years.

This resale value is only an estimate.

Example 3

An SUV has an MSRP of \$46 783. It depreciates at a rate of 25% per year. Estimate the resale value of the vehicle after 5 years.

Solution

Use the formula $V = P(1 - r)^n$.

Substitute $P = 46\ 783$, $r = 0.25$, and $n = 5$.

$V = 46\ 783(1 - 0.25)^5$
$\ \ \ = 46\ 783(0.75)^5$
$\ \ \ \doteq 11\ 101.83$

The vehicle has a resale value of approximately \$11 100 after 5 years.

Discuss

In Chapter 3, pages 152–159, you learned that depreciation is an example of exponential decay. Compare the formula $V = P(1 - r)^n$ with the general equation for exponential decay $y = Ab^x$. What do you notice?

Why do cars usually depreciate in value while houses usually appreciate in value?

 Exercises

 A

1. List 3 advantages and 3 disadvantages of buying a new vehicle versus a used vehicle.

2. Calculate the GST (7%) and PST (8%) paid on a car with each price.
   a) $12 765   b) $23 984   c) $43 679
   d) $31 796   e) $19 543   f) $28 727

3. Neil wants to buy a car and plans to arrange financing. For each set of conditions, what is the maximum loan and the maximum price of the car Neil can afford? The interest on the loan is compounded monthly.

	Maximum monthly payment	Interest rate	Length of loan	Down payment
a)	$600	4.9%	36 months	$2500
b)	$600	4.9%	48 months	$2500
c)	$600	4.9%	60 months	$2500
d)	$475	4.9%	48 months	$6000
e)	$525	4.9%	48 months	$5000
f)	$575	4.9%	48 months	$4000

4. Determine the resale value of each vehicle.
   a) a 3-year-old vehicle with an MSRP of $36 594 and an annual depreciation rate of 20%
   b) a 1-year-old vehicle with an MSRP of $18 594 and an annual depreciation rate of 25%
   c) a 5-year-old vehicle with an MSRP of $40 739 and an annual depreciation rate of 27%
   d) a 4-year-old vehicle with an MSRP of $27 840 and an annual depreciation rate of 22%
   e) a 2-year-old vehicle with an MSRP of $15 099 and an annual depreciation rate of 18%

B

5. Determine the monthly payment on a vehicle financed under each condition.

   a) $25 756 at 4.9% compounded monthly for 48 months

   b) $16 357 at 8.9% compounded monthly for 36 months

   c) $33 675 at 8.9% compounded monthly for 60 months

   d) $19 087 at 14.1% compounded monthly for 24 months

   e) $9995 at 7.5% compounded monthly for 36 months

   f) $28 682 at 1.9% compounded monthly for 42 months

6. For each loan in exercise 5, determine the total interest paid.

7. Marisa wants to sell her 3-year-old car. The car had an MSRP of $35 940. Marisa knows that the average annual depreciation of cars of her make and model is 20%. Estimate the resale value of Marisa's car.

8. **Communication** There are many factors that affect how much a vehicle depreciates over time. Explain the relationship between the depreciation of a vehicle and each item.

   a) the popularity of the vehicle

   b) the distance the vehicle is driven

   c) how well the vehicle is maintained

9. Describe a situation in which the resale value of a vehicle increases as the vehicle gets older.

10. **Knowledge/Understanding** Tony purchases a new car with an MSRP of $32 804. He negotiates a discount of $822. Tony pays these additional costs: an $895 freight charge, a $100 tire/air tax, a $75 gas tax, an $85 administration fee, a $74 licence plate fee, and a $20 gas fee. Tony does not have a trade-in. He makes a down payment of $2500 and finances the rest through the dealership at 4.9% compounded monthly for 36 months. The finance fee is $54. Complete a deal review for Tony's purchase.

11. Elinka purchases a used truck with a list price of $22 489. She has a trade-in worth $8650, which is lien free. She negotiates a discount of $835. Elinka pays these additional costs: an $85 administration fee, a $74 licence plate fee, and a $20 gas fee. Elinka finances the truck through the dealership at 8.9% compounded monthly for 48 months. The finance fee is $54. Complete a deal review for Elinka's purchase.

12. Peter trades in his 2-year-old car for a new SUV with an MSRP of $45 607. He negotiates a discount of $1500. Peter receives a trade-in allowance of $17 800 for his old car on which he owes $7200. Peter pays these additional costs: a $1030 freight charge, a $100 tire/air tax, a $75 gas tax, an $85 administration fee, a $74 licence plate fee, and a $20 gas fee. Since Peter is buying at the end of the model year, he receives a manufacturer's rebate for $3000. Peter arranges financing through the dealership at 5.9% compounded monthly for 48 months. The finance fee is $54. Complete a deal review for Peter's purchase.

13. Application Sami is buying her first vehicle. She chooses a new van with an MSRP of $27 896, and negotiates a discount of $1840. Sami pays these additional costs: a $785 freight charge, a $100 tire/air tax, a $75 gas tax, an $85 administration fee, a $74 licence plate fee, and a $20 gas fee. Since Sami pre-arranged the financing through her bank, she writes a cheque for the full amount to the dealer.

a) Complete a deal review for Sami's purchase.

b) Determine Sami's monthly payment if the bank charges 7.5% compounded monthly for 48 months.

14. Anthony has a 5-year-old car that he owns outright. He trades up to a car that is 2 years old with a list price of $19 236. He negotiates a discount of $875 and a trade-in allowance of $2500 for his old car. Anthony arranges financing through the dealership at 8.9% compounded monthly for 36 months. These costs are added to the purchase price: a $74 licence plate fee, a $20 gas fee, and a $54 finance fee. Complete a deal review for Anthony's purchase.

15. Thinking/Inquiry/Problem Solving A recent advertisement offers two ways to purchase a car.

- Cash price of $19 627
- Finance price of $20 877 at 0.9% compounded monthly for 48 months, or 1.9% compounded monthly for 60 months

The prices given include the freight charge, tire/air tax, and administration fee. Additional costs include a $74 licence plate fee and a $20 gas fee.
Suppose you can finance the cash price of the car through the bank at 3.9% compounded monthly for 48 months.

a) Which is the most economical way to purchase the car? Justify your answer.

b) Why might you not choose the most economical option?

Leasing is a popular alternative to buying a vehicle. When you sign a lease, you are paying to use a vehicle for a specified period of time. At the end of that time, the vehicle is returned to the leasing company. The lease contract specifies that the vehicle must be kept in good repair during the term of the lease. It also specifies a distance allowance and a penalty for exceeding it. In some cases, you have the option to buy the vehicle at the end of the lease.

When you lease a vehicle, you pay for the estimated depreciation in the vehicle's value over the term of the lease. Thus you are not paying for the entire value of the vehicle, but only for the loss in the vehicle's value while you use it, plus interest. For this reason, monthly lease payments may be lower than comparable vehicle loan payments.

The depreciation is the difference between the vehicle's cost today, its *net capital cost*, and its value at the end of the lease, the *residual value*. (The depreciation may be called the amount financed.) The net capital cost is the total amount paid for the vehicle. It consists of the MSRP, additional costs and fees charged by the dealership, and discounts such as a down payment or a trade-in allowance. The residual value is usually a percent of the vehicle's MSRP.

Depreciation = Net Capital Cost − Residual Value

Example 1

Jenna takes a 36-month lease on a car with an MSRP of $23 847 and a net capital cost of $24 737. The residual value is 42% of the MSRP.

a) Calculate the residual value.

b) By how much does the car depreciate during the term of the lease?

Solution

a) The residual value is 42% of the MSRP.

Thus, the residual value is 0.42 × $23 847 = $10 015.74.

b) Depreciation = Net Capital Cost − Residual Value
= $24 737 − $10 015.74
= $14 721.26

The car depreciates by $14 721.26 during the term of the lease.

In *Example 1*, the 42% is called the *residual factor*.

The total monthly payment Jenna makes on the car lease in *Example 1* consists of 3 separate charges. They are:

- payment of the depreciation, plus interest
- interest on the residual value of the car
- PST and GST

For most loans, a payment is made at the end of the payment period. If the loan is to be repaid with monthly payments, the first payment is made 1 month after the loan is taken out. A car lease, however, is an annuity in which each payment is made at the beginning of the payment period. This is called an *annuity due*. The following formula is used to calculate the monthly depreciation payment. The payment period is equal to the compounding period.

TAKE NOTE

Payment for an Annuity Due

Each payment is made at the beginning of the payment period.

$$R = \frac{Di}{1 + i - (1 + i)^{-N}}$$

R is the monthly depreciation payment in dollars.
D is the depreciation in dollars.
i is the interest rate per compounding period, as a decimal.
N is 1 less than the number of payments.

For Jenna's lease, the interest rate is 4.9% compounded monthly.
Use the formula above to calculate Jenna's monthly depreciation payment.

$$R = \frac{Di}{1 + i - (1 + i)^{-N}}$$

Substitute $D = 14\ 721.26$, $i = \frac{0.049}{12}$, and $N = 35$.

$$R = \frac{(14\ 721.26)(\frac{0.049}{12})}{1 + \frac{0.049}{12} - (1 + \frac{0.049}{12})^{-35}}$$

$$\doteq 438.76$$

The monthly depreciation payment is $438.76.

The monthly payment also includes an interest charge on the residual value of the car. Since Jenna is "borrowing" the residual value, $10 015.74, during the term of the lease, she is charged simple interest on it.

$$I = Prt$$

Substitute $P = 10\ 015.74$, $r = 0.049$, and $t = \frac{1}{12}$.

$$I = 10\ 015.74 \times 0.049 \times \frac{1}{12}$$
$$\doteq 40.90$$

Since this interest is due at the end of each month but is paid at the beginning, its present value for 1 month is calculated.

Use the formula for the present value of an amount: $P = \frac{A}{(1 + i)^n}$.

Substitute $A = 40.90$, $i = \frac{0.049}{12}$, and $n = 1$.

$$P = \frac{40.90}{\left(1 + \frac{0.049}{12}\right)^1}$$
$$\doteq 40.73$$

The interest is $40.73.

The charges of $438.76 and $40.73 are added to give the *base monthly payment*. The PST and GST are calculated on the base monthly payment and added to it to give the total monthly payment.

Base monthly payment = $438.76 + $40.73
= $479.49

PST = 0.08 × $479.49   GST = 0.07 × $479.49
$\doteq$ $38.36 $\doteq$ $33.56

Total monthly payment = $479.49 + $38.36 + $33.56
= $551.41

When Jenna leased the car, she received a *lease quote*. It is similar to the deal review for the purchase of a car. Here is Jenna's lease quote.

		LEASE QUOTE				
1	Term of Lease	36 months	9	Monthly Payment		551.41
1	MSRP	23 847.00	1	Interest Rate		4.9%
2	Gross Capital Cost	24 737.00	10	1st Payment		551.41
1	Trade-in Allowance	0.00	11	PST (Down Payment)		0.00
1	Down Payment	0.00	11	GST (Down Payment)		0.00
3	Total Capital Reduction	0.00	1	1st Year Fees		130.00
4	Net Capital Cost	24 737.00	1	Other Fees		160.00
1	Residual Factor	0.42	12	PST On Upfront		12.80
5	Residual Value	10 015.74	12	GST On Upfront		11.20
6	Depreciation	14 721.26	1	Security Deposit		475.00
7	Base Monthly Payment	479.49				
8	Monthly PST	38.36	13	Total Initial Payment		1340.41
8	Monthly GST	33.56				

The numbers in blue to the left of the items on page 337 refer to the steps below.

1 The costs, discounts, and terms associated with the lease are entered.

The 1st year fees are the licence plate fee, gas fee, and finance fee.

The other fees are the gas tax and an administration fee.

A refundable security deposit is required when a car is leased.

2 The gross capital cost includes the MSRP, freight charge, tire/air tax, less any negotiated discount off the MSRP.

3 The total capital reduction is the sum of the trade-in allowance and the down payment.

Total Capital Reduction = Trade-in Allowance + Down Payment

4 The net capital cost is the difference between the gross capital cost and the total capital reduction.

Net Capital Cost = Gross Capital Cost − Total Capital Reduction

5 The residual value is the value of the car at the end of the lease.

Residual Value = Residual Factor × MSRP

6 The depreciation is the difference between the net capital cost and the residual value.

Depreciation = Net Capital Cost − Residual Value

7 The base monthly payment includes the depreciation payment and the interest charge on the residual value. Refer to the calculations on pages 336 and 337.

8 The monthly PST and GST are calculated on the base monthly payment.

9 The monthly payment is the sum of the base monthly payment and the monthly PST and GST.

Monthly Payment = Base Monthly Payment + Monthly PST
+ Monthly GST

10 The 1st payment is paid at the beginning of the lease.

11 PST and GST are calculated on the capital reduction (the down payment). The trade-in allowance is not taxed.

12 PST and GST are calculated on the other fees.

13 The total initial payment is the sum of the entries in the second column, from 1st payment down to security deposit.

Example 2

Ludwig leases a new sports car with an MSRP of $29 080 and a residual factor of 42%. The gross capital cost of the car after he subtracts the negotiated discount and adds the freight charge and tire/air tax is $30 000. Ludwig leases the car for 36 months at 5.9% compounded monthly. He makes a down payment of $2500 and receives a trade-in allowance of $5000 on his old car. Ludwig is charged $130 in 1st year fees, $160 in other fees, and a $425 refundable security deposit.

a) Construct a lease quote for Ludwig's lease.

b) Determine the total cost of the lease.

Solution

a) The numbers in the lease quote are generated as follows.

1 The costs, discounts, and terms associated with the lease are entered.

2 Gross Capital Cost = $30 000

3 Total Capital Reduction = $5000 + $2500 = $7500

4 Net Capital Cost = $30 000 − $7500 = $22 500

5 Residual Value = 0.42 × $29 080 = $12 213.60

6 Depreciation = $22 500 − $12 213.60 = $10 286.40

7 For the base monthly payment:

Use the formula $R = \dfrac{Di}{i + 1 - (1 + i)^{-N}}$ to calculate the monthly depreciation payment.

Substitute $D = 10\ 286.40$, $i = \dfrac{0.059}{12}$, and $N = 35$.

$$R = \frac{(10\ 286.40)\left(\dfrac{0.059}{12}\right)}{\dfrac{0.059}{12} + 1 - \left(1 + \dfrac{0.059}{12}\right)^{-35}}$$
$$\doteq 310.94$$

The monthly depreciation payment is $310.94.

Use the formula $I = Prt$ to calculate the interest on the residual value.

Substitute $P = 12\ 213.60$, $r = 0.059$, and $t = \dfrac{1}{12}$.

$$I = 12\ 213.60 \times 0.059 \times \frac{1}{12}$$
$$\doteq 60.05$$

Calculate the present value of the interest.

Use the formula $P = \dfrac{A}{(1+i)^n}$.

Substitute $A = 60.05$, $i = \dfrac{0.059}{12}$, and $n = 1$.

$$P = \dfrac{60.05}{1 + \dfrac{0.059}{12}}$$
$$\doteq 59.76$$

The monthly interest charge on the residual value is $59.76.

The Base Monthly Payment = $310.94 + $59.76 = $370.70

8 Monthly PST = $0.08 \times \$370.70 \doteq \$29.66$
Monthly GST = $0.07 \times \$370.70 \doteq \$25.95$

9 Monthly Payment = $370.70 + $29.66 + $25.95 = $426.31

10 The 1st Payment is the monthly payment, $426.31.

11 PST = $0.08 \times \$2500 = \$200$
GST = $0.07 \times \$2500 = \$175$

12 PST = $0.08 \times \$160 = \$12.80$
GST = $0.07 \times \$160 = \$11.20$

13 Total Initial Payment = $426.31 + $200 + $175 + $130 + $160
$\qquad\qquad\qquad\qquad + \$12.80 + \$11.20 + \$425$
$\qquad\qquad\qquad = \$1540.31$

	LEASE QUOTE				
1	Term of Lease	36 months	9	Monthly Payment	426.31
1	MSRP	29 080.00	1	Interest Rate	5.9%
2	Gross Capital Cost	30 000.00	10	1st Payment	426.31
1	Trade-in Allowance	5000.00	11	PST (Down Payment)	200.00
1	Down Payment	2500.00	11	GST (Down Payment)	175.00
3	Total Capital Reduction	7500.00	1	1st Year Fees	130.00
4	Net Capital Cost	22 500.00	1	Other Fees	160.00
1	Residual Factor	0.42	12	PST On Upfront	12.80
5	Residual Value	12 213.60	12	GST On Upfront	11.20
6	Depreciation	10 286.40	1	Security Deposit	425.00
7	Base Monthly Payment	370.70			
8	Monthly PST	29.66	13	Total Initial Payment	1540.31
8	Monthly GST	25.95			

b) The total cost of the lease is the sum of the trade-in allowance, the down payment, the total initial payment, and the total monthly payments, less the security deposit. (You get the security deposit back if the vehicle is in good condition.)

Total cost = $5000 + $2500 + $1540.31 + $426.31 × 35 − $425
= $23 536.16

The total cost of the lease is $23 536.16.

Discuss

For the total monthly payments, why is the monthly payment multiplied by 35 and not 36? Explain.

7.2 Exercises

1. What factors affect the residual value of a vehicle?

2. Determine the residual value of each vehicle.

	MSRP	Residual factor
a)	$19 763	45%
b)	$28 956	48%
c)	$45 278	33%
d)	$37 589	28%
e)	$22 519	43%
f)	$41 835	22%

3. Determine the interest earned in one month.

	Principal	Annual interest rate
a)	$9652.00	5.9%
b)	$12 675.36	6.5%
c)	$10 806.39	2.9%
d)	$15 387.00	9.9%
e)	$23 364.82	8.75%
f)	$8541.45	4.9%

4. Determine the present value of each amount that is due one month from now, at the given annual interest rate compounded monthly.

	Amount	Annual interest rate
a)	$650.00	5.9%
b)	$438.95	1.9%
c)	$523.60	6.75%
d)	$341.58	9.7%
e)	$867.48	0.9%
f)	$705.43	8.6%

B

5. Communication List 3 possible advantages and 3 disadvantages for leasing a car instead of buying it.

6. Determine the base monthly payment on each vehicle. The interest is compounded monthly.

	Net capital cost	Residual value	Annual interest rate	Length of lease
a)	$35 659	$12 356.72	5.9%	36 months
b)	$24 749	$7920.00	4.5%	48 months
c)	$41 852	$10 463.00	9.9%	60 months
d)	$17 427	$10 630.47	1.9%	24 months
e)	$27 905	$11 999.15	10.25%	36 months
f)	$49 831	$15 945.92	0.9%	48 months

7. Knowledge/Understanding Barry leases a new truck. It has a net capital cost of $28 653 and a residual value of $13 753.34. The lease is for 48 months at 7.1% compounded monthly. Determine Barry's monthly payment.

8. A vehicle with a net capital cost of $27 964 and a residual value of $6431.72 is leased for 60 months. The interest rate is 5.45% compounded monthly. Determine the monthly payment.

9. Matt leases a new car with an MSRP of $35 265, a residual factor of 44%, and a net capital cost of $36 195. The lease is for 36 months at 4.9% compounded monthly. What is Matt's monthly payment?

10. Linda leases an SUV with a gross capital cost of $38 594 and a residual value of $17 367.30 for 36 months. Linda makes a down payment of $7500, and finances the remainder at 6.1% compounded monthly. Determine Linda's monthly payment.

11. Sylvia leases a new compact car with an MSRP of $18 678 and a residual factor of 41%. The gross capital cost of the car after she subtracts the negotiated discount, then adds the freight charge and tire/air tax is $18 000. Sylvia leases the car for 36 months at 4.9% compounded monthly. She is charged $130 in 1st year fees, $160 in other fees, and $450 as a refundable security deposit.

a) Construct a lease quote for the lease.

b) Determine the total cost of the lease.

12. Lianna leases a new truck with an MSRP of $29 405, a residual factor of 55%, and a gross capital cost of $30 000. She makes a down payment of $5000. Her lease is for 24 months at 0.9% compounded monthly. Lianna is charged $130 in 1st year fees, $160 in other fees, and $475 as a refundable security deposit.

a) Construct a lease quote for the lease.

b) Determine the total cost of the lease.

13. **Application** Milan leases a new 4-wheel drive vehicle with an MSRP of $43 375 and a residual factor of 45%. He negotiates a discount of $1000 and pays the following additional costs: an $860 freight charge and a $100 tire/air tax. Milan makes a down payment of $4000 and receives a trade-in allowance of $8640. Milan's lease is for 36 months at 5.9% compounded monthly. He is charged the following fees: a $74 licence plate fee, a $20 gas fee, a $36 finance fee, a $75 gas tax, and an $85 administration fee. Milan also pays a $525 refundable security deposit. Determine the total cost of the lease.

14. **Thinking/Inquiry/Problem Solving** Nasser leases a new SUV with an MSRP of $39 720 and a residual factor of 32%. He negotiates a discount of $850 and pays the following additional costs: an $830 freight charge and a $100 tire/air tax. Nasser receives a trade-in allowance of $11 845 for his old vehicle. Nasser's lease is for 48 months at 7.2% compounded monthly. He is charged the following fees: a $74 licence plate fee, a $20 gas fee, a $36 finance fee, a $75 gas tax, and an $85 administration fee. Nasser also pays a $495 refundable security deposit. The lease specifies a yearly distance allowance of 24 000 km and a penalty of $0.15 per kilometre driven in excess of the distance allowance. When Nasser returns the SUV at the end of the lease, he has driven 120 000 km.

a) Determine the penalty Nasser pays for exceeding the distance allowance.

b) Determine the total cost of the lease.

The purchase or lease of a vehicle represents only part of the cost of driving. There are also many costs involved in the day-to-day operation of a vehicle. These costs vary, depending on where you live, the type of vehicle you drive, and the distance you drive. The regular expenses involved in operating a vehicle include fuel costs, maintenance costs, insurance costs, and licence costs.

Fuel Costs

The amount of fuel a vehicle uses is often a factor in the choice of the type of vehicle to buy or lease. Information about the fuel consumption of a vehicle can be obtained from the salesperson from whom you buy or lease the vehicle. It can also be obtained from the web site of National Resources Canada. The web site has information on how fuel consumption ratings are determined, and provides the fuel consumption ratings for many vehicles. Ask your teacher for the web site address.

Fuel consumption ratings are expressed either in miles per Imperial gallon or in litres per 100 kilometres. Once you know the fuel consumption rating for the vehicle you drive, the approximate distance you drive in a year, and an estimate of the average cost per litre of fuel, you can estimate the yearly cost of fuel.

Example 1

Oliver's car has a fuel consumption rating of 5.8 L/100 km. Oliver estimates that he drives 20 000 km per year and the average cost of fuel during the year is $0.76/L. Estimate Oliver's fuel cost for the year.

Solution

A fuel consumption rating of 5.8 L/100 km means that 100 km are travelled on 5.8 L of fuel.

Thus, the fuel for 1 km is $\frac{5.8}{100}$ L.
Oliver drives approximately 20 000 km in a year.
The fuel for 20 000 km is $20\ 000 \times \frac{5.8}{100}$ L $= 1160$ L.
The cost of 1 L of fuel is $0.76.
The cost of 1160 L of fuel is $1160 \times \$0.76 = \$881.60$.
Oliver spends approximately $880 on fuel in a year.

Maintenance Costs

A second major expense in operating a vehicle is the cost of maintenance. Vehicle manufacturers stress the importance of regularly scheduled maintenance to keep a vehicle in good running order and to maintain its value. The manufacturer's recommended maintenance schedule for any vehicle can be obtained through the dealer or on the Internet.

Here is a sample vehicle maintenance schedule.

Vehicle Maintenance Schedule			
Recommended Service	Frequency (km)	Frequency (months)	Approximate cost ($)
Lube, oil, and filter	5000	3	29.95
Tire rotation and brake inspection	10 000	6	41.50
Wheel alignment inspection	25 000	12	69.75
Cooling system	50 000	24	72.95
Tune-up and emission control	50 000	30	225.00
Automatic transmission	85 000	51	145.00

Example 2

Velma purchases a new car. She will use the car to drive to work every day. She estimates she will drive 35 000 km in the first year. Use the vehicle maintenance schedule to estimate Velma's maintenance costs in the first year.

Solution

Velma estimates she will drive 35 000 km in the first year.

The services listed in the first three rows of the table will be performed during the year.

The lube, oil, and filter service is done every 5000 km.

Since 35 000 ÷ 5000 = 7, the service is performed 7 times in the first year.

The tire rotation and brake inspection is done every 10 000 km.

Since 35 000 ÷ 10 000 ≐ 3, the service is performed 3 times in the first year.

The wheel alignment inspection is done every 25 000 km.

Since 35 000 ÷ 25 000 ≐ 1, the service is performed once in the first year.

Total maintenance cost = 7($29.95) + 3($41.50) + $69.75
= $403.90

There is 7% GST and 8% PST on the maintenance cost.
Total tax: 15% of $403.90 = 0.15 × $403.90
$$= \$60.59$$

Maintenance cost including taxes = $403.90 + $60.59
$$= \$464.49$$

Velma spends approximately $460 in maintenance costs in the first year.

Discuss
What assumptions are made in calculating the maintenance costs?
Why is the recommended servicing frequency given in both kilometres and months?

Insurance Costs

Insurance is another item that contributes to the yearly operating cost of a vehicle.

Canadian law requires that all purchased and leased vehicles be insured. All drivers are required to have *personal liability coverage*. Personal liability provides insurance against lawsuits in the event that someone is injured in an accident in which the driver is involved. It also covers the cost of damage to other cars and property caused by the driver's car.

If you finance a vehicle, you must also have *collision and comprehensive coverage*. Collision coverage pays for damage to your car if you are in an accident or replaces a car that is damaged beyond repair. Comprehensive coverage covers theft and damage to your car from things such as falling trees, fire, hail, and flood.

The cost of car insurance varies with the type of coverage provided and with the individual driver. Some factors that influence this cost are where you live, your age and marital status, the amount you drive, your driving record, and the purposes for which you use your vehicle. Car insurance payments may be made annually, semi-annually, or monthly.

Licence Costs

Licence fees include both the driver's licence and the vehicle licence plate. At the present time, a driver's licence is renewed every 5 years, while the vehicle licence plate is renewed every year or every second year. The renewals must be done on or before your birthday in the year the renewal is required.

Example 3

In the first 3 years that Sal owns his SUV, he drives 102 653 km. The average cost of fuel is $0.81/L. Sal's SUV has a fuel consumption rating of 12.7 L/100 km. He maintains his vehicle according to the distance maintenance schedule on page 345. Sal pays $1259 insurance per year. He renewed his driver's licence at a cost of $50. His vehicle licence plate is renewed every year at a cost of $74. What was Sal's average monthly operating cost in the 3-year period?

Solution

The operating costs include the cost of fuel, maintenance costs, the cost of insurance, and licence fees.

$$\text{Fuel cost} = 102\ 653 \times \frac{12.7}{100} \times \$0.81$$
$$\doteq \$10\ 559.91$$

The maintenance costs are:

Since $102\ 653 \div 5000 \doteq 20$, the lube/oil/filter service is performed 20 times.

Since $102\ 653 \div 10\ 000 \doteq 10$, the tire rotation/brake inspection service is performed 10 times.

Since $102\ 653 \div 25\ 000 \doteq 4$, the wheel alignment inspection service is performed 4 times.

Since $102\ 653 \div 50\ 000 \doteq 2$, each of the cooling system service and the tune-up and emission control service is performed twice.

Since $102\ 653 \div 85\ 000 \doteq 1$, the automatic transmission service is performed once.

$$\begin{aligned}\text{Maintenance costs} &= 20(\$29.95) + 10(\$41.50) + 4(\$69.75) + \\ &\quad 2(\$72.95) + 2(\$225) + \$145 \\ &= \$2033.90\end{aligned}$$

There is 7% GST and 8% PST on the maintenance cost.
Total tax: 15% of $2033.90 = 0.15 \times \$2033.90 = \$305.09$

$$\text{Insurance cost} = 3 \times \$1259 \qquad \qquad \text{Licence fees} = \$50 + 3(\$74)$$
$$= \$3777 \qquad \qquad \qquad \qquad \qquad = \$272$$

There is 7% GST on the insurance cost.
7% of $1259 = 0.07 \times \$1259 = \$88.13$

$$\begin{aligned}\text{Total operating costs} &= \$10\ 559.91 + \$2033.90 + \$3777 + \$272 + \\ &\quad \$305.09 + \$88.13 \\ &= \$17\ 036.03\end{aligned}$$

$$\text{Average monthly cost} = \frac{\$17036.03}{36} = \$473.22$$

Sal's average monthly operating cost was approximately $470.

7.3

A

1. Determine the amount of fuel required to drive each distance at the given fuel consumption rating.
   a) 10 000 km at 4.2 L/100 km
   b) 50 450 km at 7.4 L/100 km
   c) 35 700 km at 12.3 L/100 km
   d) 125 400 km at 6.8 L/100 km
   e) 27 385 km at 9.1 L/100 km
   f) 84 867 km at 10.4 L/100 km
   g) 20 378 km at 5.8 L/100 km
   h) 248 000 km at 8.3 L/100 km

2. Determine the cost to drive each distance at the given fuel consumption rating and average cost of fuel.
   a) 15 000 km at 6.9 L/100 km and $0.78/L
   b) 4900 km at 4.2 L/100 km and $0.71/L
   c) 36 700 km at 9.8 L/100 km and $0.83/L
   d) 47 260 km at 12.3 L/100 km and $0.67/L
   e) 150 700 km at 5.7 L/100 km and $0.75/L
   f) 67 572 km at 11.6 L/100 km and $0.94/L

3. Josie drives about 25 000 km per year. The average cost of fuel is $0.79/L. Determine the average monthly cost of fuel if Josie drives a vehicle with each fuel consumption rating.
   a) 3.8 L/100 km
   b) 5.6 L/100 km
   c) 7.1 L/100 km
   d) 6.2 L/100 km
   e) 8.7 L/100 km
   f) 13.1 L/100 km

B

4. **Communication** The cost of insurance varies with the type of insurance coverage and with the individual driver. To research the cost of insurance, use radio, television, and newspaper advertising, the Internet, your parents or guardians, friends, and local insurance agents. Write a brief report on your findings to explain how the cost of insurance is determined.

5. **Knowledge/Understanding** Tim drove about 19 000 km last year. The average cost of fuel for the year was $0.82/L. Tim's truck has a fuel consumption rating of 12.1 L/100 km. Tim follows the distance maintenance schedule on page 345. How much did Tim spend on fuel and maintenance last year?

6. Victor drives about 27 000 km per year. His car has a fuel consumption rating of 7.2 L/100 km. Victor follows the distance maintenance schedule on page 345. The average cost of fuel is $0.78/L. Determine Victor's average monthly cost for fuel and maintenance.

7. Dalia works in sales. She drives about 95 000 km per year. Her truck has a fuel consumption rating of 8.7 L/100 km. Since she relies on her truck for work, Dalia follows the distance maintenance schedule on page 345. The average cost of fuel is $0.79/L. Determine the average monthly fuel and maintenance cost for Dalia's truck.

8. Use the information in exercise 7. Assume Dalia follows the time maintenance schedule on page 345. Determine the average monthly maintenance cost for Dalia's truck.

9. **Application** The Wongs have 2 cars. Last year, one car was only driven about 9500 km. For this car, Mrs. Wong followed the time maintenance schedule on page 345. How much did she spend to maintain the car?

10. John's van has a fuel consumption rating of 11.7 L/100 km. Last year, John drove about 45 000 km. The average cost of fuel was $0.84/L. How much would John have saved by driving a vehicle with a fuel consumption rating of 4.1 L/100 km?

11. In a one-year period, the cost of fuel rose from $0.49/L to $0.78/L. A vehicle with a fuel consumption rating of 13.6 L/100 km was driven 65 600 km during the year. Estimate the cost of fuel for the year. Explain any assumptions you made.

12. Michelle's car has a fuel consumption rating of 5.9 L/100 km. During the first 3 years that Michelle owns her car, she drives 72 460 km. Michelle maintains her car according to the distance maintenance schedule on page 345. Her insurance is $975 per year and her vehicle licence plate is $74 each year. During those 3 years, Michelle pays $50 to renew her driver's licence. The average cost of gasoline over the 3 years is $0.78/L. Determine Michelle's average monthly operating cost over the 3 years.

13. Lynn drives her van an average of 18 000 km per year. She paid $1240 insurance the first year she owned the van, and $1480 the second year. Lynn's van has a fuel consumption rating of 9.3 L/100 km. The average cost of fuel was $0.87/L in the first year and $0.79/L in the second year. Lynn pays $74 per year for the licence plate. During those 2 years, Lynn paid $50 for her driver's licence. Lynn maintains her van according to the distance maintenance schedule on page 345. Determine Lynn's average monthly operating cost for her van over the 2 years.

14. In the first 3 years that Gordon owns his van, he drives 143 759 km. Gordon maintains his van according to the distance maintenance schedule on page 345. Gordon's van has a fuel consumption rating of 10.8 L/100 km. Gordon's insurance averages $1790 per year and his vehicle licence plate costs $74 each year. Gordon renews his driver's licence at a cost of $50. The average cost of fuel over the 3 years is $0.85/L. Determine Gordon's average monthly operating cost over the 3 years.

15. Thinking/Inquiry/Problem Solving Greg plans to buy a new sports car that he expects to keep for 5 years. Before he makes the financial commitment, he wants to be sure that he can afford the monthly operating costs. The car has a fuel consumption rating of 8.9 L/100 km. Greg estimates that the average cost of fuel during the 5 years will be $0.90/L. He estimates he will drive 200 000 km in the 5 years. Greg expects his annual insurance payment to be $1500, and his annual licence fee to be $74. Greg will follow the distance maintenance schedule on page 345. Because of the time period and the distance driven, he expects to replace the following items at the given costs: tires $600, exhaust system $870, and brakes $580. He also plans to add 10% to his estimate for emergencies. How much should Greg budget per month for the operating expenses on his car? Explain.

1. Determine the resale value of each vehicle.

   a) a 3-year-old vehicle with an MSRP of $27 356 and an annual depreciation rate of 20%

   b) a 1-year-old vehicle with an MSRP of $14 739 and an annual depreciation rate of 22%

2. Determine the monthly payment on each financed vehicle.

   a) $28 463 at 5.1% compounded monthly for 36 months

   b) $12 945 at 9.9% compounded monthly for 48 months

3. For each loan in exercise 2, determine the total interest paid.

4. Zachary leases a new van with a net capital cost of $27 791 and a residual value of $12 987.54. The lease is for 36 months at 5.9% compounded monthly. Determine Zachary's monthly payment.

5. Determine the amount of fuel required to drive each distance at the given fuel consumption rating.

   a) 12 000 km at 4.7 L/100 km   b) 48 370 km at 7.7 L/100 km

6. Determine the cost to drive each distance at the given fuel consumption rating and average cost of fuel.

   a) 16 000 km at 5.7 L/100 km and $0.75/L

   b) 5800 km at 7.2 L/100 km and $0.72/L

7. Beth trades in her 2-year-old car for a new sports car with an MSRP of $45 594. She negotiates a discount of $1200. Beth receives a trade-in allowance of $11 200 for her old car on which she owes $5137.42. She finances her sports car through the dealership at 4.9% compounded monthly for 48 months. Beth pays the following additional costs: a $690 freight charge, a $100 tire/air tax, a $75 gas tax, an $85 administration fee, a $74 licence plate fee, a $20 gas fee, and a $54 finance fee. Create a deal review for Beth's purchase.

8. Rick's truck has a fuel consumption rating of 9.8 L/100 km. In the first 4 years he owns the truck, Rick drives a total of 175 728 km. Rick follows the distance maintenance schedule on page 345. His insurance is $1565 per year and his vehicle licence plate is $74 each year. During those 4 years, Rick renews his driver's licence at a cost of $50. The average cost of fuel over the 4 years was $0.78/L. Determine Rick's average monthly operating cost over the 4 years.

In Sections 7.1 to 7.3, you calculated the costs involved to buy, lease, and operate a vehicle. The skills you developed will help you complete the investigations that follow.

Case Study 1

Bernard has chosen the car he wants, and must now decide whether to buy or lease it. The car has an MSRP of $21 977 and a residual factor of 34%. Bernard negotiates a $500 discount, and must pay the following additional costs: $660 freight charge, $100 tire/air tax, $75 gas tax, $85 administration fee, $74 licence plate fee, and $20 gas fee. Regardless of whether Bernard buys or leases the car, the financing is 6.9% compounded monthly for 48 months. If Bernard buys the car, the finance fee is $54. If he leases the car, the finance fee is $36.

a) Create a deal review and a lease quote for Bernard's car.

b) What is the difference in monthly payments?

c) What is the total cost in each case?

d) What factors should Bernard consider as he decides whether to buy or lease?

Investigation 1 Should I Buy or Lease?

1. With a partner, discuss the possible advantages and disadvantages of owning a vehicle versus leasing it.

a) Write a list of conditions under which you think it is a good idea to buy a vehicle.

b) Write a similar list of conditions for leasing a vehicle.

Share your lists with your classmates.

2. Choose a vehicle that you would like to buy or lease.

a) Research the costs involved. If possible, visit a dealership and obtain quotes for buying or leasing the vehicle. Alternatively, obtain information from newspapers or the Internet.

b) Write a report that compares the cost to buy and the cost to lease the vehicle. Include all necessary calculations.

c) Would you buy the vehicle or lease the vehicle? Explain why you made the decision you did.

Case Study 2

Bernice wants to buy her first car. She knows the make and model she wants, but has not decided whether it will be new or used. The new car has an MSRP of $24 572. Bernice negotiates a discount of $650, and would pay the following additional costs: $685 freight charge, $100 tire/air tax, $75 gas tax, $85 administration fee, $74 licence plate fee, $20 gas fee, and $54 finance fee. Bernice has also found a used car of the same make and model that is 2 years old and has been driven 38 547 km. The price of the used vehicle is $14 950. Additional costs include an $85 administration fee, a $74 licence plate fee, a $20 gas fee, and a $54 finance fee. The interest rate on the loan for the new car is 4.9% compounded monthly. The interest rate on the loan for the used car is 9.9% compounded monthly. In each case, the car will be financed for 36 months.

a) Create two deal reviews: one for the new car, the other for the used car.

b) What is the difference in monthly payments?

c) What is the total cost in each case?

d) What factors should Bernice consider as she decides whether to buy the new car or the used car?

Should I Buy New or Used?

1. With a partner, discuss the possible advantages and disadvantages of buying a new vehicle versus a used vehicle.

   a) Write a list of conditions under which you think it is a good idea to buy a new vehicle.

   b) Write a similar list of conditions for buying a used vehicle.

   Share your lists with your classmates.

2. Choose a model and make of vehicle that you would like to buy, new or used.

   a) To obtain a quote for a new model and a used model, visit a dealership, read newspapers, or use the Internet.

   b) Write a report that compares the cost of the new vehicle and the cost of the used vehicle. Include all the necessary calculations.

   c) Would you buy the new vehicle or the used vehicle? Explain why you made the decision you did.

Choosing the Vehicle of your Dreams

Choose the "vehicle of your dreams" and write a report that contains the following information. Include a picture of your vehicle in your report.

a) Why is the chosen vehicle the "vehicle of your dreams"?

b) Would you want a new or used vehicle? Would you buy or lease this vehicle? Research then present all relevant costs, including the cost of financing. Explain why you made the decisions to buy or lease the new or used vehicle.

c) Estimate the cost to drive your vehicle over a 5-year period. Include the following costs: fuel, maintenance, insurance, and licensing.

Career Profile

Paralegal

Paralegals or legal assistants help lawyers in case preparatory work, so lowering the legal fees for a client. An assistant may research, interview clients, maintain records, do pre-trial paperwork, and any other tasks that a lawyer assigns. As with lawyers, paralegals may specialize in a particular aspect of the law, such as family law, wills and estates administration, corporate law, immigration, process serving, tribunal hearings, or taxation, and so on. A paralegal cannot represent a client in court.

Paralegals often work in law offices, corporations, government offices, financial institutions, and real estate companies. However, some paralegals may work independently, dealing with immigration issues, small claims, and traffic offenses, where the client does not need representation in court. Success in this career requires excellent communication, research, and analytical skills, and the facility to read and comprehend complex legal documents. Because the legal system functions on deadlines, the paralegal's job can be stressful and demanding, and involve long and irregular work hours. Paralegals must be diligent and adaptable in changing situations.

Computer skills are mandatory as legal databases and computerized filing systems are commonly used in the legal workplace. Paralegals also have to be sensitive and kind when dealing with anxious and upset clients.

Where's the Math?
The head of the Paralegal Department at Prime Tech Institute states, "Mathematical applications play an integral part in almost every aspect of the legal profession. Whether you are determining the damages your client has suffered plus any interest and costs, or calculating the amount a vendor (seller) is entitled to in a real estate transaction, accuracy with numbers is essential."

What plans do you have for the future? What lifestyle do you hope to achieve once you live on your own? A budget can help you plan your spending and save for your future goals.

A *budget* is a list that compares income (money earned) and expenditures (money spent). Governments and businesses typically develop annual budgets. However, for personal budgeting, it is a good idea to plan monthly. There are no rules for developing a budget since situations vary from person to person. The table below provides suggested guidelines from the finance industry.

Expense category	Portion of monthly net income (%)
Housing and utilities	27 – 33
Food and clothing	20 – 26
Health and personal care	3 – 5
Transportation	12 – 14
Recreation and education	6 – 8
Savings	6 – 10
Miscellaneous	12 – 18

In the table above, *net income* is the income you have after all taxes have been paid. On the worksheet on page 364, the final item is *discretionary income*. This is the money you can spend how you want.

Example 1

Kelly and Maria will share an apartment while they attend college. Their net monthly income is $2100. According to the guidelines above, approximately how much can they afford for accommodation?

Solution

Kelly and Maria have a net income of $2100.

The guidelines recommend spending 27% to 33% of net income on housing and utilities.

27% of $2100 is $0.27 \times \$2100 = \$567$

33% of $2100 is $0.33 \times \$2100 = \$693$

Kelly and Maria can afford to spend between $567 and $693.

A budget should be reviewed and revised regularly to respond to changing financial and lifestyle situations. *Example 2* models a process for analysing and modifying a budget.

Example 2

This table summarizes Mel's monthly budget. He wants to move to a new apartment and expects to increase his housing and utilities costs to $1000 a month. Mel has monthly car payments of $475, which are included in the Transportation category. Describe the decisions Mel could make to be able to afford the new apartment.

Expense category	Amount ($)
Housing and utilities	750
Food and clothing	550
Health and personal care	75
Transportation	700
Recreation and education	200
Savings	75
Miscellaneous	250

Solution

Determine Mel's net monthly income by adding the numbers in the *Amount* column.

Net monthly income = $750 + $550 + $75 + $700 + $200 + $75 + $250
= $2600

Express each expense as a percent of Mel's net monthly income.

For example, Housing and utilities $= \frac{750}{2600} \times 100\%$
$\doteq 28.8\%$

Expense category	Actual percent (%)	Recommended percent (%)
Housing and utilities	28.8	27 – 33
Food and clothing	21.2	20 – 26
Health and personal care	2.9	3 – 5
Transportation	26.9	12 – 14
Recreation and education	7.7	6 – 8
Savings	2.9	6 – 10
Miscellaneous	9.6	12 – 18

Compare the percents of Mel's monthly expenditures to the guidelines.

- Mel is spending nearly twice the recommended percent on transportation.
- If Mel moves to the new apartment, his housing expense will increase to $\frac{1000}{2600} \times 100\%$, or 38.5%, which also exceeds the recommended percent.
- Mel's savings and miscellaneous expenses are lower than the recommended percent.

There are many ways Mel could modify his budget. Here are two possibilities.

- Sell or trade his car for a cheaper model so he can afford to move to a new apartment now.
- Delay the move to a new apartment, continue to save, and pay off the car loan.

There are other solutions Mel may be tempted to try, but they may not be effective.

- Mel may cut expenses for food or health, or reduce the amount he sets aside for savings and miscellaneous expenses. This could lead to problems if he gets sick, or if emergencies occur such as losing his job or a major repair bill for the car.
- Mel might try to reduce his transportation expenses. However, this may not work. He needs an additional $250 per month for housing, but there is only $700 − $475 = $225 per month in this category that is not used for the car payments.

In making his final decision, Mel needs to recognize that the car has put him in debt. He is over-extended in his transportation expenses. Moving to a new apartment will increase his debt: he will be carrying both a car loan and an increased rental payment. If emergencies arise, it is unlikely that a bank would grant him another loan, which means he may miss payments on the car or the rent for the apartment.

Mel may need to acknowledge that he cannot have everything at once. Either he has to delay the move or sell the car and buy something more modest. Due to depreciation, he will not receive the original value of the car when he sells. He may prefer to make the apartment move a long-term goal, working toward it while he pays off the loan for the car.

A

1. Write the first number as a percent of the second number. Where necessary, round the answer to the nearest tenth.

    a) 12, 60   b) 85, 200   c) 375, 1500   d) 74, 398

    e) 17, 39   f) 238, 2306   g) 850, 3590   h) 125, 50

2. Susan has a net monthly income of $2875. She saves $330 per month.

    a) What percent of her monthly income does Susan save?

    b) What percent of her monthly income does Susan spend?

3. Will has a net monthly income of $2480. He spends about $560 per month on food and clothing. What percent of his monthly income does Will spend on food and clothing?

B

4. **Communication** There are many ways to stretch your budget. For example, you could rent a video instead of going to a movie. You could eat at home more often. Explain 4 other ways to stretch your budget.

5. Use the information in the table.

    a) What percent of the monthly income is spent in each category?

    b) Compare the spending to the guidelines on page 355. In which categories is the person:

       i) overspending?

       ii) underspending?

       iii) spending within the guidelines?

Expense category	Amount ($)
Housing and utilities	650
Food and clothing	350
Health and personal care	50
Transportation	600
Recreation and education	150
Savings	50
Miscellaneous	150

6. Carmen has a net monthly income of $1260. Her monthly car payment is $255, and she spends about $150 per month on gas and maintenance. Carmen pays $850 car insurance every 6 months. What percent of her monthly income does Carmen spend on transportation?

7. Eric's net annual income is $32 000. Use the suggested guidelines to determine the range of money Eric should budget monthly in each category.

    a) Housing and utilities   b) Food and clothing

    c) Transportation   d) Savings

8. This circle graph represents a monthly budget.

   a) What is the monthly budget?

   b) Refer to the guidelines on page 355. Identify the categories in which the person is:

   i) overspending

   ii) underspending

   iii) spending within the guidelines

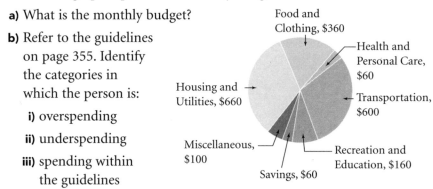

Food and Clothing, $360

Health and Personal Care, $60

Transportation, $600

Recreation and Education, $160

Savings, $60

Miscellaneous, $100

Housing and Utilities, $660

9. **Knowledge/Understanding** Nyles spends his net monthly income as shown in the table.

Expense category	Amount ($)
Housing and utilities	400
Food and clothing	325
Health and personal care	50
Transportation	450
Recreation and education	140
Savings	25
Miscellaneous	150

   a) What percent of his net monthly income does Nyles spend in each category?

   b) Compare Nyles' budget to the guidelines. In which categories is Nyles:
   i) overspending?

   ii) underspending?

   iii) spending within the guidelines?

10. Cindy is a single mother with a preschool child. She has a net monthly income of $3300. Cindy spends her monthly income as shown in the table.

Expense category	Amount ($)
Housing and utilities	1000
Food and clothing	660
Health and personal care	165
Transportation	430
Recreation and education	145
Savings	200
Miscellaneous	700

a) What percent of her monthly income does Cindy spend in each category?

b) Compare Cindy's budget to the guidelines. In which categories is Cindy:

   i) overspending?

   ii) underspending?

   iii) spending within the guidelines?

c) What monthly expenses might Cindy have that cause her to overspend in the Miscellaneous category?

11. Melissa is in her last year of high school. She works part-time after school and on weekends. Melissa's net monthly income is $760. She spends it as shown in the table.

Expense category	Amount ($)
Housing and utilities	0
Food and clothing	75
Health and personal care	35
Transportation	150
Recreation and education	100
Savings	350
Miscellaneous	50

a) What percent of her monthly income does Melissa spend in each category?

b) Suggest why Melissa does not spend any of her monthly income on housing and utilities.

c) Melissa does not own a vehicle. Suggest why she spends $150 per month on transportation.

d) Suggest why Melissa saves such a large percent of her monthly income.

e) Suppose Melissa purchases a used car and makes monthly payments of $195. Construct a new budget for Melissa, keeping in mind that she wants to save as much as possible. Explain why you made the changes you did.

12. Application The Zunigas have two children. Both parents work outside the home. The table on page 361 shows their monthly budget. The budget must be revised to reflect two changes. First, due to increased interest rates, their monthly mortgage payment will increase by $200. Second, their older child is starting grade 1.

Expense category	Amount ($)
Housing and utilities	1200
Food and clothing	800
Health and personal care	150
Transportation	700
Recreation and education	100
Savings	50
Miscellaneous	600

a) What percent of their monthly income do the Zunigas currently spend in each category?

b) Construct a new budget for the Zunigas. Explain the changes you made.

✓ **13. Thinking/Inquiry/Problem Solving** The table shows Pat and Steve's monthly budget. They were both working when they created this budget. The transportation expense reflects their purchase of a new car, with monthly loan payments of $750. Steve earns a net income of $1900 per month but has just learned that his job will be terminated. He will receive 2 months' severance pay. Steve predicts that he can find a new job with a comparable salary within 6 months. Currently, Pat and Steve have $1000 in savings.

Expense category	Amount ($)
Housing and utilities	1500
Food and clothing	700
Health and personal care	150
Transportation	1000
Recreation and education	200
Savings	100
Miscellaneous	100

a) Construct two budgets for Pat and Steve. Base the first budget on the next 2 months, in which monthly net income will not change. Base the second budget on the following 4 months, when only Pat is earning a salary. Explain the decisions you make to get them through the period of unemployment.

b) Financial planners recommend people have 3 months' net earnings in their savings. Does this seem reasonable? Explain.

A budget can be prepared quickly and efficiently with a computer. There are many commercial software programs and web sites that can help you prepare a budget. You can begin your search from our web site. www.pearsoned.ca/onmath11

If you do not have access to software programs or the Internet, you can use a spreadsheet program to create your own budget worksheet. Ask your teacher for more information.

To create a budget on a computer, follow these steps.

1. Determine the monthly net income.
2. Determine the monthly expenditures. The budget worksheet on page 364 may be helpful to organize expenses and expenditures before you enter them in the computer.
3. Enter the information from steps 1 and 2 in the budgeting software of your choice.
4. Compare monthly income and expenses. A positive amount can go toward fulfilling financial goals. A negative amount indicates that there is not enough income to cover expenses.
5. Revise the estimates as necessary. The computer automatically adjusts amounts as you revise the estimates.

A budget is a personal document that varies from person to person. In the following case studies, create a budget appropriate for the financial situation of the person or family. Try to make the budget as realistic as possible by researching to estimate expenses and by using the guidelines in Section 7.5, page 355.

Case Study 1

Cara has just completed high school, and will be working full-time at a grocery store. Cara is paid $14.85/h for a regular 40-h week. She receives time-and-a-half for overtime. On average, Cara expects to work 5 h overtime per week. Cara has $4000 in savings, which she will use for a down payment on a car, and for first and last month's rent on a furnished apartment. Create and print out a budget for Cara.

Case Study 2

Janice and Rick Palmer have two preschool children. Both the Palmers work full-time and have a combined net monthly income of $4200. They own their own home, and have recently bought a new station wagon. The Palmers employ a nanny. Create and print out a budget for the Palmers.

Case Study 3

Liam is a single father with a 2-year-old daughter. He will be returning full-time to a job that pays a net weekly salary of $650. Liam's daughter will attend daycare while Liam works. Liam will be moving to a new apartment for which he has saved first and last months' rent. He owns a car on which he is making monthly payments.

a) Create and print out a budget for Liam.

b) Suppose Liam's father agrees to take care of his granddaughter while Liam works. Revise the budget in part a to reflect this change. Print out the revised budget.

Case Study 4

Jodi has recently completed high school. She will attend college away from home. Jodi has saved $15 000 toward her education. Her parents will contribute $3000 per year while Jodi attends college. Jodi qualifies for a student loan, which she will take out if necessary.

a) Create and print out a budget for Jodi. If Jodi's finances are in a negative position, redo the budget with the student loan to make it balance.

b) Suppose Jodi decides to attend college and live at home. Revise the budget in part a to reflect this change. Print out the revised budget.

Investigation 1 — Budgeting for a Long-Term Goal

1. Design a personal budget. Use the worksheet on page 364 to help you keep track of your personal expenses for one week. Estimate your expenses for one month.

2. Consider your long-term goals. They may include: attending college; buying a car; moving into an apartment; buying a house; or owning your own business.

Choose a long-term goal. Design a financial plan to enable you to achieve your goal. Here are some points to consider:

- Do you have, or should you get, a part-time job now?
- Do you have any debts? If you do, how soon can they be paid off?
- What are your current monthly expenses?
- How much can you save each month? Calculate how much monthly savings might amount to in 1 year, in 5 years, and in 10 years.

Write a report on your long-term goal and how you intend to achieve it.

Monthly Budget Worksheet for _____

Average Monthly Net Income _____

Expenses

1. HOUSING and UTILITIES

   Rent or Mortgage _____

   Utilities _____

   Cable _____

   Insurance _____

   Taxes _____

   Repairs _____

   _____ _____

   TOTAL _____

   % of Net Income _____

2. FOOD and CLOTHING

   Groceries _____

   Eating Out _____

   Clothing _____

   Footwear _____

   _____ _____

   TOTAL _____

   % of Net Income _____

3. HEALTH and PERSONAL CARE

   Prescriptions _____

   Dental _____

   Other Medical _____

   Skin and Hair Care _____

   _____ _____

   TOTAL _____

   % of Net Income _____

4. TRANSPORTATION

   Public Transit _____

   Taxis _____

   Car Payments _____

   Car Licence _____

   Car Insurance _____

   Gas, Oil, and so on _____

   Repairs _____

   _____ _____

   TOTAL _____

   % of Net Income _____

5. RECREATION and EDUCATION

   Entertainment _____

   Hobbies _____

   Vacations _____

   Lessons _____

   School Expenses _____

   _____ _____

   TOTAL _____

   % of Net Income _____

6. SAVINGS

   Short Term _____

   Long Term _____

   _____ _____

   TOTAL _____

   % of Net Income _____

7. MISCELLANEOUS

   Gifts _____

   Donations _____

   _____ _____

   _____ _____

   TOTAL _____

   % of Net Income _____

Summary

Net Income _____

1. Housing and Utilities _____

2. Food and Clothing _____

3. Health and Personal Care _____

4. Transportation _____

5. Recreation and Education _____

6. Savings _____

7. Miscellaneous _____

Total Monthly Expenses _____

Discretionary Income _____

In Chapters 1 and 2, you studied investing money in Canada Savings Bonds, GICs, term deposits, and savings accounts. In Chapters 4 and 5, you learned how investing money in an RRSP at an early age could help make you more financially secure in the future.

When money is invested, you receive money for someone else's use of that money. This can be interest on the investment or profit from the sale of the investment. The money you receive is called the *return* on your investment. The *rate of return* is your earnings expressed as a percent of the initial investment. For example, suppose you invest $200 and it amounts to $220. The return is $20 and the rate of return is $\frac{20}{200} \times 100\% = 10\%$.

Your money is safe when it is invested in a financial institution that guarantees protection of all funds up to a certain amount. Major banks protect up to $60 000. Some credit unions protect up to $100 000.

Canada Savings Bonds are a safe investment because they are fully backed by the government of Canada. A disadvantage of CSBs and bank investments is that they earn interest at a lower rate than other types of investments. However, with these alternative investments, you may lose some or all of your original investment.

The following investigations introduce alternatives to those investment options studied earlier. The information you need to complete these investigations may be obtained through your bank, a financial planner, newspapers, books, and your parents, guardians, or friends. If you have Internet access, much of the information is available through the Investor Learning Centre of Canada. Ask your teacher for the web site address. The web sites of major mutual fund companies also contain much information. You could begin your search from our web site.
www.pearsoned.ca/onmath11

With a partner, and using the Toronto Stock Exchange (TSE) as a source of information, answer these questions.

1. What is a stock?
2. What is the stock market?
3. How do I buy a stock?
4. How is the price of a stock determined?
5. How could I make money on the stock market?
6. How could I lose money on the stock market?
7. What are the risks involved in investing in stocks?
8. What is a "blue chip" stock?
9. How do I minimize the risks of stock ownership?
10. What return should I expect when I invest money in the stock market?
11. What fees do I pay?

With a partner, select a financial planner or a financial institution that sells mutual funds. Obtain information to answer these questions.

1. What is a mutual fund?
2. Where do I purchase mutual funds?
3. What types of mutual funds are there?
4. How is the price of a particular mutual fund determined?
5. How could I make money buying mutual funds?
6. How could I lose money buying mutual funds?
7. What are the risks involved in investing in mutual funds?
8. How do I minimize the risk involved in buying mutual funds?
9. What return should I expect when I invest money in mutual funds?

Bonds

Earlier, you studied Canada Savings Bonds. However, the purchase of bonds in Canada is not limited to CSBs. Other levels of government and incorporated companies also issue bonds to be sold to the public.

With a partner, select a financial institution that sells bonds. Obtain information to answer these questions.

1. Where may bonds be purchased?

2. How do the bonds sold on the bond market differ?

3. How is the price of a specific bond determined?

4. How do I make money buying bonds?

5. Can I lose money buying bonds? Explain.

6. What are the risks involved in buying bonds?

7. What return should I expect when I invest money in bonds?

Real Estate

Money may be invested in real estate by purchasing property to rent or resell.

With a partner, contact a real estate agent or broker. With her or his help, answer these questions.

1. What determines the price of property?

2. What properties are best suited for investment?

3. How could I make money buying real estate?

4. How could I lose money buying real estate?

5. What are the risks involved in buying real estate as an investment?

6. How do I minimize the risks involved in investing in real estate?

7. What return should I expect when I invest money in real estate?

Summary

Write a brief summary that compares the investment options in *Investigations 1–4* from the point of view of risk versus return.

Review Exercises

MATHEMATICS TOOLKIT

Algebra Tools

> To calculate the regular payment on a loan:

$$R = \frac{(PV)(i)}{1 - (1 + i)^{-n}}$$

  R is the regular payment in dollars.
  PV is the present value of the loan in dollars.
  i is the interest rate per compounding period, as a decimal.
  n is the number of payments.

> To estimate the resale value of a vehicle:

$$V = P(1 - r)^n$$

  V is the resale value in dollars.
  P is the MSRP in dollars.
  r is the annual depreciation rate, as a decimal.
  n is the age of the car in years.

> To calculate the monthly depreciation payment on a car lease:

$$R = \frac{Di}{1 + i - (1 + i)^{-N}}$$

  R is the monthly depreciation payment in dollars.
  D is the depreciation in dollars.
  i is the interest rate per compounding period, as a decimal.
  N is 1 less than the number of payments.

7.1

1. Determine the monthly payment on a vehicle financed under each condition.

   a) $18 569 at 7.9% compounded monthly for 48 months

   b) $25 075 at 4.7% compounded monthly for 24 months

   c) $36 948 at 11.9% compounded monthly for 30 months

   d) $41 187 at 13.2% compounded monthly for 36 months

2. For each loan in exercise 1, determine the total interest paid.

3. Determine the resale value of each vehicle.

   a) a 4-year-old vehicle with an MSRP of $14 350 and an annual depreciation rate of 24%

b) a 2-year-old vehicle with an MSRP of $25 687 and an annual depreciation rate of 19%

c) a 3-year-old vehicle with an MSRP of $31 594 and an annual depreciation rate of 22%

d) a 1-year-old vehicle with an MSRP of $41 938 and an annual depreciation rate of 30%

4. Harold wants to trade in his 4-year-old truck. The truck had an MSRP of $29 465. Harold researched and found that the average annual depreciation for his truck is 22%. Estimate the resale value of Harold's truck.

5. Yoshiko trades in her 3-year-old car for a new SUV with an MSRP of $38 998. She negotiates a discount of $1250. Yoshiko receives a trade-in allowance of $18 550 for her old car on which she owes $4100. Since Yoshiko is buying at the end of the model year, she receives a manufacturer's rebate of $2500. She finances her vehicle through the dealership at 4.9% compounded monthly for 60 months. Yoshiko pays these additional costs: an $860 freight charge, a $100 tire/air tax, a $75 gas tax, an $85 administration fee, a $74 licence plate fee, a $20 gas fee, and a $54 finance fee. Create a deal review for Yoshiko's purchase.

6. A recent advertisement for a car offers 2 ways to purchase the car.
- Cash price of $18 548
- Finance price of $19 820 at 0.9% compounded monthly for 48 months, or 1.9% compounded monthly for 60 months, plus a $54 finance fee

These prices include the freight charge, tire/air tax, and administration fee. Additional costs include a $74 licence plate fee and a $20 gas fee.

Assume the cash price can be financed through a bank at 3.9% compounded monthly for 48 months.

a) What is the most economical way to purchase the car?

b) Why might a person not choose the most economical option?

7. Olaf purchases a used car with a list price of $17 543. He receives a trade-in allowance of $3550 for his old car, which is lien free. Olaf negotiates a discount of $1090. He pays these additional costs: an $85 administration fee, a $74 licence plate fee, and a $20 gas fee. Olaf finances the car through the dealership at 8.9% compounded monthly for 36 months. The finance fee is $54. Create a deal review for Olaf's purchase.

8. Hal buys a new car. He finances $23 785 at 8.9% compounded monthly for 48 months.

a) Determine Hal's monthly payment.

b) Determine the total interest paid.

9. Determine the resale value of a 3-year-old vehicle with an original MSRP of $28 960. Assume the annual depreciation rate for the vehicle is 23%.

7.2 **10.** Determine the residual value of each vehicle.

	MSRP	Residual factor
a)	$18 763	65%
b)	$24 762	43%
c)	$44 986	37%
d)	$33 051	32%

11. Determine the present value of each amount that is due one month from now, at the given annual interest rate compounded monthly.

	Amount	Annual interest rate
a)	$720.00	5.8%
b)	$384.70	2.9%
c)	$482.97	5.25%
d)	$297.48	11.4%

12. Determine the interest earned in one month.

	Principal	Annual interest rate
a)	$10 524	9.9%
b)	$9672	5.5%
c)	$18 596	4.9%
d)	$13 382	8.9%

13. Determine the base monthly payment on each vehicle. The interest is compounded monthly.

	Net capital cost	Residual value	Annual interest rate	Length of lease
a)	$25 853	$11 375.32	7.5%	36 months
b)	$18 974	$11 763.88	5.75%	24 months
c)	$34 577	$9982.88	6.9%	60 months
d)	$21 692	$8885.04	3.9%	48 months

14. Determine the residual value of a leased vehicle with an MSRP of $35 275 and a residual factor of 39%.

7.3 **15.** Determine the amount of fuel required to drive each distance at the given fuel consumption rating.

a) 15 000 km at 5.2 L/100 km   **b)** 52 675 km at 9.3 L/100 km

c) 35 900 km at 7.7 L/100 km   **d)** 156 974 km at 14.3 L/100 km

16. Determine the cost to drive each distance at the given fuel consumption rating and average cost of fuel.

a) 18 000 km at 7.3 L/100 km and $0.76/L

b) 4700 km at 10.8 L/100 km and $0.73/L

c) 24 690 km at 4.8 L/100 km and $0.85/L

d) 56 728 km at 14.1 L/100 km and $0.66/L

17. In the first 2 years that Madge owns her car, she drives 47 348 km. She does maintenance on her vehicle according to the distance maintenance schedule on page 345. The fuel consumption rating for her car is 6.7 L/100 km. Each year, Madge pays $785 for insurance and $74 for her vehicle licence plate. During those 2 years, she renewed her driver's licence at a cost of $50. The average cost of fuel during the 2 years is $0.81/L. Determine Madge's average monthly operating cost during the 2 years.

18. An SUV has a fuel consumption rating of 11.7 L/100 km. How much fuel will be needed to drive 5389 km?

19. Victor and a friend are planning a vacation trip to the west coast. Victor estimates that they will drive about 11 000 km. His car has a fuel consumption rating of 7.8 L/100 km. The average cost of fuel is $0.84/L. Estimate the fuel cost for Victor's trip.

20. In the first 3 years that Gill owns her sports car, she drives 63 350 km. Gill maintains her vehicle according to the distance maintenance schedule on page 345. The fuel consumption rating for her sports car is 8.3 L/100 km. Each year, Gill pays $1660 for insurance and $74 for her vehicle licence plate. During those 3 years, Gill renews her driver's licence at a cost of $50. The average cost of fuel is $0.79/L. Determine Gill's average monthly operating cost during the 3 years.

7.5 **21.** Alfred has a net monthly income of $1648. He spends $375 a month on transportation. What percent of his monthly income does Alfred spend on transportation?

22. Chantal's annual net income is $41 000. Use the guidelines on page 355 to determine the range of money Chantal should budget monthly in each category.

a) Housing and utilities   **b)** Food and clothing

c) Recreation and education   **d)** Health and personal care

23. Alice's annual net income is $25 800. Use the guidelines on page 355 to determine the range of money Alice should budget monthly in each category.

a) Housing and utilities   **b)** Savings

24. Josh's monthly budget is shown below.

Expense category	Amount ($)
Housing and utilities	980
Food and clothing	500
Health and personal care	140
Transportation	170
Recreation and education	280
Savings	600
Miscellaneous	130

a) What percent of his monthly income does Josh spend in each category?

b) Compare Josh's budget to the guidelines on page 355. In which categories is Josh overspending? underspending? spending within the guidelines?

c) Suggest why Josh is able to save more than the guideline limits.

1. **Knowledge/Understanding** A vehicle with a net capital cost of $32 584 and a residual value of $13 685.28 is leased for 36 months. Determine the base monthly payment when the interest is 5.9% compounded monthly.

2. **Communication**

   a) State two possible advantages and two disadvantages of buying a used car instead of a new car.

   b) State two possible advantages and two disadvantages of leasing a car instead of buying a car.

3. **Thinking/Inquiry/Problem Solving** Alexia has chosen a vehicle and is deciding whether to buy or lease it. The 4-wheel drive truck has an MSRP of $37 254 and a residual factor of 32%. Alexia negotiates a discount of $1475. She receives a trade-in allowance of $7800 for her old car on which she owes $2500. Alexia pays these additional costs: a $750 freight charge, a $100 tire/air tax, a $75 gas tax, an $85 administration fee, a $74 licence plate fee, and a $20 gas fee. Regardless of whether Alexia buys or leases the truck, the financing is 0.9% compounded monthly for 60 months. If she buys the truck, the finance fee is $54; if she leases the truck, the finance fee is $36. Should Alexia buy or lease the truck? Explain your recommendation.

4. **Application** Scott has a monthly net income of $1500. The table shows his monthly budget. Scott plans to enroll part-time at a local business school. He can continue working while he attends school at night and on weekends. The school costs will be approximately $200 per month for 2 years. Construct a new budget for Scott that allows him to attend school. Explain the decisions you made.

Expense category	Amount ($)
Housing and utilities	570
Food and clothing	240
Health and personal care	60
Transportation	390
Recreation and education	105
Savings	75
Miscellaneous	60

Careers

Background

Do you already know what job you would like when you enter the workforce? Many Canadians can no longer expect to spend their working life in the same job. Even if you are sure about the career you would like, you may have to reassess your plans at some stage in your life and, possibly, retrain. This project will help you explore career options and make informed decisions about them.

- What are your personal aptitudes?
- What are your interests and skills?
- Do you know which occupations seem to be in high demand?
- What do you hope to do after you complete high school? Will you attend a college, or a university, or enter the workplace directly?
- What lifestyle would you like 10 years from now? 15 years from now?

Explore

Self-assessment is the process of looking at yourself as you are now. When you know your personal strengths and challenges, you can set realistic goals and choose a career path suited to you. As you get older, your views may change. So, you should self-assess whenever you think of making career choices.

1. Obtain, then complete, a self-assessment activity. Your school may have software available, or a questionnaire you can complete. The Internet has many self-assessment sites, some provided by government agencies. You can start your search from our web site.

   www.pearsoned.ca/onmath11

Suggested Group Size: 1

Materials:

Self-Assessment software

Internet access

Career Information, Outlook and Education, and Wages and Educational Costs worksheets

A folder for project presentation (optional)

Curriculum Expectations

By the end of Explore, Research, Report, you will:

> Design an effective financial plan to facilitate the achievement of a long-term goal.

> Describe a decision involving a choice between alternatives.

> Collect relevant information related to the alternatives to be considered in making a decision.

> Summarize the advantages and disadvantages of the alternatives to a decision, using lists and organization charts.

> Compare alternatives by rating and ranking information, and by applying mathematical calculations and analysis, as appropriate, using technology.

> Explain the process used in making a decision and justify the conclusions reached.

> Identify the advantages and disadvantages of a variety of occupations of personal interest.

> Compare the expected income for a variety of occupations with the costs of education or training required.

> Analyse employment trends to identify some occupations that are in high demand, and identify the skills required and the education paths recommended to qualify for these occupations.

2. Consider the results of the self-assessment activity. If you have already identified potential careers, use the self-assessment results to see if your career choices match your personality and skills. If you are undecided, use the assessment to help identify at least two suitable careers. Use books or the Internet as sources of information.

3. Write a short report on your self-assessment activity. Describe your personality, skills, and interests. Describe at least two suitable careers. Include a bibliography of your sources and web sites. Save this report and the questionnaires for your career portfolio.

Research

You will create a career portfolio that documents your investigation of career opportunities.

To research the careers you have identified as suitable, you need access to current information. You may use the library, a Career Guidance Centre, or the Internet.

As you work through the following exercises, you will determine the demand for the careers you chose. If you find some, or all, of your career choices have a poor job outlook, you should reconsider your options.

Before you begin, obtain the worksheets *Career Information*, *Outlook and Education*, and *Wages and Educational Costs* from your teacher. Read through the worksheets and this section first. As you research, you may find information for several of the exercises, so you may want to work on all of them simultaneously. Keep all your responses. They will form part of your portfolio and can be part of your final project presentation.

Career Comparisons

1. List the careers that have a high demand for personnel and are suited to your interests, aptitudes, and abilities.

2. Complete the *Career Information* table for 4 careers.
   Here are some items to consider when you list the advantages and disadvantages of each career.
   - Regular hours/overtime/shift work/flex hours
   - Wages
   - Responsibilities
   - Safety and health issues

- Personal satisfaction
- Work environment
- Travel/relocation opportunities or requirements
- Physical demands and activities
- Opportunities for promotion
- Benefits such as health or dental plans

Analyse your findings. Rank each job on a scale of 1 to 4, where 1 is least desirable and 4 is most desirable. Write a brief explanation of your reasoning.

3. Complete the *Outlook and Education* table.
   - Determine whether each job outlook (that is, the possibility of future employment) is poor, fair, average, or good.
   - Describe any opportunities for advancement, or whether this job leads to more challenging jobs.
   - Provide details of education or training required, and how long it takes to get them.
   - Note any required high school courses for admittance to post-secondary education for this career.

Analyse your findings. Rank each job on a scale of 1 to 4, where 1 is least desirable and 4 is most desirable. Write a brief explanation of your reasoning.

4. Complete the *Wages and Educational Costs* table.
   - What salary can you expect to earn at the beginning of your career? What salary does the average worker earn?
   - Convert the average salary to an annual income.
   - Calculate the approximate total cost of education for each career. Include tuition, books, supplies, and equipment.
   - Calculate $\dfrac{\text{Education cost}}{\text{Average annual income}}$. This value will enable you to rate your job according to the number of years of gross earnings your education will cost you.

Analyse the education costs versus the salary benefits. What are your findings? Is the education for each career a good investment? Explain.

5. Examine your completed tables.

   a) Are there any careers you would eliminate based on your findings? If so, why?

   b) Which careers, if any, are you interested in pursuing?

   c) If you decide that a different career would hold more interest, complete tables for this new career.

   d) Which career is the most attractive to you? This will be called your chosen career.

   e) Which career would you consider as an alternative?

6. Use the information from the tables to prepare a report for your chosen career. This report should include:

   • A detailed description of the career

   • Your reasons for choosing this career

   • Educational requirements: include the name of the educational institution you would attend, and its costs.

   • Current and future employment opportunities

   • Starting position and salary

   • Advancement opportunities and future salary expectations

   • Advantages and disadvantages

   • The most appealing aspects of this career, and the least appealing aspects

7. Prepare a one-page report for your alternative career. This report should include:

   • A detailed description of the career

   • Educational requirements: include the name of the educational institution you would attend, and its costs.

   • Current and future employment opportunities

   • Starting position and salary

   • Advancement opportunities and future salary expectations

   • Advantages and disadvantages

Save the completed tables and your reports for your career portfolio.

Lifestyle Assessment

Your choice of career should provide the money for the lifestyle you want.

You will now research and describe the lifestyle you expect once you are established in your chosen career. You must visualize yourself established in your chosen career, in the future. This may be difficult. If so, discuss the exercises that follow with family members, friends, or older acquaintances.

8. Career information and personal information
Visualize yourself at an age when you are established in your career; perhaps after 6 years. Write a paragraph that gives a snapshot of you. Include information on:
- Your employer, your position, and annual salary
- Benefits, including pension, health, dental, and insurance plans
- Your family unit: will you live alone or with a partner? In a city or rural area?
- Children: do you hope to have children? How many?

9. Housing information
Describe the accommodation you hope to have.
- Use information from Chapter 6 to help with your housing choice.
- Estimate your costs. Include any costs for rent or mortgage, heating, water, telephone, electricity, cable or satellite television, and Internet connection.

10. Transportation expenses
Describe the transportation you hope to use.
- Use information from Chapter 7.
- Estimate your costs. Include costs for insurance, servicing, and repairs for a vehicle.

11. Other expenses
- Identify other costs you may encounter for items such as clothing, entertainment, home furnishings and electronics, food costs, and investments such as RRSPs.

12. Use your results from exercises 8 to 11, and the skills you learned in Chapter 7, to prepare a monthly budget.

Validating Your Choice

To gain an accurate understanding of the work itself and lifestyle provided by your chosen career, find someone who is working in that career. Interview her or him on how the career has developed and the lifestyle it provides. Use the interview and verbal skills you learned in other courses, and take notes.

Cover topics such as the prospects for advancement, the range of salaries, and the perks, or non-monetary benefits. Ask the person to identify any particular advantages or disadvantages to the job. Would he or she recommend the job? Why, or why not?

After the interview, transcribe your notes into a question and answer format.

Report

Prepare a portfolio that documents your work. Include all the questionnaires, tables, and reports you completed. Organize your work. Make a table of contents.

Write a conclusion that reflects what you discovered during the project. Points to consider:

- If you had a particular career in mind, are you still planning to pursue it?
- If you had several careers in mind, did you narrow your choices? Are you still undecided?
- Did you find a completely different career that you had not considered before? Why are you considering it now?
- If you did not have a career choice in mind before the project, do you have some options now? Explain.
- What is the most important thing you learned from this project?

Career Information

Career Option	Career Title	Advantages	Disadvantages	Rank
1				
2				
3				
4				

Outlook and Education

Career Option	Job Outlook	Opportunities for Advancement	Description of Post-Secondary Education or Training	Years of Education or Training Required	High School Course Requirements	Rank
1						
2						
3						
4						

Wages and Educational Costs

Career Option	Expected Starting Salary	Average Salary	Average Annual Income	Total Cost of Education or Training	Education Cost / Average Annual Income
1					
2					
3					
4					

1. Kalandra works in an electronics store. She receives a weekly salary of $300, plus a commission of 4.2% on her gross sales. For the last three weeks, her sales were $8400, $7500, and $15 350. How much did she earn altogether during the last 3 weeks?

2. The general term of a sequence is $t_n = 3n^2 - 2$. Determine each term.

   a) t_1 **b)** t_2 **c)** t_3 **d)** t_7

3. For the arithmetic sequence 2, 7, 12, 17..., determine:

   a) t_n **b)** t_{14} **c)** n when $t_n = 137$

4. Determine the sum of the series $5 + 3 + 1 - 1 - \ldots - 43$.

5. A principal of $2400 is invested at 8% per year. Determine the interest earned in 5 years if the interest is

   a) simple interest

   b) compound interest, compounded annually

   c) compound interest, compounded monthly

6. Without using technology, state the value of each expression.

   a) 2^8 **b)** 20^2 **c)** 10^6

   d) 300^3 **e)** 4^0 **f)** $3^2 \times 2^3$

7. Evaluate. Round to 2 decimal places where necessary.

   a) 5^4 **b)** $(-2)^2$ **c)** $\left(\frac{1}{3}\right)^{-1}$

   d) $2.5^{1.25}$ **e)** $2^0 \times 3^{0.23}$ **f)** $3.65^{-0.1}$

8. Determine the amount of each investment.

   a) $8000 at 5.3% compounded annually for 4 years

   b) $23 000 at 8.2% compounded quarterly for 7 years

9. Determine the present value of each amount.

   a) $1000 in 6 years at 3% compounded semi-annually

   b) $12 800 in 4 years at 7.8% compounded monthly

10. How long will it take a principal of $7000 to double if it is invested at 10% compounded semi-annually? Use a scientific calculator to calculate the time to the nearest year.

11. Determine the value of i.

   a) $1.8061 = (1 + i)^{20}$ **b)** $514.2648 = 350(1 + i)^5$

12. The population of a certain insect colony doubles every day. Suppose there are 5000 insects today.

a) Find a formula for the number of insects in n days.

b) Determine how many insects there will be in two weeks.

13. a) Copy and complete this table of values for $y = 3^x$.

x	0	1	2	3	4
y					

b) Graph $y = 3^x$.

c) Use the graph to estimate the value of x when $y = 30$.

d) What is the x-intercept? What is the y-intercept?

e) What is the domain? What is the range?

14. Carla bought a new truck. The truck decreases in value exponentially after it is purchased. Its value, V dollars, after n years given by the equation $V = 29\ 000(0.82)^n$.

a) What was the purchase price of the truck?

b) By what percent does the value decrease each year?

c) Estimate the value of the truck after 7 years.

15. Evaluate without using a calculator.

a) $16^{\frac{3}{4}}$ **b)** $8^{\frac{2}{3}}$ **c)** $25^{\frac{3}{2}}$

16. Solve each equation.

a) $5^{x+3} = 5^7$ **b)** $4^x = 64$ **c)** $10^{x+1} = 1000$

17. Consider the geometric sequence $3, -12, 48, -192, \ldots$

a) Find an expression for the general term, t_n.

b) Calculate the value of t_{10}.

18. Consider the geometric series $2 + 6 + 18 + \ldots + 39\ 366$.

a) Find an expression for the sum of the series, S_n.

b) Find S_8.

19. Determine whether each sequence is arithmetic, geometric or neither. For each arithmetic sequence, identify a and d. For each geometric sequence, identify a and r.

a) $96, 48, 24, 12, \ldots$ **b)** $96, 48, 24, 0, \ldots$

c) $48, 24, 0, -24, \ldots$ **d)** $1, 4, 9, 16, \ldots$

e) $0.1, 0.2, 0.3, 0.4, \ldots$ **f)** $3, -15, 75, -375, \ldots$

20. Calculate the amount of each annuity on the date of the last deposit.

a) A deposit of $8000 at the end of each year for 5 years at 6.5% compounded annually

b) A deposit of $250 at the end of each month for 3 years at 9% compounded monthly

21. Calculate the regular deposit at the end of each quarter for an annuity that amounts to $3500 in 5 years at 7.6% compounded quarterly.

22. Garnet has two options for investing money over a 10-year period.

A Invest $50 at the end of each month for 10 years at 6% compounded monthly.

B Wait 5 years, then invest $100 at the end of each month for 5 years at 6% compounded monthly.

a) How much does each option amount to at the end of 10 years?

b) Which option earns more money? Explain why.

23. Determine the present value of an annuity that pays $3050 at the end of every 6 months for 7 years at 9% compounded semi-annually.

24. Determine the regular payment at the end of each month of an annuity with present value $50 000 at 6.75% compounded monthly for 20 years.

25. Kayla inherited $25 000. She invests in an annuity that will pay her $500 per month for 4 years at 9% compounded monthly.

a) How much of her money must she invest in the annuity?

b) How much money will be left after she buys the annuity?

26. Eric borrowed $15 600 at 10.8% compounded monthly.

a) Determine the monthly payment for a 48-month loan.

b) Determine the monthly payment for a 60-month loan.

27. Both Sabrina and Sebastien borrow $10 000. The money is to be repaid in 36 monthly payments with interest compounded monthly. Sabrina has a poor credit rating and pays interest at 13.8%. Sebastien has an excellent rating and pays interest at 7.2%.

a) Calculate the monthly payments for Sebastien and Sabrina.

b) Calculate the total interest each person pays.

c) How much more interest does Sabrina pay than Sebastien?

28. Describe two important features of each item.

a) RRSP   **b)** GIC

c) debit card   **d)** amortization period

29. A mortgage of $150 000 is amortized over 25 years at 7.5% compounded semi-annually.

a) Determine the monthly interest rate that is equivalent to 7.5% compounded semi-annually.

b) Determine the monthly payment.

c) Determine the total interest paid.

30. A mortgage of $250 000 is amortized over 30 years at 8% compounded monthly. It has an initial term of 5 years.

a) Determine the monthly payment.

b) Calculate the principal owing on the mortgage after 5 years.

c) Calculate the principal owing on the mortgage after 20 years.

31. A mortgage of $175 000 at 9.4% compounded monthly with a 7-year term is amortized over 25 years. After 7 years the mortgage is re-negotiated at 7.7% compounded monthly. Determine the new monthly payment.

32. Ray and Jana are buying a condominium and can afford to make monthly payments of $1400. They can get a mortgage at 8.5% compounded semi-annually with a 30-year amortization period.

a) Determine the monthly interest rate equivalent to 8.5% compounded semi-annually.

b) Determine the amount, or present value, of the mortgage they can afford.

c) The mortgage is for 75% of the cost of the condominium. How much does the condominium cost?

33. A guideline for budgeting suggests that 27–33% of net income should be spent on housing, and 12–14% on transportation. Brianna has a net yearly income of $19 800. She spends $700 a month on her apartment, and an average of $155 a month on transportation. What percent of her monthly income does Brianna spend on housing and on transportation?

34. Sunita purchased a new car for which the delivery price was $18 699. She made a down payment of $3000 and received a manufacturer's rebate of $350. The financing fee was $75. The dealer offers 2.9% financing compounded monthly for 36 months.

a) How much does Sunita finance?

b) What is her monthly payment?

35. A car that has a MSRP of $18 540 and a net capital cost of $19 362 is leased for 48 months. At the end of the lease, the car has a residual value of 38% of the MSRP.

a) Calculate the residual value.

b) By how much did the car depreciate during the term of the lease?

Using a Calculator to Evaluate Financial Formulas

To evaluate many financial formulas, a calculator must be able to evaluate powers. It should also have bracket keys. These functions are included on scientific calculators, but are not usually present on basic calculators. The power key is labelled $\boxed{x^y}$, $\boxed{y^x}$, or $\boxed{\wedge}$. It should not be confused with the $\boxed{\text{Exp}}$ key that is used to enter numbers written in scientific notation. Determine the type of logic your calculator uses; check the User's Guide.

Most basic calculators evaluate the expression $1 + 2 \times 5$ and display 15, which is incorrect. This calculator performs the operations in the order in which they are entered. So, $1 + 2 = 3$, then $3 \times 5 = 15$.

To obtain the correct answer, 11, you must either enter the expression with the correct order of operations, $2 \times 5 + 1$, or use brackets, $1 + (2 \times 5)$.

Most scientific calculators use *algebraic precedence*. This means that powers are evaluated before multiplication and division, which will be performed before addition and subtraction. A scientific calculator that uses algebraic precedence evaluates the expression above by first performing the multiplication $2 \times 5 = 10$, then the addition, $1 + 10$, to display the correct answer, 11. However, brackets should be used when evaluating complex expressions, even when using a scientific calculator.

For example, consider this expression:

$$\frac{32.75 - 56.42}{0.326 \times 100.2}$$

The fraction bar acts as a grouping symbol, like brackets. To evaluate this expression, the numerator and denominator should be evaluated completely, then divided. So, brackets must be inserted around the numerator and the denominator to ensure the calculator evaluates correctly.

$$\frac{(32.75 - 56.42)}{(0.326 \times 100.2)}$$

Before starting any new calculation, always clear any numbers stored in the calculator that you do not need. On the TI-30X IIS, press $\boxed{\text{CLEAR}}$ to clear the display, and $\boxed{\text{2nd}}$ $\boxed{\text{MEMVAR}}$ to clear the memories. If your calculator is different, the User's Guide will explain how to do this.

Key in: $\boxed{(}$ 32.75 $\boxed{-}$ 56.42 $\boxed{)}$ $\boxed{\div}$ $\boxed{(}$ 0.326 $\boxed{\times}$ 100.2 $\boxed{)}$ $\boxed{\text{ENTER}\atop=}$ to display -0.724624371.

$$\frac{32.75 - 56.42}{0.326 \times 100.2} \doteq -0.725$$

Evaluate each expression.

1. $\dfrac{300[(1 + 0.025)^{12} - 1]}{0.025}$

2. $\dfrac{0.055 \times 2586}{(1 + 0.055)^{36} - 1}$

3. $\dfrac{350[(1 - (1 + 0.06)^{-8}]}{0.06}$

Using the Memory Feature on a Calculator

When you use a calculator to perform a series of calculations, you should not round intermediate values.

For example, consider this expression:

$$\frac{50\left[\left(1 + \frac{0.08}{12}\right)^{120} - 1\right]}{\frac{0.08}{12}}$$

The correct answer is approximately 9147.30. If you round $\frac{0.08}{12}$ and use 0.0067, you will obtain approximately 9167.74, which is 20.44 more than the correct answer. To avoid this problem, use the memory, or store and recall, feature of the calculator.

Most scientific calculators permits the user to store one or more values that can later be recalled and used. The TI-30X IIS has 5 memories. Check your calculator to discover how many memories it has. Listed below are the memory keys commonly found on calculators. Not all calculators have these keys. Consult your User's Guide for information about your calculator.

[Min], [MS] or [STO▸]: stores a value in the memory. If multiple values can be stored in the memory, a location variable (usually a letter or a number) must also be specified.

[MR] or [RCL]: recalls the stored memory value.

[MC] or [CLRVAR]: clears the value from the memory. On some calculators, [MR] and [MC] are 2 functions on one key: the value is recalled by

pressing the key once and cleared by pressing the key twice.

[M+]: adds the value displayed to the value stored in the memory. On some calculators, this key replaces the [Min] key.

[M-]: subtracts the value displayed from the value stored in the memory.

To evaluate the expression given:

1. Clear the memory of the calculator. Press [2nd] [MEMVAR] for CLRVAR.

2. Divide 0.08 by 12 then store the result in the memory. Key in: 0.08 [÷] 12 [STO▸] [ENTER =]

3. Enter the expression using the memory recall key for the stored value of $\frac{0.08}{12}$.

   Key in: 50 [(] [(] 1 [+] [2nd] [STO▸] [)] [^] 120 [-] 1 [)] [÷] [2nd] [STO▸] [ENTER =] [ENTER =] to display 9147.301758.

Evaluate each expression.

1. $\dfrac{250\,000 \times \frac{0.14}{12}}{\left(1 + \frac{0.14}{12}\right)^{360} - 1}$

2. $\dfrac{1\,000\,000 \times \frac{0.07}{12}}{\left(1 + \frac{0.07}{12}\right)^{300} - 1}$

3. $\dfrac{350\,000 \times \frac{0.1}{12}}{\left(1 + \frac{0.1}{12}\right)^{144} - 1}$

Using the TVM Solver on the TI-83

The TI-83 can carry out financial calculations. It has a feature called the TVM (Time Value of Money) Solver. When interest is paid on a principal, the amount changes with time. This change is the time value of money.

To access the TVM Solver on the TI-83, press [2nd] [x⁻¹] [ENTER]. The screen below appears.

To access the TVM Solver on the TI-83 Plus, press [APPS] **1 1**. The screen above appears.

The variables represent these quantities.

N: total number of payments

I%: annual interest rate as a percent

PV: present value

PMT: payment each period

FV: future value, or amount

P/Y: number of payments per year

C/Y: number of compounding periods per year

The calculator displays either positive or negative values for PV, PMT, and FV.

When you make a payment on a loan, PMT is negative. When you calculate the amount of an investment, the principal is the present value, and PV is negative.

When you input four of the first five quantities, the calculator can provide the fifth. The five examples that follow demonstrate this. In each case, to input the known quantities use the arrow and [ENTER] keys.

1. Solve for N (the number of payments):

   To buy a new car, you take out a loan of $10 593.30. You can afford a payment of $238 per month. The finance company charges an annual interest rate of 3.75% compounded monthly. How many payments must you make?

   Enter the values shown, below left, in the TVM Solver:

   The payment will be made at the end of a payment period, so the word END should be highlighted.

   To find the number of payments, move the cursor to the row for N, then press [ALPHA] [ENTER] to obtain the screen above right.

   You must make 48 payments. That is one payment each month for 4 years.

2. Solve for I (the interest rate):

A certain college program will cost $20 000. You can save $288.50 per month for the next 5 years and hope to have the money for the course saved at that time. What annual interest rate, compounded monthly, must you obtain?

Enter the values shown, below left, in the TVM Solver.

Move the cursor to the row for I%. Press ALPHA ENTER to obtain the screen above right.

You must obtain an annual interest rate of at least 5.75% compounded monthly.

3. Solve for PV (the present value):

You plan to buy a car. You can make payments of $525 per month. The interest rate is 6.25% compounded monthly. The finance company offers the loan for 2 years. How much can you afford to borrow?

Enter the values shown, below left, in the TVM Solver.

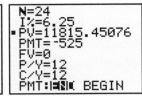

Move the cursor to the row for PV. Press ALPHA ENTER to obtain the screen above right.

You can afford to borrow $11 815.45.

4. Solve for PMT (the payment):

You want to buy a house. You have a 30-year mortgage of $100 000 at 8% compounded monthly. What is the monthly payment?

Enter the values shown, below left, in the TVM Solver.

Move the cursor to the row for PMT. Press ALPHA ENTER to obtain the screen above right.

The monthly payment is $733.76.

5. Solve for FV (the future value or amount):

You invest $6500. The interest rate is 8.25% compounded annually. What will the amount be in 7 years?

Enter the values shown, below left, in the TVM Solver.

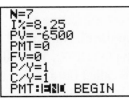 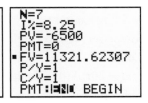

Move the cursor to the row for FV. Press ALPHA ENTER to obtain the screen above right.

The amount will be $11 321.62.

What Is a Spreadsheet?

A spreadsheet is a calculator that can perform many calculations at one time. The diagram below shows part of a typical spreadsheet document. A spreadsheet has small rectangles called cells, which are arranged in rows and columns. In most spreadsheets, the rows are numbered from top to bottom and the columns are named using letters, beginning with A on the left.

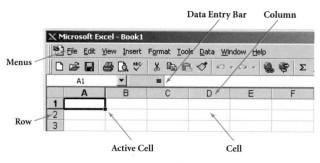

The diagram above was generated by Microsoft® Excel. Most spreadsheet packages have similar features. If you are using a different spreadsheet, refer to its User's Guide for specific commands.

A cell is named using the column name and row name. For example, in the diagram, the Cell label arrow is pointing to cell D2. The cell that is currently selected is called the active cell, which in this case is cell A1. There are three ways to move to a particular cell in a spreadsheet. You can move the mouse pointer to the cell then click the mouse button, or use the arrow keys to move to the cell, or use the **Go To** command from the **Edit** menu. The data entry bar shows the contents of the active cell; in this example, it is empty because there are no data in cell A1. Whatever you type is displayed in the data entry bar until you press the **Enter**, **Return**, or **Tab** key. It is then displayed in the cell.

Any cell can contain one of three things: numbers (including dates and times), letters (text), or formulas. When a cell contains a mixture of letters and numbers, the data in the cell are usually treated as text. A formula may contain numbers, cell names, and mathematical operations or **Functions** from the **Insert** menu. In most spreadsheet programs, a cell that contains a formula must begin with =, and will usually display the number that is the result of the mathematical calculation. To see the formula, click on the cell and the formula is displayed in the data entry bar. By changing a number in the spreadsheet, all the formulas that involve that cell will recalculate and display the new results. This allows the user to quickly explore how changing a value will affect a particular result.

Making Tables Using a Spreadsheet

A spreadsheet is an excellent tool for exploring mathematical patterns. This Utility illustrates some common ways to create tables. You will create a table for an investment that earns interest compounded annually. Work through this Utility at a computer with spreadsheet software.

1. **Start a new document.**
   - Start the spreadsheet application on your computer and begin a new spreadsheet document. If the program is already running, from the **File** menu, select **New**, then click **OK**.
   - Before you enter any data, save the document using a name, such as **Compound**. From the **File** menu, select **Save As**. Enter a new file name at the prompt, and click **Save**.

2. **Give the spreadsheet a title.**
   - If the cursor is not on cell A1, click on A1. Type **Exploring Compound Interest**, then press **Return**.

3. **List and enter the variables.**
   - Type **Interest Rate** in cell A3, **Initial Investment** in cell A4, **Years** in cell A6, and **Value** in cell B6.
   - In cell B3, enter 0.08 as the interest rate. In cell B4, enter 2000 as the initial investment.

4. **Enter the years in increments of 5 in column A.**
   - In cell A7, type 0. For each subsequent cell, we want to add 5 to the value of the cell that is directly above it.
   - In cell A8, type the formula **=A7+5**, then press **Return**.

5. **Copy a formula to other cells.**
   - Select the cell with the formula and the cells to which you wish to copy it. Then, use the Fill command.

   - Use the mouse to select cells A8 to A21. From the **Edit** menu, select **Fill** and **Down**. Select cell A9. The formula should be **=A8+5**.

When a cell location is specified in this way, it is called a relative reference since it describes the location of the cell in relation to the active cell. In this example, the specified cell is always one cell above the active cell. If you change the value of cell A7, the value of each cell below it will also change. To change the increment, edit the formula in cell A8, then repeat the Fill command.

6. Enter a formula to calculate the value of the investment.

- Select B7, then enter
  =$B$4*(1+$B$3)^A7

When a dollar sign is placed before the column or row name, it is called an absolute reference. An absolute reference describes a specific cell by its cell name, and it will remain the same when it is copied to other cells.

- Select cells B7 to B21, then use the Fill Down command to copy this formula. Select cell B8. The formula should be **=$B$4*(1+$B$3)^A8**, since A7 was the only relative reference used in the initial formula.

7. Investigate. Try changing the values in cells B3 or B4. The value of the investment will quickly be recalculated. You can use this spreadsheet to see how changing the interest rate or initial investment changes the value of the investment over time.

Formatting a Spreadsheet

Here are some basic formatting commands to change the look of a spreadsheet.

1. If a cell is not wide enough to hold a particular number, that cell will display #####. There are 2 ways to change the width of a column.
   - A column can be made wider, or narrower, by dragging on a side line that represents the left or right side of the column label at the top of the spreadsheet.
   - From the **Format** menu, select **Column**, then **Width**. Enter a numerical value for the width of the column.

   The height of a row can be changed similarly, either by dragging on the top or bottom line, or by using the Format menu. Changing the height or width of one cell will change all the cells in that row or column.

2. To insert a row, highlight the row above which you wish to insert a row by clicking on the row label. From the **Insert** menu, select **Row**. Any formulas that involve the contents of a cell that has been shifted will be adjusted automatically. To delete a row, highlight the row, then from the **Edit** menu, select **Delete**. If a cell that is used in a formula is deleted, the affected cell will display an error message. To undo a command, select **Undo** in the **Edit** menu.

A column can be inserted to the left of a selected column, or deleted, using a similar approach.

3. To format a cell(s), highlight the cell(s) you wish to format. To highlight the whole spreadsheet, click the rectangle that is to the left of column label A. From the **Format** menu, select **Cells**. By clicking on the tabs at the top of the window you can change: the way numbers are displayed, the horizontal and vertical alignment of the data in the cell, the size, colour and style of font, the border surrounding the cell, and the colour of the cell.

4. Headings and text may be too wide to fit in a cell. To make these fit, highlight the cell(s). From the **Format** menu, select **Cells**. Click the **Alignment** tab, then click so the box in front of **Wrap Text** is checked. Press **OK**. The text will be wrapped within the cell, as in a word processing program.

5. Numbers in cells can be formatted. For example, to format a number in a cell as currency, highlight the number. From the **Format** menu, select **Cells**. Click the **Number** tab and highlight **Currency**. Press **OK**.

6. Try these at the computer.
- Start a new spreadsheet.
- Type "Formatting a Spreadsheet" in cell A1, "by" in cell B1, your name in cell C1, and 125.34 in cell A3.
- Highlight cells A1 to C1. Wrap the text in these cells. Adjust the height and width of the cells so the entry in cell A1 is displayed on 2 lines.
- Format cell A3 to show a percent to 3 decimal places.
- Investigate the other ways of formatting the number in cell A3. Enter your own text in cell B1, then adjust the cell height and width until it looks pleasing to you.

Formatting numbers

Look at the following ways of writing the same number.

$$\frac{1}{4} \qquad 0.250 \qquad 25\% \qquad \$0.25$$

A number that is typed in a spreadsheet cell can be displayed in all of the ways above except the first. A fraction can only appear with the numerator and denominator side by side separated by a slash, rather than one above the other. In any spreadsheet program, if you enter **=1/4**, the spreadsheet will divide 1 by 4 and display the result as a decimal.

1. Start a new spreadsheet document.

a) In cells A1 to E1, type each representation of $\frac{1}{4}$ shown above. What does the program display? In Microsoft Excel, click on the cell, go to the **Format** menu, choose **Cells** and **Number**. Choose the method of writing the number that matches what you want.

b) In cells A2 to E2, enter $3\frac{3}{4}$ using the same format as the the cells above. For cell C2, think carefully about how to write this number as a percent.

2. a) In cell B3, enter a formula to subtract the number in cell B1 from the number in cell B2. Does the format of the answer match that of the cells referenced in the formula? If not, format cell B3 so that it does match.

b) Copy the formula into cells C3 to E3. What do you notice about the results? What must you remember when copying formulas from or into formatted cells? Format cells C3 to E3 to match the cells above.

c) What happens if you try to copy the formula from B3 into cell A3? Why does this happen?

ANSWERS

Chapter 1 Linear Growth

Necessary Skills

1 Review: Percent
Exercises, page 6

1. a) 0.24 **b)** 0.06 **c)** 0.50 **d)** 0.12
e) 0.95 **f)** 0.01 **g)** 0.25 **h)** 1.00

2. a) 0.046 **b)** 0.142 **c)** 0.008 **d)** 0.0725
e) 0.1675 **f)** 0.641 **g)** 0.0025 **h)** 1.05

3. a) 0.0625 **b)** 0.151 25 **c)** 0.005 **d)** 0.0275
e) 0.246 25 **f)** 1.105 **g)** 0.053 75 **h)** 1.0425

4. a) 85% **b)** 30% **c)** 7% **d)** 3.5%
e) 130% **f)** 12.5% **g)** 15% **h)** 800%

5. a) $1.96 **b)** $50.75 **c)** $137.50 **d)** $4.44
e) $91.68 **f)** $3.44 **g)** $2035.00 **h)** $27.25

2 Review: Solving Linear Equations
Exercises, page 8

1. a) $x = 2$ **b)** $x = 3$ **c)** $x = 8$ **d)** $y = -8$
e) $m = -7$ **f)** $n = -3$ **g)** $x = 8$ **h)** $x = 10$
i) $r = 5$ **j)** $m = -5$ **k)** $x = 6$ **l)** $x = -5$

2. a) $x = 7$ **b)** $b = 3$ **c)** $y = -4$
d) $a = 5$ **e)** $m = 3$ **f)** $p = 9$
g) $x = 12$ **h)** $m = 32$ **i)** $x = 35$

3. a) $x = \frac{9}{4}$ **b)** $n = \frac{1}{5}$ **c)** $x = \frac{11}{2}$
d) $x = 2$ **e)** $x = 12$ **f)** $n = 1.6$
g) $x = \frac{5}{8}$ **h)** $x = -\frac{4}{5}$ **i)** $x = 0.6$

3 New: Evaluating a Formula
Exercises, page 9

1. a) $p = 42.2$ **b)** $A = 10.03$
c) $I = 108.28$ **d)** $P = 259$
e) $V \doteq 768.10$ **f)** $C \doteq 109.96$
g) $A \doteq 284.38$

2. a) $S = 3828$ **b)** $A = 32.96$
c) $r \doteq 0.02$ **d)** $P = 656.94$
e) $V \doteq 146.11$ **f)** $V \doteq 179.59$

1.1 Exercises, page 12

1. a) $20.00 **b)** $80.00 **c)** $72.00 **d)** $82.50
e) $135.00 **f)** $206.25 **g)** $219.00 **h)** $158.10

2. $148.00

3. $85.80

4. $62.48

5. $46.13

6. $193.50

7. $238.50

8. a) $500.00

b)

Hours worked	Earnings ($)
0	0
10	125.00
20	250.00
30	375.00
40	500.00

c)

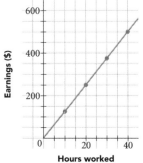

Jeong's Earnings

d) Yes. Jeong's earnings show linear growth because her earnings increase by a constant amount.

9. $7125.00

10. $950.00

11. $5520.00

12. a)

Sales ($)	Commission ($)	Weekly earnings ($)
0	0	500
4 000	120	620
8 000	240	740
12 000	360	860
16 000	480	980
20 000	600	1100

b)

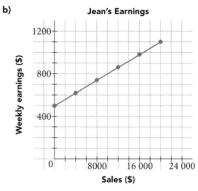

Jean's Earnings

(graph: x-axis "Sales ($)" 0 to 24 000; y-axis "Weekly earnings ($)" 0 to 1200)

c) Yes. Jean's earnings are an example of linear growth because his earnings increase by a constant amount.

13. $222.90

14. $32 760 for 33 weeks

15. a) Time-and-a-half means that you receive 1.5 times your regular salary for the time you work overtime.

b) $984.38

c)

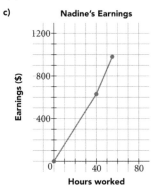

Nadine's Earnings

(graph: x-axis "Hours worked" 0 to 80; y-axis "Earnings ($)" 0 to 1200)

d) The graph of Nadine's earnings shows 2 different linear growth rates. From 0 to 40 hours, the constant growth rate is $15.75/h. After 40 hours, the constant growth rate is $23.63/h (time-and-a-half).

16. $848.80

17. $139.83

18. $857.00

1.2 Exercises, page 17

1. a) e, f, g   **b)** i, k, m   **c)** ae, af, ag
  d) 11111, 111111, 1111111
  e) 12345, 123456, 1234567
  f) 151, 161, 171
  g) →, ↘, ↓   **h)** ▼, ▽, ◀

2. a) 5, 6, 7   **b)** 9, 11, 13
  c) 25, 30, 35   **d)** 50, 60, 70
  e) 15, 18, 21   **f)** 20, 24, 28
  g) 6, 5, 4   **h)** 1.5, 1, 0.5
  i) 24, 20, 16   **j)** 12, 10, 8
  k) 18, 15, 12   **l)** 19, 14, 9

3. a) 16, 32, 64   **b)** 81, 243, 729
  c) 80, 160, 320   **d)** 10 000, 100 000, 1 000 000
  e) 162, 486, 1458   **f)** 625, 3125, 15 625
  g) 256, 1024, 4096   **h)** 4, 2, 1
  i) $1, \frac{1}{3}, \frac{1}{9}$ **j)** $1, -\frac{1}{3}, \frac{1}{9}$

4. a) 10, 12, 14   The difference between consecutive terms is 2.
  b) 32, 64, 128   Multiply a term by 2 to get the next term.
  c) 12, 17, 23   The difference between terms increases by 1 starting with a difference of 1, then 2, then 3, and so on.
  OR 13, 21, 34   Add the two previous terms to get the next term.
  d) 21, 31, 43   The difference between terms increases by multiples of 2 starting with a difference of 2, then 4, then 6, and so on.
  e) 48, 96, 192   Multiply a term by 2 to get the next term.
  f) 55, 44, 33   The difference between consecutive terms is −11.
  g) $\frac{1}{6}, \frac{1}{7}, \frac{1}{8}$ The numerator remains as 1 while the denominator increases by 1.
  h) 0.555 55, 0.666 666, 0.777 777 7
       For the nth term, repeat n for n digits after the decimal point.

5. a) 13, 15, 17   The difference between consecutive terms is 2.
  b) 25, 36, 49   Square n for the nth term.
  c) $\frac{5}{6}, \frac{6}{7}, \frac{7}{8}$ Add 1 to both the numerator and the denominator.
  d) $\frac{9}{10}, \frac{11}{12}, \frac{13}{14}$ Add 2 to both the numerator and the denominator.
  e) 125, 216, 343   Cube n for the nth term.
  f) 90, 85, 79   The difference between terms decreases by 1 starting with a difference of −1, then −2, then −3, and so on.
  g) $\frac{1}{32}, \frac{1}{64}, \frac{1}{128}$ Multiply a term by $\frac{1}{2}$ to get the next term.
  h) $\frac{35}{36}, \frac{48}{49}, \frac{63}{64}$ The numerator's difference increases by 2 starting with a difference of 5, then 7, then 9, and so on. The denominator is the sequence of square numbers starting at 2^2.

6. a) 24, 39, 34   Add 5 to a term to get the next term.
  b) 9, 5, 1   Subtract 4 from a term to get the next term.
  c) 20 000, 200 000, 2 000 000
       Multiply a term by 10 to get the next term.
  d) 2500, 12 500, 62 500
       Multiply a term by 5 to get the next term.
  e) 1, 4, 7   Add 3 to a term to get the next term.
  f) 1, −1, 1   Multiply a term by −1 to get the next term.
  g) $\frac{9}{32}, \frac{11}{64}, \frac{13}{128}$ For each term, add 2 to the numerator and multiply the denominator by 2 to get the next term.
  h) 48, −96, 192   Multiply a term by −2 to get the next term.

7. Answers may vary.

1, 2, 3, 4, …   Add 1 to the term to get the next term.

1, 2, 4, 8, …   Multiply a term by 2 to get the next term.

1, 2, 4, 7, …   The difference between terms increases by 1 starting with a difference of 1, then 2, then 3, and so on.

1, 2, 3, 5, …   Add the two previous terms to get the next term.

8. a) 1, 2, 3, 4   **b)** 2, 3, 4, 5

c) 1, 4, 9, 16   **d)** −3, −6, −9, −12

e) 3, 5, 7, 9   **f)** −2, −1, 0, 1

g) 11, 10, 9, 8   **h)** $1, \frac{1}{2}, \frac{1}{3}, \frac{1}{4}$

9. a) 3, 4, 5, 6   **b)** 2, 5, 10, 17

c) −5, −10, −15, −20   **d)** 2, 5, 8, 11

e) 1, 8, 27, 64   **f)** 1, 6, 15, 28

g) 2, 12, 36, 80   **h)** −1, 1, 5, 11

10. a) 0, 2, 6, 12, 20   **b)** $\frac{1}{2}, \frac{2}{3}, \frac{3}{4}, \frac{4}{5}, \frac{5}{6}$

c) 7, 6, 5, 4, 3   **d)** $\frac{1}{2}, 1, \frac{3}{2}, 2, \frac{5}{2}$

e) 6, 14, 24, 36, 50   **f)** $\frac{1}{2}, \frac{4}{3}, \frac{9}{4}, \frac{16}{5}, \frac{25}{6}$

g) 5, 8, 11, 14, 17   **h)** 1, 3, 6, 10, 15

11. Answers may vary.

$t_n = 2n + 1$

3, 5, 7, 9   Add 2 to a term to get the next term.

12. a) −20   **b)** 43   **c)** 300   **d)** −68

e) 1001   **f)** $\frac{1}{5}$ **g)** 81   **h)** 990

13. a) 13, 27   **b)** 50, 401   **c)** −36, −200

d) −4, −30   **e)** $-\frac{9}{2}, -\frac{39}{2}$ **f)** 110, 600

g) 5.3, 20.5   **h)** 10 000 000, 1 000 000 000 000

14. a) $t_n = n^2$ **b)** $t_n = 10^n$ **c)** $t_n = \sqrt{n}$ **d)** $t_n = \frac{1}{n}$

15. a) 1   The numbers 1, 2, 3 repeat.

b) 7   There is a 2 between consecutive odd numbers.

c) 21   After the first 2 terms, add the previous two terms to get the next term.

d) 48   After the first 2 terms, add all the previous terms to get the next term.

16. a) 23   The difference between terms increases by 1 starting with a difference of 1, then 2, then 3, and so on.

b) 34   After the first 2 terms, add the previous two terms to get the next term.

c) 80   After the first 2 terms, add all the previous terms to get the next term.

d) 11   Add 1, then add 2. Repeat this pattern to get the next terms.

1.3 Exercises, page 24

1. a) Arithmetic, $d = 2$ **b)** Not arithmetic

c) Arithmetic, $d = -3$ **d)** Arithmetic, $d = 0.5$

e) Not arithmetic   **f)** Not arithmetic

g) Arithmetic, $d = 6$ **h)** Arithmetic, $d = 3$

2. a) 3; 24, 27, 30   **b)** −8; 13, 5, −3

3. a) 2; 10, 12, 14   **b)** −4; 20, 16, 12

c) −11; 11, 0, −11   **d)** 7; 37, 44, 51

e) −5; −13, −18, −23   **f)** 6; 14, 20, 26

g) −5; 30, 25, 20   **h)** −25; −25, −50, −75

i) 12; 60, 72, 84   **j)** −9; −28, −37, −46

4. a) 4, 9, 14, 19   **b)** −2, 6, 14, 22

c) 38, 35, 32, 29   **d)** 3.4, 5.9, 8.4, 10.9

e) 2, 3.1, 4.2, 5.3   **f)** −12, −17, −22, −27

g) −8, −4, 0, 4   **h)** 101, 76, 51, 26

i) 5.6, 5.8, 6.0, 6.2

5. a) $t_n = 5n - 1$ **b)** $t_n = 8n - 10$

c) $t_n = -3n + 41$ **d)** $t_n = 2.5n + 0.9$

e) $t_n = 1.1n + 0.9$ **f)** $t_n = -5n - 7$

g) $t_n = 4n - 12$ **h)** $t_n = -25n + 126$

i) $t_n = 0.2n + 5.4$

6. a) 1, 4, 7; $d = 3$ **b)** 6, 12, 18; $d = 6$

c) 4, 3, 2; $d = -1$ **d)** 0, 3, 8; not arithmetic

e) 5, 3, 1; $d = -2$ **f)** $\frac{1}{2}, 1, \frac{3}{2}; d = \frac{1}{2}$

g) 2, 4, 8; not arithmetic   **h)** 0.9, 1.3, 1.7; $d = 0.4$

7. a) Yes. The sequence is arithmetic since the sequence has a common difference of 5.

b) $135

8. a) 12, 16, 20, 24, 28   **b)** −1, 3, 7, 11, 15

c) −14, −11, −8, −5, −2   **d)** $\frac{2}{3}, \frac{1}{2}, \frac{1}{3}, \frac{1}{6}, 0$

e) −19, −11, −3, 5, 13   **f)** 0.5, 1.7, 2.9, 4.1, 5.3

g) −5, 10, 25, 40, 55   **h)** −29, −7, 15, 37, 59

9. a) $t_n = 2n + 2$ **b)** $t_n = -n + 11$

c) $t_n = 0.5n + 1.6$ **d)** $t_n = 5n - 22$

e) $t_n = -8n + 38$ **f)** $t_n = 10n - 19$

g) $t_n = 2.8n - 0.2$ **h)** $t_n = 2n - 1$

10. a) 57   **b)** 131   **c)** 49   **d)** 298

e) 152.3   **f)** 40   **g)** −66   **h)** 48

i) 5.5   **j)** −350

11. $5.00

12. $140.00

13. 34th term

14. 106th term

15. 6

16. a) 191   **b)** 312   **c)** 50   **d)** 90

e) 93   **f)** 46   **g)** 58   **h)** 22

i) 42   **j)** 53

17. $a = 7, \ d = 3$

1.4 Exercises, page 31

1. a) 15   **b)** 42   **c)** 80

d) 80   **e)** 20   **f)** 5

2. a) 220   **b)** 365   **c)** 510

d) 340   **e)** −25   **f)** −150

3. a) 285   **b)** 495   **c)** 1200   **d)** 1425

e) 0   **f)** −450   **g)** 240   **h)** 675

4. 145

5. 4960

6. 5050

7. 2550

8. a) 121   **b)** 1280

9. a) −40   **b)** −400

10. a) 1060   **b)** 975
     c) 1912.5   **d)** −198
     e) 1936   **f)** 0
     g) 1000   **h)** 248

11. a) 31   **b)** 1457

12. a) 24   **b)** 1068

13. 62 750

14. 19

15. 500 500

16. 900

17. $S_n = \frac{n(n+1)}{2}$; 20 100

18. a) $S_n = n^2$ **b)** 20

19. a) 174   **b)** 2270

Self-Check 1.1–1.4, page 33

1. $170.63

2. a) 20, 27, 35   **b)** $-\frac{1}{2}, \frac{1}{4}, -\frac{1}{8}$
    c) 80, 160, 320   **d)** 25, 36, 49

3. a) 2, 5, 8, 11   **b)** 2, 9, 28, 65
    c) −3, −6, −9, −12   **d)** 3, 9, 27, 81

4. To determine if a sequence is arithmetic, calculate the differences between consecutive terms. If the differences are common, then the sequence is arithmetic.

5. a) Not arithmetic   **b)** Not arithmetic
    c) Arithmetic; $d = -2$ **d)** Arithmetic; $d = \frac{1}{4}$

6. −5, 2, 9, 16

7. 9, 15, 21, 27, 33

8. 75

9. a) $t_n = 4n + 1$ **b)** $S_n = 2n^2 + 3n$
    c) 324

10. a) −124   **b)** −1593

11. 7475

12. 13 361

13. 4 501 500

1.5 Exercises, page 38

1. a) $15.00   **b)** $18.00   **c)** $24.00
    d) $48.00   **e)** $4.00

2. a) $11.25   **b)** $10.94   **c)** $81.90
    d) $20.01   **e)** $1.29

3. a) $93.50   **b)** $81.97   **c)** $312.50
    d) $55.92   **e)** $13.09   **f)** $1470.00
    g) $38.91   **h)** $22 395.83

4. $98.63

5. $46.67

6. $53.12

7. $35.85

8. $513.44

9. a)

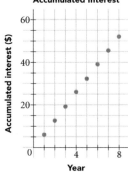

b) Linear growth

10. Yes. Since $I = Prt$, $2t$ will double the interest earned.

11. Yes. Since $I = Prt$, $2r$ will double the interest earned.

12. $158.49

13. $528.00

14.

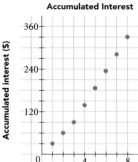

1.6 Exercises, page 41

1. a) $t = 4$ **b)** $r = 10$ **c)** $r = 0.5$
    d) $t = 8$ **e)** $P = 1250$ **f)** $r = 0.08$

2. a) $200.00   **b)** $1500.00
    c) $525.00   **d)** $3000.00

3. a) 2%   **b)** 3.04%
    c) 1.75%   **d)** 2%

4. a) 2 years   **b)** 2 years
    c) 1.5 years   **d)** 4 years

5. a) 3 years   **b)** $1200.00
    c) 7%   **d)** $144.00
    e) $800.00   **f)** 3 years
    g) 6%   **h)** 12 years
    i) $2000.00   **j)** 5%

6. a) Approximately 3.5 years **b)** $1449.75
  c) 5.25% **d)** $170.16
  e) $5024.93 **f)** 6.5 years
  g) 8.4% **h)** Approximately 6 months
  i) $875.09 **j)** 7.6%

7. a) $P = \dfrac{I}{rt}$, $r = \dfrac{I}{Pt}$, $t = \dfrac{I}{Pr}$
  b) Approximately 3.5 years, $1449.75, 5.25%
  c) The advantage of using the rearranged formulas for
   $I = Prt$ is that the unknown variable is isolated. The
   disadvantage is that four formulas must be remembered.

8. $8000

9. a) 1.75% **b)** 1.5 years **c)** $3250

10. 4%

11. $742.04

12. $682.67

13. 1.2 years

14. 6 years

15. Approximately 4.5%

16. Approximately 50.21%

17. Approximately 90 days

18. $5555.56

19. $1744.56

20. Approximately 3.05%

Self-Check 1.5, 1.6, page 45

1. a) $30 **b)** Approximately 6 months
  c) Approximately 3% **d)** $6.15
  e) $998.00 **f)** Approximately 30 days
  g) Approximately 4% **h)** $247.97

2. $50

3. $560

4. $4.01

5. $500

6. Approximately 5.65%

7. Approximately 180 days

8. Yes. If t is doubled, then Prt becomes $Pr(2t) = 2Prt = 2I$.

1.7 Project, page 47

1. March: $5.26, April: $5.42, May: $5.86, June: $7.21, July:
$7.77, August: $8.14, September: $7.97, October: $8.78,
November: $9.18, December: $9.75; Yearly total: $78.73

2. $98.00

3. $177.98

4. $244.83

Chapter 1 Review Exercises, page 50

1. $137.38

2. a) $460.00

b)

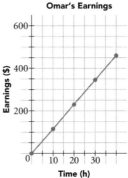

Omar's Earnings

c) Yes. Omar's earnings illustrate linear growth because
there is a constant increase in his earnings.

3. $3482.71

4. 4, 7, 12, 19

5. 27, 39, 53, 69

6. a) 1, 7, 17 **b)** $2, \dfrac{3}{4}, \dfrac{4}{9}$
  c) 8, 16, 24 **d)** 4, 7, 10

7. a) 4, 15 **b)** 143, 1295
  c) 4912, 215 **d)** $-24, -600$

8. a) Arithmetic; 2 **b)** Not arithmetic
  c) Arithmetic; -5 **d)** Not arithmetic
  e) Not arithmetic **f)** Arithmetic; $\dfrac{3}{2}$

9. a) 4, 13, 22, 31, 40 **b)** $1, -3, -7, -11, -15$
  c) 21, 16, 11, 6, 1 **d)** 0, 0.75, 1.5, 2.25, 3.0

10. a) $t_n = 3n + 1$; $t_{15} = 46$
  b) $t_n = -n + 16$; $t_{15} = 1$
  c) $t_n = 0.5n + 1.6$; $t_{15} = 9.1$
  d) $t_n = 7n - 56$; $t_{15} = 49$
  e) $t_n = \dfrac{3}{4}n - \dfrac{1}{2}$; $t_{15} = \dfrac{43}{4}$
  f) $t_n = -8n + 78$; $t_{15} = -42$

11. a) 163 **b)** 149 **c)** 96
  d) 89 **e)** 111 **f)** 46

12. a) 416 **b)** 117 **c)** 145.6
  d) -130 **e)** -468 **f)** 0

13. a) $t_n = 8n - 5$ **b)** $S_n = 4n^2 - n$ **c)** 1914

14. 24 hours

15. 125 250

16. 31 375

17. 160 400

18. $61.03

19. a) $21, $42, $63, $84, $105

b) Arithmetic

c)

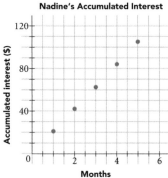

Nadine's Accumulated Interest

d) Linear growth. The graph shows linear growth because there is a constant increase in the accumulated interest.

20. $562.50

21. $7.14

22. $1800.00

23. 7 years

24. Approximately 1.78%

Chapter 1 Self-Test, page 53

1. a) $3406.40

b)

Janet's Monthly Earnings

2. $962.94

3. −8, −5, −2, 1

4. a) $t_n = 6n - 3$ **b)** $S_n = 3n^2$

c) 1200   **d)** 687

5. 157

6. 2662

7. 250

8. $S_n = 850n$, where n is the number of weeks worked

9. $41.42

10. $1850.02

11. Approximately 5.25%

12. Approximately 180 days

13. Yes. If the term is doubled, the value of t in the equation $I = Prt$ doubles, which doubles the interest.

Chapter 2 Compound Interest

Necessary Skills

1 Review: Evaluating Powers

Exercises, page 56

1. a) 16   **b)** 125   **c)** 36   **d)** 27   **e)** 64
  f) 16   **g)** 81   **h)** 128   **i)** 49   **j)** 243
  k) 64   **l)** 121   **m)** 8   **n)** 100   **o)** 1024

2. a) 100 000   **b)** 100 000 000
  c) 10 000   **d)** 1 000 000
  e) 1 000 000 000   **f)** 1000
  g) 10 000 000   **h)** 10 000 000 000
  i) 1 000 000 000 000

3. a) 216   **b)** 256   **c)** 625
  d) 64   **e)** 256   **f)** 400
  g) 8000   **h)** 900   **i)** 2500
  j) 6400   **k)** 64 000   **l)** 3 200 000

4. a) 625   **b)** 2025   **c)** 1225
  d) 5625   **e)** 4225   **f)** 3025

5. a) The answer ends in 25 and begins with the product of the first digit in the number to be squared and the next consecutive integer.

  b) i) 225   **ii)** 7225   **iii)** 11 025

2 Review: Exponent Laws for Positive Integral Exponents

Exercises, page 60

1. a) 2^5 **b)** 3^5 **c)** $(-2)^6$
  d) 4^7 **e)** $(1.02)^7$ **f)** $(-3)^8$
  g) $(\frac{1}{2})^8$ **h)** $(\frac{1}{3})^6$ **i)** $(\frac{2}{5})^7$

2. a) 2^2 **b)** 3^2 **c)** $(-2)^4$
  d) 4^3 **e)** $(-10)^4$ **f)** $(-3)^5$
  g) 5^5 **h)** $(-3)^3$ **i)** 6^4

3. a) c^8 **b)** a^5 **c)** e^{11}
  d) d^5 **e)** m^7 **f)** $(\frac{a}{2})^7$

4. a) c^2 **b)** a **c)** e
  d) d^3 **e)** m **f)** $(-x)^5$

5. a) 12^{15} **b)** 20^3 **c)** $(-7)^{14}$
  d) $(-8)^2$ **e)** $(1.09)^{26}$ **f)** 16

6. a) x^{70} **b)** x^2 **c)** $(-a)^{11}$
  d) $(-a)^3$ **e)** m^8 **f)** r^2

7. a) 2^6 **b)** 3^{24} **c)** 10^8
  d) 10^8 **e)** $(-2)^{12}$ **f)** $(-5)^{12}$

8. a) x^6 **b)** a^{20} **c)** $(-x)^6$
  d) $(-a)^{20}$ **e)** m^9 **f)** $(-n)^4$

2.1 Exercises, page 63

1. a) $5.00   **b)** $2.00   **c)** $1.50   **d)** $25.00

2. a) $6.00   **b)** $2.75   **c)** $8.80   **d)** $6.11
  e) $11.45   **f)** $73.15

3. a) $16.32   **b)** $8.08   **c)** $10.13   **d)** $142.45

4. With simple interest, the interest earned is the same each year. With compound interest, the interest earned increases each year because the interest is added to the principal.

5. a) $22.44   **b)** $31.44   **c)** $85.28   **d)** $167.24

6. a) $30.75   **b)** $187.30   **c)** $100.41   **d)** $524.95

7. a) $30.00, $180.00, $96.00, $480.00
   b) $0.75, $7.30, $4.41, $44.95

8. a) $184.64   **b)** $626.53   **c)** $259.15   **d)** $215.88

9. $281.53

10.

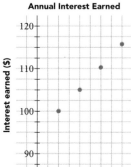

Annual Interest Earned

The graph does not show linear growth. Since the principal increases each year, the interest also increases and the difference between consecutive values of the interest earned is not constant. The graph is a curve.

11.

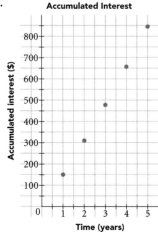

Accumulated Interest

The graph does not show linear growth. The interest earned increases every year, so the accumulated interest grows at an increasing rate. The graph is a curve.

12. The GIC at 5.5% compounded annually for 5 years earns $13.92 more in interest.

2.2 Exercises, page 68

1. a) $450, 5%, 4 years; $546.98
   b) $5000, 7.5%, 8 years; $8917.39
   c) $875, 3.75%, 5 years; $1051.84
   d) $1535, 8.25%, 7 years; $2673.64
   e) $915, 6.6%, 6 years; $1342.65
   f) $1200, 5.2%, 2 years; $1328.04

2. a) $844.26   **b)** $1791.08   **c)** $131.08
   d) $3187.70   **e)** $973.32   **f)** $13 458.68
   g) $1264.44   **h)** $6332.18

3. a) $79.64   **b)** $184.50   **c)** $212.26
   d) $215.51   **e)** $36.54   **f)** $1365.85
   g) $1392.75   **h)** $153.30

4. a) $862.03   **b)** $17 787.25   **c)** $3028.66
   d) $33 526.05   **e)** $1230.92   **f)** $803.99
   g) $122 712.39   **h)** $11 329.63   **i)** $48 231.47
   j) $5096.76

5. a) $55.32   **b)** $60.23   **c)** $94.71
   d) $177.87   **e)** $16.91   **f)** $171.22
   g) $60.70   **h)** $238.67

6. a) $1086.81   **b)** $1181.15   **c)** $1338.24

7. a) $86.81   **b)** $181.15   **c)** $338.24

8. a) $669.12   **b)** $1338.24   **c)** $2007.35

9. a) $169.12   **b)** $338.24   **c)** $507.35

10. a) $3345.59   **b)** $845.59

11. a) $523.75   **b)** $2226.05   **c)** $4730.44
   d) $4078.17   **e)** $13 700.87

12. a)

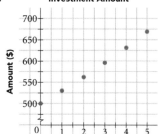

Investment Amount

b) Since the differences are not constant, the growth of the investment is not linear. Also, the points on the graph do not lie in a straight line.

13. a)

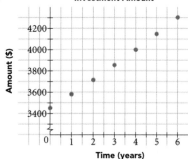

Investment Amount

b) Since the differences are not constant, the growth of the investment is not linear. Also the points on the graph do not lie in a straight line.

14. $3025.94

15. $4 052 694.23

16. a) Alexie's investment   **b)** $1.45

17. Yes. Marie doubles her money since it amounts to $793.23 after 18 years, which is more than twice $375.

18. No. Compound interest is not represented by linear growth, so more interest will be earned in the last three years than in the first three years.

2.3 Exercises, page 76

1. a) 0.08   **b)** 0.04   **c)** 0.02   **d)** 0.0067

2. a) 6   **b)** 12   **c)** 24   **d)** 72

3. a) $200, 4.5%, 10; $310.59
   b) $750, 17.5%, 15; $8426.15
   c) $225, 8.7% , 8; $438.55
   d) $1475, $\frac{0.055}{12}$ %, 36; $1738.95
   e) $3000, $\frac{0.0525}{365}$ %, 1825; $3900.46
   f) $483, $\frac{0.15}{12}$ % , 72; $1181.38

4. a) $886.47   **b)** $2437.99   **c)** $1902.36
   d) $1368.33   **e)** $1813.28   **f)** $1432.69

5. a) $1012.19   **b)** $2231.69   **c)** $3458.56
   d) $21 419.20   **e)** $487.25   **f)** $1669.82
   g) $189.25   **h)** $1666.71

6. a) $597.90   **b)** $1047.68   **c)** $164.10
   d) $469.66   **e)** $491.80   **f)** $15 625.91
   g) $447.76   **h)** $662.58

7. $2457.92

8. $976.15

9. $2774.26

10.

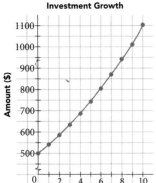
Investment Growth

a) After 10 years, the amount of the investment is $1104.02, which is more than twice $500.
b) The growth of the investment is not linear as the differences are not constant and the points on the graph do not lie in a straight line.

11. $19.89

12. $16 059.18

13. a) $1221.00, $1489.85   **b)** $221.00, $489.85
   c) No. When the interest rate is doubled, the interest earned more than doubles, since the interest compounds every year.

14.

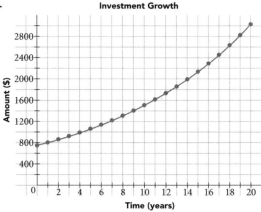
Investment Growth

a) Yes. After 20 years, the amount of the investment is $3029.05, which is more than triple $750.
b) The growth of the investment is not linear as the differences are not constant. Also, the points on the graph do not lie in a straight line.

15. Mark should invest in Plan B as the amount at maturity is greater.

16.

Compounding frequency	Number of compounding periods per year	Calculations	Amount ($)
Annually	1	$1000(1 + 0.1)$	1100.00
Semi-annually	2	$1000\left(1 + \frac{0.1}{2}\right)^2$	1102.50
Quarterly	4	$1000\left(1 + \frac{0.1}{4}\right)^4$	1103.81
Monthly	12	$1000\left(1 + \frac{0.1}{12}\right)^{12}$	1104.71
Weekly	52	$1000\left(1 + \frac{0.1}{52}\right)^{52}$	1105.06
Daily	365	$1000\left(1 + \frac{0.1}{365}\right)^{365}$	1105.16
Hourly	8760	$1000\left(1 + \frac{0.1}{8760}\right)^{8760}$	1105.17
Every minute	525 600	$1000\left(1 + \frac{0.1}{525\ 600}\right)^{525\ 600}$	1105.17
Every second	31 536 000	$1000\left(1 + \frac{0.1}{31\ 536\ 000}\right)^{31\ 536\ 000}$	1105.17

b) The amount earned increases as the interest is compounded more often. When the compounding periods are very small (minutes, seconds), the difference is minimal. The maximum amount earned in one year is $1105.17.

c) Banks rarely compound by the hour, minute, or second as more calculations must be performed, and the difference in the amount earned is very small (as shown in the table).

17. Pat should make the investment at 5.1% compounded semi-annually for 6 years, as it is worth more at maturity.

18. a) $38.82, $80.65, $125.72, $174.30, $226.65, $283.06, $343.85

b)

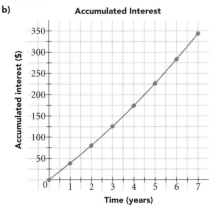

Accumulated Interest

c) Approximately 5.5 years

19. Answers are approximate.
   a) 10.5 years   **b)** 13.5 years
   c) 8 years, 3 months

Self-Check NS, 2.1–2.3, page 79

1. a) 4   **b)** 8   **c)** 16
   d) 32   **e)** 64   **f)** 128

2. a) 49   **b)** 27   **c)** 81
   d) 16   **e)** 1000   **f)** 625

3. a) 25^9 **b)** x^3 **c)** 5^{12} **d)** $(1.04)^5$

4. a) $638.14   **b)** $557.27   **c)** $12 115.47
   d) $965.73   **e)** $1725.39

5. a) $69.97   **b)** $129.31   **c)** $70.07
   d) $5.27   **e)** $446.82

6. $177.82

7. Investment 2 is the better choice as it is worth more at maturity.

8. Doubling the interest rate with compound interest more than doubles the amount earned.

9. $571.41

2.4 Exercises, page 82

1. a) $90.70   **b)** $161.99   **c)** $208.63
   d) $451.05   **e)** $798.85   **f)** $1355.23

2. a) $82.19   **b)** $89.00   **c)** $88.85

3. a) $172.46   **b)** $170.70   **c)** $177.70

4. a) $807.22   **b)** $804.91   **c)** $803.72

5. a) $559.66   **b)** $1154.95
   c) $704.30   **d)** $363.65

6. a) $2033.31   **b)** $659.04
   c) $424.07   **d)** $507.17

7. a) $1114.09   **b)** $498.51
   c) $7099.30   **d)** $1539.15

8. a) $8548.04   **b)** $8227.02
   c) $7920.94   **d)** $7628.95

9. $2234.97

10. $673.53

11. $6810.49

12. $41.32

13. Paula should choose the savings account, as she can invest a smaller principal to have $5000 after 4 years.

14. $950.00

15. $1865.63

16. $10 970.40

17. $1200.00

2.5 Exercises, page 90

Answers may be approximate.

1. a) 0.05   **b)** 0.07   **c)** 11
   d) 11   **e)** 0.05   **f)** 16

2. a) 7 years   **b)** 19 years
   c) 29 years   **d)** 37 years

3. a) 1.5%   **b)** 3.0%
   c) 5.0%   **d)** 7.0%

4. a) 15 years   **b)** 23 years
   c) 31 years   **d)** 46 years

5. a) 6 years   **b)** 10.5 years
   c) 15 years   **d)** 22.5 years

6. a) 12   **b)** 0.07   **c)** 0.075
   d) 9   **e)** 13   **f)** 0.075

7. a) 18 years   **b)** 15 years
   c) 12 years   **d)** 11 years

8. a) 17.5 years   **b)** 14 years
   c) 12 years   **d)** 9 years

9. a) 18.5 years   **b)** 14 years
   c) 11.25 years   **d)** 9.5 years

10. 8%

11. 5 years

12. 2.5 years

13. 1.96%

14. 0.56%

15. 17 years

16. 5 years

17. 4.5%

18. 5.5%

19. 10.31%

Self-Check 2.4, 2.5, page 92

1. a) $613.91 **b)** $581.25 **c)** $551.26 **d)** $522.96

2. a) $790.31 **b)** $730.69 **c)** $821.93 **d)** $759.92

3. a) $836.39 **b)** $2090.97 **c)** $3010.99 **d)** $4934.69

4. a) $562.14 **b)** $1064.96 **c)** $2379.49

5. a) 0.01 **b)** 0.025 **c)** 0.0325
   d) 0.05 **e)** 0.045 **f)** 0.0475

6. a) 20 **b)** 50 **c)** 60
   d) 10 **e)** 45 **f)** 100

7. 4%

8. 5.6 years

9. $1288.71

10. The interest earned after 30 years more than triples when the time period is tripled. Because interest is earned on interest, the principal grows at an increasing rate.

2.6 Project, page 94

1. a) Regular interest CPB = $550.00
   Compound interest CPB = $708.14
   Regular interest CSB = $485.00
   Compound interest CSB = $605.77
   b) $65.00
   c) $102.37
   d) The differences are not the same because regular interest is linear growth and compound interest is non-linear growth.

e)

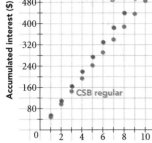
Accumulated Interest

f)

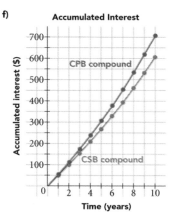
Accumulated Interest

2. a) Regular interest CPB **b)** $1100.00

3. a) Compound interest CPB **b)** $5124.43

4. a) Compound interest CSB
   b) $40.42, $112.68

5. a) Regular interest CSB **b)** $1455.00

6. a) $275.00, $285.00, $295.00
   b) $110.00, $120.27, $131.59

7. a) i) $37.50 **ii)** $12.80 **iii)** $26.25
   b) $182.50
   c) $4614.33
   d)

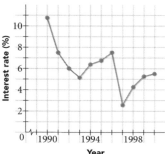
CSB Interest Rates

The graph shows that the rates decreased from 1990 to 1993, then increased from 1993 to 1996. The rates dropped from 1996 to 1997 then increased until the year 2000.

8. The government follows interest rate changes in the financial market to stay competitive, and so pays out no more than the going rate.

Chapter 2 Review Exercises, page 97

1. a) 8 **b)** 27 **c)** 64 **d)** 125
   e) 1000 **f)** 8000 **g)** 27 000 **h)** 64 000
   i) 125 000 **j)** 216 000

2. a) 25 **b)** 32 **c)** 36 **d)** 16
   e) 81 **f)** 100 **g)** 225 **h)** 144
   i) 400 **j)** 625

3. a) 3^7 **b)** 3^3 **c)** a^6 **d)** c^5
   e) b^{11} **f)** 4^0

4. a) 3^8 **b)** 4^{10} **c)** a^9 **d)** 10^{18}

5. a) $3   **b)** $175   **c)** $90   **d)** $165

6. a) $19.47   **b)** $117.05   **c)** $724.50   **d)** $1772.25

7. a) $442.57   **b)** $1477.31   **c)** $397.84   **d)** $153.19

8. a) $911.58   **b)** $1702.19   **c)** $1663.08   **d)** $596.65
   e) $679.98   **f)** $2821.65

9. a) $1070.58   **b)** $2021.10   **c)** $1605.78   **d)** $311.59

10. a) $1191.56   **b)** $3728.07   **c)** $183.03
   d) $443.89   **e)** $13 140.67   **f)** $3247.65
   g) $414.78

11. a) $2226.25   **b)** $242.07   **c)** $110.21
   d) $2259.97   **e)** $48 226.47   **f)** $5665.32
   g) $683.38

12. a) $67.81   **b)** $423.94   **c)** $84.23
   d) $666.13   **e)** 1783.98   **f)** $586.40
   g) $332.05   **h)** $501.54

13. a) $133.01   **b)** $3834.97   **c)** $198.87

14. a) $739.73   **b)** $1012.29   **c)** $418.89
   d) $2132.35   **e)** $210.71   **f)** $64.59

15. a) $548.02   **b)** $638.80   **c)** $1137.34
   d) $2095.30   **e)** $349.02   **f)** $2586.16

16. Answers are approximate.
   a) 0.05   **b)** 9   **c)** 0.055
   d) 15   **e)** 0.065   **f)** 60

17.

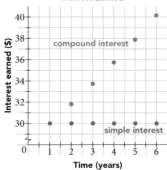

Interest Earned

18. Approximately 6.5 years

19. $837.84

20. $53.48

21. Approximately 5.5%

22. The 4.9% investment is the better choice as its amount is greater upon maturity.

23. The amount earned on an investment increases as the compounding periods increase. However, compounding periods as small as minutes yield an insignificant difference.

24. Approximately 9 years

25. $5149.76

Chapter 2 Self-Test, page 101

1. a) a^5 **b)** m^6 **c)** c^3 **d)** m^{12}

2. a) $500.00   **b)** $1250.00

3. a) $2950.73   **b)** $1332.45   **c)** $2987.62

4. a) $356.91   **b)** $3263.19

5. a) $1150.00   **b)** $675.00

6. a) $687.00   **b)** $1000.00

7. a) 0.0625   **b)** 18

8. Approximately 8 years

9. If the interest rate is doubled, the principal grows faster with each compounding period. Therefore, the interest earned more than doubles.

10. $654.32

11. 5.25% compounded annually

Explore, Research, Report: Travelling Abroad

Explore, page 104

1.

Location	Price ($ CAD)	Price for 3 nights ($ CAD) Nov.	Price for 3 nights ($ CAD) May
London	264.64	793.92	760.89
Oslo	126.34	379.02	334.97
Paris	1304.92	3914.76	3396.35
Warsaw	40.82	122.46	118.92
Prague	41.81	125.43	109.50
Zurich	238.58	715.74	645.23
Total cost		6051.33	5365.86

2.

Hotel	Price ($ CAD)
Qent	41.81
Jalta Praha	250.45
Obora	84.44

Cheapest hotel is Qent.

4. a) London: $760.89; Oslo: $334.98; Paris: $3396.36; Warsaw: $118.92; Prague: $109.50; Zurich: $645.24; Total: $5365.89

   b) Exchange rates have gone down from November to May, so expenses such as hotels and food will cost less, leaving more money for other items.

5.

Location	Convert to $ CAD	Convert to:
London	$60.15	324 NOK
Oslo	$102.19	67 EUR
Paris	$64.48	190 PLZ
Warsaw	$34.02	814 CSK
Prague	$50.17	53 CHF
Zurich	$19.09	19 CAD

6. a) Because this allows currency exchanges to make a profit
b) The value of your money is reduced.

Chapter 3 Exponential Growth

Necessary Skills
1 Review: Number Systems
Exercises, page 113

1. Answers may vary.
  a) 0, 3, 7
  b) $\frac{1}{2}$, 0, −3
  c) −6, −2, 3
  d) 3, 4, 5
  e) $\sqrt{8}$, 3.134 729..., π
  f) $\sqrt{3}$, $\frac{2}{3}$, 6

2. a) Natural, integer, rational **b)** Integer, rational
  c) Rational **d)** Irrational
  e) Integer, rational **f)** Rational
  g) Natural, integer, rational **h)** Rational

3.

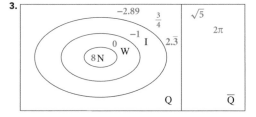

2 Review: Zero and Negative Exponents
Exercises, page 115

1. a) $\frac{1}{3}$ **b)** 1 **c)** 1 **d)** $\frac{1}{64}$
  e) $\frac{1}{9}$ **f)** 1 **g)** $\frac{1}{6}$ **h)** $\frac{1}{25}$
  i) $\frac{1}{10}$ **j)** $\frac{1}{49}$ **k)** $\frac{1}{4}$ **l)** $\frac{1}{4}$

2. a) $\frac{1}{100}$ **b)** $\frac{1}{16}$ **c)** $\frac{1}{8}$ **d)** 100
  e) 16 **f)** 8 **g)** $\frac{1}{36}$ **h)** $\frac{1}{32}$
  i) $\frac{1}{81}$ **j)** 64 **k)** 64 **l)** 10

3. a) 2 **b)** 3 **c)** $\frac{3}{2}$ **d)** $\frac{64}{27}$
  e) $\frac{81}{25}$ **f)** $\frac{8}{27}$ **g)** 32 **h)** $\frac{81}{16}$
  i) $\frac{64}{49}$

4. a) 2 **b)** $\frac{5}{6}$ **c)** 99 **d)** $\frac{5}{4}$
  e) $\frac{4}{3}$ **f)** 0 **g)** $\frac{81}{5}$ **h)** $\frac{5}{6}$
  i) $\frac{13}{36}$

5. a) $\frac{1}{3}$ **b)** 3 **c)** $\frac{1}{2}$ **d)** $\frac{3}{2}$
  e) $\frac{4}{3}$ **f)** $\frac{1}{18}$ **g)** 3 **h)** $\frac{1}{3}$
  i) 2

3 New: Evaluating Expressions with Negative Exponents
Exercises, page 117

1. a) 0.143 **b)** 0.001 **c)** 0.007
  d) 0.012 **e)** 0.016 **f)** 0.008
  g) 0.037 **h)** 0.003 **i)** 0.005

2. a) 18 **b)** 0.205 **c)** 0.142
  d) 11.246 **e)** 9.252 **f)** 985.149

3. a) 0.054 **b)** 2.495 **c)** 54.925
  d) 1.8 **e)** 1483.827 **f)** 11.379

4. a) 8.111 **b)** 0.091 **c)** 0.908
  d) 8.875 **e)** −21.907 **f)** 0.712

5. a) 1.185 **b)** 16.04 **c)** −0.105
  d) 6.321 **e)** 0.141 **f)** 0.070
  g) 855.980 **h)** −31.999 **i)** 13.847

4 New: Exponent Laws for Integer Exponents
Exercises, page 120

1. a) 2 **b)** 3^3 **c)** 10^{-7}
  d) $(\frac{1}{2})^{-2}$ **e)** $(-2)^{-6}$ **f)** $(\frac{2}{5})^{-8}$

2. a) 2^{-7} **b)** 2^{-3} **c)** 2^{-7}
  d) 2^3 **e)** 3^9 **f)** 3^{-3}

3. a) c^2 **b)** a^{-1} **c)** m^{-3}
  d) c^{-8} **e)** a^0 or 1 **f)** m^3

4. a) x^{-1} **b)** 1 **c)** n^{-5}
  d) m^{-5} **e)** x^2 **f)** b^7

5. a) m^{-8} **b)** m^{-8} **c)** m^8
  d) x^{-6} **e)** x^6 **f)** a^{15}

6. a) x^3y^3 **b)** a^4b^2 **c)** $25b^4$
  d) $a^{-2}b^{-2}$ **e)** $\frac{1}{9}b^{-2}$ **f)** $\frac{1}{4}x$

7. a) $\frac{4}{9}$ **b)** $\frac{a^2}{64}$ **c)** $\frac{1}{64}$
  d) $\frac{27}{b^6}$ **e)** $\frac{9}{100}$ **f)** $\frac{a^{15}}{125}$

8. a) 4 **b)** 6 **c)** 6
  d) $\frac{8}{27}$ **e)** 81 **f)** $\frac{27}{8}$
  g) 25 **h)** $\frac{16}{9}$ **i)** $\frac{9}{16}$

9. a) $\frac{a^6}{b^{-2}}$ **b)** $\frac{x^4}{y^4}$ **c)** $\frac{m^{-3}}{n^{-2}}$
  d) $\frac{b^4}{a^{-6}}$ **e)** $\frac{b^2}{a^3}$ **f)** $\frac{m^3}{n^6}$

10. a) $\frac{1}{a^2}$ **b)** $\frac{1}{a^2}$ **c)** $\frac{1}{x^6}$

d) $\frac{1}{a^7}$ **e)** x^1 **f)** $\frac{1}{m^{12}}$

g) x^6 **h)** $\frac{1}{a^2}$ **i)** $\frac{1}{b^{10}}$

j) $\frac{a^9}{b^6}$ **k)** a^9b^6 **l)** $\frac{1}{x^2y^4}$

m) $\frac{a^2}{b^2}$ **n)** $\frac{y^6}{x^6}$ **o)** $\frac{g^6}{f^4}$

3.1 Exercises, page 129

1. The exponential functions have the form $y = Ab^x$.
  a) No   **b)** Yes   **c)** Yes
  d) Yes   **e)** No   **f)** No

2. a) $75.00   **b)** 18 years

3. a) $1000   **b)** 3 years

4. a) 10.76 million
  b) 11.65 million
  c) 12.61 million

5. a) 87%   **b)** 65.85%   **c)** 49.84%

6. a) $2382.03   **b)** $2837.04   **c)** $3581.70

7. a) 0.70 m   **b)** 4.28 m

8. a)

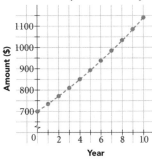

Amount of a $700 Investment at 5% Compounded Annually

  b) 7; after 7 years the interest on the principal has compounded and the amount is $985.
  c)

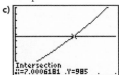

Intersection
X=7.0006181 Y=985

9. a) By the year 2000
  b) The population of Canada is unlikely to reach 50 000 000 in the near future, but people may have multiple cell phones, so the number of subscribers may reach 50 000 000.

10. a) $A = 1200(1 + 0.06)^n$
  b) Approximately $2149.00
  c) Approximately 7 years

3.2 Exercises, page 134

1. a) 4   **b)** 6   **c)** 2   **d)** 10
  e) 5   **f)** 7   **g)** 8   **h)** 9

2. a) 5   **b)** 4   **c)** 2   **d)** 10

3. a) $\frac{1}{7}$ **b)** $\frac{1}{2}$ **c)** $\frac{1}{10}$ **d)** $\frac{1}{5}$
  e) $\frac{1}{9}$ **f)** $\frac{1}{6}$ **g)** $\frac{1}{4}$ **h)** $\frac{1}{3}$

4. a) $\frac{1}{2}$ **b)** $\frac{1}{10}$ **c)** $\frac{1}{4}$ **d)** $\frac{1}{5}$

5. a) 8   **b)** 243   **c)** 256   **d)** 8
  e) 9   **f)** 10 000   **g)** 32   **h)** 125

6. Write 64 as 4^3.

7. a) $\frac{1}{4}$ **b)** $\frac{1}{1000}$ **c)** $\frac{1}{32}$ **d)** $\frac{1}{32}$
  e) $\frac{1}{25}$ **f)** $\frac{1}{64}$ **g)** $\frac{1}{32}$ **h)** $\frac{1}{27}$

8. a) 3.16   **b)** 3.87   **c)** 3.42   **d)** 1.48
  e) 1.28   **f)** 0.71   **g)** 1764.12   **h)** 1.38

9. a) 0.10   **b)** 0.20   **c)** 0.65   **d)** 0.56
  e) 1.18   **f)** 0.46   **g)** 5.49   **h)** 2.34

10.

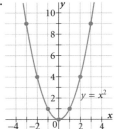

$y = x^2$

  a) To estimate the square root of a number, locate the number on the y-axis and find the corresponding x-values.
  b) Since the square root of x is $x^{\frac{1}{2}}$, the graph is used to evaluate a rational exponent.

11. To 3 decimal places where necessary: 2, 1.414, 1.260, 1.189; 0.5, 0.707, 0.794, 0.841

12. a) 25.75   **b)** 0.52   **c)** 0.98   **d)** 15.00
  e) 0.20   **f)** 1.26   **g)** 1.41   **h)** 0.71

13. a) 0.71   **b)** 0.58   **c)** 0.87   **d)** 0.91
  e) 1.40   **f)** 1.84   **g)** 0.96   **h)** 0.84

14. a) 1.19   **b)** 2.00   **c)** 1.15   **d)** 1.16
  e) 4.35   **f)** 1.99   **g)** 0.70   **h)** 1.15

3.3 Exercises, page 140

1. a) i) 2   **ii)** 4   **iii)** 8
  iv) 16   **v)** 32   **vi)** $\frac{1}{2}$
  b) i) 3   **ii)** 9   **iii)** 27
  iv) 81   **v)** 243   **vi)** $\frac{1}{3}$
  c) i) $\frac{1}{10}$ **ii)** 1   **iii)** 10
  iv) 100   **v)** 1000   **vi)** 10 000

2. a) i) 0.02   **ii)** 0.06   **iii)** 0.25
  iv) 1   **v)** 4
  b) i) 64   **ii)** 16   **iii)** 4
  iv) 1   **v)** 0.25

3. The equations must have the form $y = Ab^x$.
  a) No   **b)** Yes   **c)** Yes
  d) Yes   **e)** Yes   **f)** No

4. a) iv   **b)** ii   **c)** iii   **d)** i

5. a)

x	−1	0	1	3	5	7
y	0.33	1	3	27	243	2187

b)

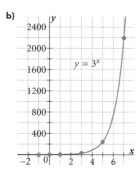

c) i) $x = 2$ **ii)** $x = 6$ **iii)** $x = 4$

6. a)

x	−1	0	1	2	3
y	0.1	1	10	100	1000

b)

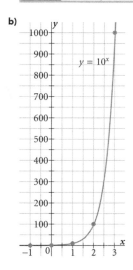

c) There is no x-intercept; the y-intercept is 1.
d) The x-axis is the asymptote because the curve approaches the x-axis but never intersects it.
e) $y = 3$

7. a)

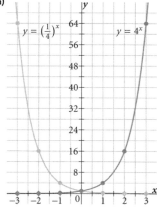

b) Both graphs have y-intercept of 1, no x-intercept, domain all real numbers, range $y > 0$, and the x-axis is an asymptote.
c) $y = 4^x$ increases as x increases, and $y = \left(\frac{1}{4}\right)^x$ decreases as x increases.

8. a) i)

$y = 5^x$						
x	−3	−2	−1	0	1	2	3
y	0.008	0.04	0.2	1	5	25	125

$y = \left(\frac{1}{5}\right)^x$						
x	−3	−2	−1	0	1	2	3
y	125	25	5	1	0.2	0.04	0.008

ii)

$y = 6^x$						
x	−3	−2	−1	0	1	2	3
y	0.005	0.03	0.17	1	6	36	216

$y = \left(\frac{1}{6}\right)^x$						
x	−3	−2	−1	0	1	2	3
y	216	36	6	1	0.17	0.03	0.005

b) For each x-value, the y-values of the functions are reciprocals of each other. The functions are mirror images of each other.

c) i)

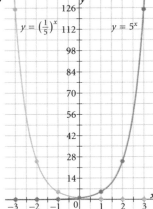

$y = \left(\frac{1}{5}\right)^x$ $y = 5^x$

ii)

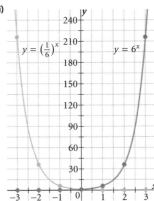

$y = \left(\frac{1}{6}\right)^x$ $y = 6^x$

d) The graphs are mirror images of each other, reflected in the x-axis.

9. a)

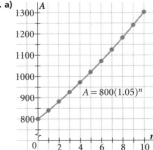

$A = 800(1.05)^n$

b) Approximately 4.6 years

c)

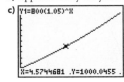

10. a)

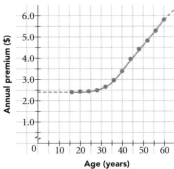

The function is increasing, and approximates an exponential function.

b) i) $2.42   **ii)** $2.43
iii) $2.57   **iv)** $2.90
v) $4.62
c) i) $5.90   **ii)** $6.35
iii) $7.05   **iv)** $2.35
v) $2.30

d) It is assumed that the graph approximates an exponential function.

11.

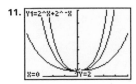

a) y-intercept of 2; the parts of the graph will be closer together.
c) The graph of $y = \left(\frac{1}{2}\right)^x + \left(\frac{1}{2}\right)^{-x}$ is the same as the graph of $y = 2^x + 2^{-x}$.
e) A catenary is the curve made by the cables of a suspension bridge.

Self-Check NS, 3.1–3.3, page 143

1. a) $\frac{1}{2}$ **b)** $\frac{1}{9}$ **c)** $\frac{1}{8}$ **d)** 3
    e) 2   **f)** 3   **g)** $\frac{1}{2}$ **h)** 27

2. a) 0.04   **b)** Approximately 12.51
    c) Approximately 4.71   **d)** Approximately 1.15

3. a) a^6 **b)** x^6 **c)** $\frac{1}{b^8}$ **d)** $\frac{1}{x^4 y^2}$

4. a) No   **b)** Yes   **c)** No   **d)** Yes

5. a) 27.3 million   **b)** 32 million   **c)** 37.5 million

6.

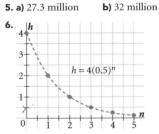

$h = 4(0.5)^n$

7.

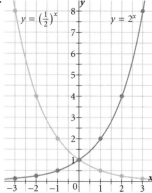

$y = \left(\frac{1}{2}\right)^x$ $y = 2^x$

a) $(0, 1)$ because x^0 is always 1
b) $y = 2^x$ is increasing; $y = \left(\frac{1}{2}\right)^x$ is decreasing.
c) $y = 2^x$ illustrates exponential growth; $y = \left(\frac{1}{2}\right)^x$ illustrates exponential decay.

3.4 Exercises, page 149

1. a) 1.12   **b)** 1.06   **c)** 1.034
   d) 1.082   **e)** 1.105

2. a) 20%   **b)** 5%   **c)** 2.5%   **d)** 0.4%   **e)** 15%

3. a) $y = 1200(2)^n$ **b)** $y = 1200(3)^n$ **c)** $y = 1200(5)^n$

4. a) 2.238 million   **b)** 1.4%
   c) 3.903 million, assuming a constant rate of growth
   d) Economic changes, employment opportunities

5. a) $y = 10.1(1.0125)^x$ **b)** 18.8 million

6. a) $y = 24(1.06)^x$ **b)** \$69 900 000 000

7. a) $y = 4000(2)^x$
   b) i) 64 000   **ii)** 256 000   **iii)** 2 048 000

8. a) $y = 65(1.08)^x$
   b)

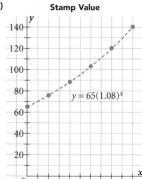

Stamp Value

$y = 65(1.08)^x$

   c) 9 years

9. a) $y = 800(1.02)^x$
   b)

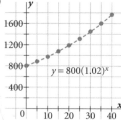

$y = 800(1.02)^x$

   c) 11 years   **d)** 35 years

10. a) $y = 600(1.05)^x$ **b)** \$844.26
   c)

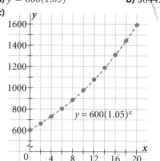

$y = 600(1.05)^x$

   d) 14.3 years from now
   e) 14.3 years

11. Answers may vary.

12. Answers may vary.

13. a) $y = 2000(1.04)^x$
   b) Answers may vary. **Problem:** Determine the value of the investment 20 years from now. **Answer:** \$43 822.46

14. a) 7.18 billion
   b) 2044

3.5 Exercises, page 156

1. a) $y = 1000(1.03)^x$ **b)** $y = 1000(0.97)^x$

2. a) 0.88   **b)** 0.94   **c)** 0.966   **d)** 0.918   **e)** 0.895

3. a) 20%   **b)** 5%   **c)** 2.5%   **d)** 4%   **e)** 55%

4. a) One-half of the radioactive material decays every day.
   b)

x (number of days)	y (mass remaining in grams) $y = 1000\left(\frac{1}{2}\right)^x$
1	$1000\left(\frac{1}{2}\right)^1 = 500$
2	$1000\left(\frac{1}{2}\right)^2 = 250$
3	$1000\left(\frac{1}{2}\right)^3 = 125$
4	$1000\left(\frac{1}{2}\right)^4 = 62.5$
n	$1000\left(\frac{1}{2}\right)^n$

5. a) i) 1   **ii)** 2   **iii)** 3   **iv)** 4   **v)** 10

b)

x (number of half-lives)	y (mass remaining in grams)
$\frac{30}{30} = 1$	$300\left(\frac{1}{2}\right)^1 = 150$
$\frac{60}{30} = 2$	$300\left(\frac{1}{2}\right)^2 = 75$
$\frac{90}{30} = 3$	$300\left(\frac{1}{2}\right)^3 = 37.5$
$\frac{120}{30} = 4$	$300\left(\frac{1}{2}\right)^4 = 18.75$
$\frac{5 \times 60}{30} = 10$	$300\left(\frac{1}{2}\right)^{10} \doteq 0.29$

6. a) $y = 500\left(\frac{1}{2}\right)^x$ **b)** 6 half-lives   **c)** 7.81 g

7. a) $y = 24\left(\frac{1}{2}\right)^x$ **b)** 25 half-lives   **c)** 7.15×10^{-7} g

8. a) $20\ 000   **b)** 16%   **c)** $7025.96

9. a) The number of children who die under the age of one
   b) 6 deaths   **c)** 5

10. a) $y = 100(0.96)^x$ **b)** 83.22%

11. a) $y = 4000(0.95)^x$
   b) i) 3095   **ii)** 2395

12. 13.5 years

13. a) $y = 20\ 000(0.88)^x$

b)

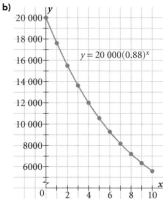

c) Approximately 5.4 years

14. a) $y = 100(0.87)^x$

b)

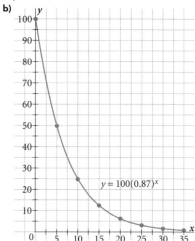

c) i) After 10 h   **ii)** After 17 h   **iii)** After 33 h
d) The graphs and equations are identical. The y-axis in *Example 4* represents the percent of caffeine, while in this exercise it represents the mass of caffeine.

15. a) 0.5 m   **b)** 5 bounces

16. Answers may vary.

17. a) $y = 22\ 234(0.958)^x$
   b) Answers will vary. **Problem:** What was the town's population in 1995? **Answer:** 17 941

18. a) For growth, when x increases, y increases. For decay, when x increases, y decreases.
   b) The equation has the form $y = Ab^x$. For exponential decay, $b > 0$ and $b < 1$; for exponential growth, $b > 1$
   c) The graph for exponential decay goes down to the right. The graph for exponential growth goes up to the right.

19. a) $y = 100(0.95)^x$ **b)** 77.38%

c)

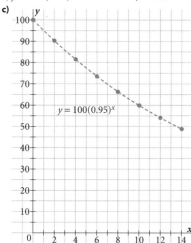

d) 70%
e) Approximately 13 layers

3.6 Exercises, page 166

1. Table c because the differences increase by a factor of 3, which is the greatest rate of change.

2. Table b because the values of y increase by the least amount.

3. Graph b because the values of y increase most quickly.

4. Graph a because the values of y increase most slowly.

5. a) Linear growth because $8 is added each hour.
  b) Exponential growth because each succeeding amount is multiplied by a constant.
  c) Linear growth because 100 students are added each year.
  d) Linear growth because the same constant is added to the amount each period.
  e) Exponential growth because the population is multiplied by 1.016 each year.

6. a)

x	$y = 6x$	$y = 3(2x)^2$	$y = 3(2)^x$
0	0	0	3
1	6	$3(2)^2 = 12$	$3(2)^1 = 6$
2	12	$3(4)^2 = 48$	$3(2)^2 = 12$
3	18	$3(6)^2 = 108$	$3(2)^3 = 24$
4	24	$3(8)^2 = 192$	$3(2)^4 = 48$
5	30	$3(10)^2 = 300$	$3(2)^5 = 96$

b)

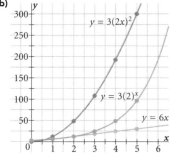

c) $y = 3(2x)^2$ shows the greatest rate of change because the y-values increase the quickest. $y = 6x$ shows the least rate of change because the y-values increase the slowest.

7. a)

x	$y = 3x$	$y = 3x^2$	$y = 3^x$
0	0	0	1
1	3	3	3
2	6	12	9
3	9	27	27
4	12	48	81
5	15	75	243

b)

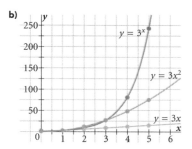

c) $y = 3^x$ shows the greatest rate of change because successive values of y are multiplied by 3.
$y = 3x$ shows the least rate of change because successive values of y have 3 added to them.

8. a) Let the number of offences be x and the value of fines in dollars be y.

Plan A		Plan B	
x	y	x	y
0	0	0	0
1	10	1	10
2	20	2	$10 \times 2 = 20$
3	30	3	$20 \times 2 = 40$
4	40	4	$40 \times 2 = 80$
5	50	5	$80 \times 2 = 160$
6	60	6	$160 \times 2 = 320$

b)

c) Plan A represents linear growth as the number 10 is repeatedly added. Plan B represents exponential growth as the number 2 is repeatedly multiplied.
d) Plan B, because for all offenders with more than 2 fines, the fine is higher.
e) It is unlikely that Plan B would be adopted as citizens would object to the very high fines for multiple offences.

9. a) Option A

Number of years	Earnings per hour	Difference
0	$10	
1	$11	$1
2	$12	$1
3	$13	$1
4	$14	$1
5	$15	$1

b) Option B

Number of years	Earnings per hour	Difference
0	$10	
1	$10 × 1.10 = $11	$1
2	$11 × 1.10 = $12.10	$1.10
3	$12.10 × 1.10 = $13.31	$1.21
4	$13.31 × 1.10 = $14.64	$1.33
5	$14.64 × 1.10 = $16.10	$1.46

c) Linear growth because a constant amount is added each year.
d) Exponential growth because each amount is multiplied by a constant.
e) Exponential growth because the amount added gets larger every year.

10. a)

Year, n	Population, P
0	800
1	880
2	960
3	1040
4	1120
5	1200

b)

Year, n	Population, P
0	800
1	880
2	968
3	1065
4	1172
5	1289

c)

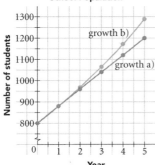
School Population

d) Linear growth because a constant amount is added each year.

e) Exponential growth because each amount is multiplied by a constant.
f) Exponential growth because the amount added gets larger every year.

11. a)

Year, n	Population, P
0	30 000 000
1	30 100 000
2	30 200 000
3	30 300 000
4	30 400 000
5	30 500 000
6	30 600 000
7	30 700 000
8	30 800 000

b)

Year, n	Population, P
0	30 000 000
1	30 990 000
2	32 012 670
3	33 069 088
4	34 160 368
5	35 287 660
6	36 452 153
7	37 655 074
8	38 897 691

c)

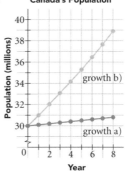
Canada's Population

d) Linear growth because a constant amount is added each year.
e) Exponential growth because each amount is multiplied by a constant.
f) Exponential growth because the amount added gets larger every year.

12. a)

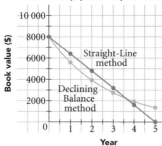

Business Equipment Depreciation

b) Using straight-line depreciation, the value of the item will be $0 after 5 years. Using the declining balance method of depreciation, the value of the item will be $1344.56 after 5 years.

c) Answers may vary. Straight-line depreciation leads to a zero balance. A declining balance method has more rapid depreciation at the beginning, slower depreciation at the end, and never reaches zero.

Self Check 3.4–3.6, page 171

1. With exponential growth, y increases as x increases. With exponential decay, y decreases as x increases.

2. a) $y = 50(1.025)^x$ **b)** $y = 50(0.975)^x$

3. a) $0.05   **b)** 8%   **c)** $2.35

4. a) $y = 3.7(1.171)^x$ **b)** 17.94 million

5. a) $y = 100(0.975)^x$

b)

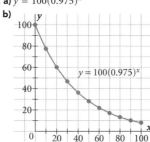

$y = 100(0.975)^x$

c) Approximately 27 m

6. a) 10 mg   **b)** 5 mg   **c)** 1.25 mg

7. $y = 2^x$ has the highest rate of growth as the y-values increase most rapidly as x increases.

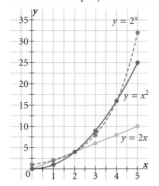

3.7 Project, page 172

1. $21 051.50

3. a)

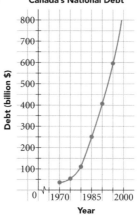

Canada's National Debt

b) Exponential growth.

f) The national debt will continue to follow the model of exponential growth, and that the government will not take steps to reduce its growth.

Chapter 3 Review Exercises, page 175

1. a) a^1 **b)** $\frac{1}{x^2}$ **c)** $3ab$
   d) $\frac{243}{x^{10}}$ **e)** 1   **f)** x^2

2. a) 0.02   **b)** 110.61   **c)** 0.5
   d) 2.67   **e)** −7.96   **f)** 1

3. a) $1788.78   **b)** $1953.39   **c)** $2229.14

4. a)

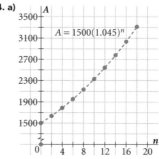

$A = 1500(1.045)^n$

b) 3.5 years   **c)** 15.5 years

5. a) 100 000   **b)** 16   **c)** 216
   d) 81   **e)** 243   **f)** 625

6. a) 500.49   **b)** 0.08   **c)** 30.75
   d) 0.91   **e)** 17 677.67   **f)** 0.78

7. a)

x	−1	0	1	2	3	4
y	0.67	1	1.5	2.25	3.375	5.0625

b)

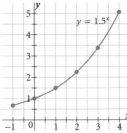

c) No x-intercept; y-intercept is 1.
d) The asymptote is the x-axis.
e) i) $x \doteq 2.5$ **ii)** $x \doteq 1.2$ **iii)** $x \doteq 1.5$

8. a) $y = 100(2)^{2x}$
   b) i) 25 600   **ii)** 409 600   **iii)** 104 857 600

9. Answers may vary. Assume the school population grows exponentially. **Problem:** Determine the population in the year 2005. **Answer:** 672

10. a)

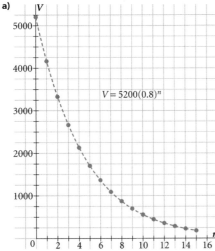

$V = 5200(0.8)^n$

b) $357   **c)** After 14 years
d) For part b: $V \doteq \$357.34$

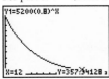

For part c: $n \doteq 13.60$ years

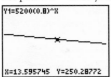

11. a) $y = 100\left(\frac{1}{2}\right)^x$ **b)** 0.10 g

12. a) Method A

Year	0	1	2	3	4	5	6
Earnings ($)	12.00	12.50	13.00	13.50	14.00	14.50	15.00

Method B

Year	0	1	2	3	4	5	6
Earnings ($)	12.00	12.60	13.23	13.89	14.59	15.32	16.08

b) Method A–linear growth because a constant amount is added each year
Method B–exponential growth because each amount is multiplied by a constant
c) Method B because after the first year Alun will be paid more

Chapter 3 Self-Test, page 177

1. a) $\frac{y^4}{x^8}$ **b)** 1   **c)** $\frac{r^6}{s^9}$
   d) $\frac{x^8}{y^{12}}$ **e)** $\frac{1}{a^9}$ **f)** $\frac{1}{x^{12}y^6}$

2. a) 97.668   **b)** 2.000   **c)** 15.326

3. a)

x	−1	0	1	2	3
y	1.333	1	0.75	0.5625	0.422

b)

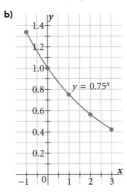

$y = 0.75^x$

c) i) $x \doteq 2.5$ **ii)** $x \doteq -0.5$ **iii)** $x \doteq 1.25$

4. a)

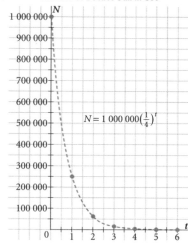

Number of Bottles Still In Use

$N = 1\,000\,000\left(\frac{1}{4}\right)^t$

b) After 5 years

5. a) 175 years

b) 100 years

6. Use the equation $A = 50(2)^x$. Substitute $x = 7$ to calculate that $A = 6400$ bacteria.

Chapter 4 Annuities

Necessary Skills

1 Review: Arithmetic Sequences
Exercises, page 181

1. a) 3, 6, 9, 12   arithmetic, common difference = 3
b) 2, 8, 14, 20   arithmetic, common difference = 6
c) $1, \frac{1}{2}, \frac{1}{3}, \frac{1}{4}$ not arithmetic
d) 3, 6, 11, 18   not arithmetic
e) 6, 5, 4, 3   arithmetic, common difference = −1
f) 2, 4, 8, 16   not arithmetic
g) $\frac{1}{3}, \frac{2}{3}, 1, \frac{4}{3}$ arithmetic, common difference = $\frac{1}{3}$
h) 12, 36, 108, 324   not arithmetic

2. a) −7   **b)** 105   **c)** 82   **d)** −792
e) −48   **f)** 352   **g)** 303   **h)** −269

2 New: Solving Exponential Equations
Exercises, page 183

1. a) $x = 3$ **b)** $x = -1$ **c)** $x = 7$
d) $x = -2$ **e)** $x = 2$ **f)** $x = -4$

2. a) $x = 8$ **b)** $x = 5$ **c)** $x = -4$
d) $x = 6$ **e)** $x = 8$ **f)** $x = -1$

3. a) $x = 5$ **b)** $x = -3$ **c)** $x = -3$
d) $x = 4$ **e)** $x = -5$ **f)** $x = 4$

4. a) $x = 4$ **b)** $x = -2$ **c)** $x = 1$
d) $x = 2$ **e)** $x = -5$ **f)** $x = -3$

5. a) $x = 3$ **b)** $x = 2$ **c)** $x = 2$
d) $x = 5$ **e)** $x = 3$ **f)** $x = 1$
g) $x = 2$ **h)** $x = 3$ **i)** $x = 2$

6. a) $x = 2$ **b)** $x = 1$ **c)** $x = 3$
d) $x = 1$ **e)** $x = 1$ **f)** $x = 1$

7. a) $x = 12$ **b)** $x = 4$ **c)** $x = 6$
d) $x = -2$ **e)** $x = -3$ **f)** $x = \frac{10}{3}$

8. a) $x = -2$ **b)** $x = -3$ **c)** $x = -2$
d) $x = -5$ **e)** $x = -1$ **f)** No solution

9. a) $x = 9$ **b)** $x = -32$ **c)** $x = 8$
d) $x = -3$ **e)** $x = 3$ **f)** $x = -\frac{9}{5}$

4.1 Exercises, page 190

1. a) Geometric; common ratio is 2
b) Not geometric
c) Not geometric
d) Not geometric
e) Geometric; common ratio is 1.5
f) Geometric; common ratio is $\frac{1}{3}$
g) Geometric; common ratio is 1.07
h) Not geometric

2. a) Arithmetic; common difference of 1
b) Arithmetic; common difference of 2
c) Geometric; common ratio of 2
d) Neither; no common difference or ratio
e) Geometric; common ratio of 2
f) Neither; no common difference or ratio

3. a) 2, 4, 8, 16, 32   **b)** 2, −4, 8, −16, 32
c) 2, 6, 18, 54, 162   **d)** 2, −6, 18, −54, 162
e) 2, 8, 32, 128, 512   **f)** 2, −8, 32, −128, 512

4. a) 1, −2, 4, −8, 16   **b)** −1, 2, −4, 8, −16
c) 2, −4, 8, −16, 32   **d)** −2, 4, −8, 16, −32
e) 3, −6, 12, −24, 48   **f)** −3, 6, −12, 24, −48

5. a) $\frac{1}{3}$; 2, $\frac{2}{3}$, $\frac{2}{9}$
b) 5; 625, 3125, 15 625
c) 1.5; 5.0625, 7.593 75, 11.390 625
d) 2; 4, 8, 16
e) −4; −1280, 5120, −20 480
f) $\frac{1}{2}$; 6, 3, 1.5
g) 5; 1875, 9375, 46 875
h) 2; 160, 320, 640

6. a) Geometric; common ratio of 3
b) Neither; no common ratio or difference
c) Arithmetic; common difference of 4
d) Neither; no common ratio or difference
e) Geometric; common ratio of $\frac{1}{2}$
f) Arithmetic; common difference of −7

7. a) Geometric; common ratio of 10
b) Neither; no common ratio or difference
c) Arithmetic; common difference of 4
d) Neither; no common ratio or difference
e) Arithmetic; common difference of −7
f) Geometric; common ratio of 3

g) Geometric; common ratio of -1
h) Arithmetic; common difference of 4
i) Geometric; common ratio of $\frac{1}{2}$
j) Arithmetic; common difference of 3

8. a) 5, 10, 20, 40
b) 3, -12, 48, -192
c) -7, -4.2, -2.52, -1.512
d) $\frac{5}{8}$, $\frac{5}{2}$, 10, 40
e) -1, $-\frac{1}{5}$, $-\frac{1}{25}$, $-\frac{1}{125}$
f) 200, 209, 218.405, 228.233 225
g) -10, 30, -90, 270
h) 100, 1000, 10 000, 100 000
i) -5, 2.5, -1.25, 0.625

9. a) $t_n = 5(2)^{n-1}$ **b)** $t_n = 3(-4)^{n-1}$
c) $t_n = 7(0.6)^{n-1}$ **d)** $t_n = \frac{5}{8}(4)^{n-1}$
e) $t_n = -1(\frac{1}{5})^{n-1}$ **f)** $t_n = 200(1.045)^{n-1}$
g) $t_n = -10(-3)^{n-1}$ **h)** $t_n = 100(10)^{n-1}$
i) $t_n = -5(-\frac{1}{2})^{n-1}$

10. a) $t_n = 4(2)^{n-1}$ **b)** 256   **c)** 8192
11. a) $t_n = 4(-2)^{n-1}$ **b)** 256   **c)** -8192

12. a) 2, 7, 12   not geometric
b) 2, 6, 18   geometric, common ratio is 3
c) 1, 8, 27   not geometric
d) 1, 5, 25   geometric, common ratio is 5
e) 4, -8, 16   geometric, common ratio is -2
f) $\frac{1}{2}$, 1, 2   geometric, common ratio is 2
g) 3, 9, 27   geometric, common ratio is 3
h) 0.5, 1, 1.5   not geometric

13. a) 2, 4, 8, 16, 32   **b)** 1, 3, 9, 27, 81
c) 1.25, -2.5, 5, -10, 20   **d)** 1, $\frac{1}{2}$, $\frac{1}{4}$, $\frac{1}{8}$, $\frac{1}{16}$
e) 1, 1.8, 3.24, 5.832, 10.4976
f) 1, 1.7, 2.9, 4.9, 8.3
g) $-\frac{16}{5}$, 16, -80, 400, -2000
h) 12, 48, 192, 768, 3072

14. a) $t_n = 4(2)^{n-1}$; 512
b) $t_n = 10(-3)^{n-1}$; -21 870
c) $t_n = 11(11)^{n-1}$; 214 358 881
d) $t_n = -8(\frac{1}{2})^{n-1}$; -0.0625
e) $t_n = 4(3)^{n-1}$; 8748
f) $t_n = \frac{5}{3}(\frac{3}{5})^{n-1}$; $\frac{729}{15\ 625}$
g) $t_n = 2(1.2)^{n-1}$; $2(1.2)^7$
h) $t_n = 50(\frac{1}{2})^{n-1}$; 0.390 625
i) $t_n = \frac{1}{12}(2)^{n-1}$; $\frac{32}{3}$
j) $t_n = 4(0.1)^{n-1}$; 0.000 000 4

15. a) $n = 11$; sequence has 11 terms
b) $n = 10$; sequence has 10 terms
c) $n = 7$; sequence has 7 terms
d) $n = 9$; sequence has 9 terms
e) $n = 10$; sequence has 10 terms
f) $n = 8$; sequence has 8 terms
g) $n = 21$; sequence has 21 terms
h) $n = 12$; sequence has 12 terms

16. a) 100, 200, 400, 800
b) 3200 insects

17. The exponent for each power of 10 is one less than the term number. 10 000 000 000 000 = 10^{13}, so $n = 14$.

18. Common ratio is 3 or -3

19. 128 great-great-great-great-great-grandparents

20. a) 0.9 m, 0.81 m, 0.729 m
b) Common ratio of 0.9
c) Approximately 0.349 m

21. $t_2 = 12$; $t_3 = 36$

4.2 Exercises, page 196

1. a) 62   **b)** 22   **c)** -22
d) 138   **e)** 66   **f)** -66

2. a) 63   **b)** 1092   **c)** 682
d) 77.5   **e)** -21 **f)** 27.5

3. a) 1562   **b)** 484   **c)** 93
d) 46.5   **e)** 605   **f)** 55

4. a) 2046   **b)** 2 441 406   **c)** 44 286
d) 59 048   **e)** 1 398 100   **f)** 1598.4375
g) 113.33   **h)** 1 111 111 111

5. a) 5115   **b)** -1705 **c)** 1.50
d) 0.75   **e)** 9.99   **f)** 3.33

6. a) 19 683   **b)** 3280

7. a) 0.02   **b)** 7.98

8. a) 19 531.25   **b)** 6.66   **c)** 2.00
d) 22.87   **e)** 24.00   **f)** 2 615 088 300
g) 0.59   **h)** 128.36

9. a) Geometric
b) $t_n = 100(1.04)^{n-1}$
c) 3908.26

10. a) 12 terms   **b)** 12 285

11. a) 16 terms   **b)** -21 845

12. 597.66

13. 2.00

14. Prize 2 because the total value is higher

15. a) 2046 ancestors
b) Answers may vary. Mortality rates were higher in previous generations.

Self-Check 4.1, 4.2, page 198

1. a) Geometric, common ratio is 2
b) Arithmetic, common difference is 2
c) Geometric, common ratio is $\frac{1}{3}$
d) Neither
e) Arithmetic, common difference is -2
f) Neither

2. a) 4, 12, 36, 108   **b)** 2, -10, 50, -250
c) -3, 6, -12, 24

3. a) 2, 5, 8   arithmetic, common difference is 3
b) 3, 6, 12   geometric, common ratio is 2
c) 1, 4, 9   neither
d) 1, 4, 16   geometric, common ratio is 4

4. a) $t_n = 2(2)^{n-1}$; 512
b) $t_n = 500(\frac{1}{5})^{n-1}$; 0.001 28

5. a) 3, 192, 768   **b)** 4.5, 9, 72
c) 320, −160, 80   **d)** 1, 27, 81

6. a) 14 348 906   **b)** Approximately 2047.94
c) −3 587 227   **d)** Approximately 873 787.78

7. a) $t_n = 4^{n-1}$
b) $S_n = \frac{4^n - 1}{3}$, $S_9 = 87\ 381$

8. a) −6825
b) Approximately 73 438.58
c) Approximately 5081.56

9. 354 292

10. 7

4.3 Exercises, page 204

1. a) $4607.11   **b)** $9214.23
c) $5318.31   **d)** $10 912.27

2. a) $541.63   **b)** $1293.68
c) $945.75   **d)** $1061.62
e) $1259.08   **f)** $3112.32

3. a) $646.84   **b)** $1642.46
c) $5955.62   **d)** $4129.74
e) $5379.71   **f)** $2899.98

4. a) $4600.59   **b)** $1658.24
c) $2034.56   **d)** $23 003.87
e) $1070.62   **f)** $73 105.94

5. a) $1302.68   **b)** $24 988.00
c) $5813.00   **d)** $48 604.30
e) $15 384.52   **f)** $53 333.62

6. $11 274.19

7. $1146.39

8. $3488.50

9. a) $2876.04   **b)** $959.74
c) $2457.66   **d)** $9675.71

10. a) $2011.81   **b)** $459.06
c) $4326.74   **d)** $12 686.91

11. $24 724.52

12. $1420.68

13. $1038.91

14. $53 283.00

15. The amount is $841 188.87. The interest is $761 188.87.

16. $6961.39

17. $192 330.44

18. Annuity A

19. Annuity A has the greater amount because the interest is compounded more often so the amount grows faster.

20. Annuity A has the greater amount because the interest is compounded more frequently.

21. $21 079.72

22. $20 842.53

4.4 Exercises, page 211

1. a) $95.33   **b)** $832.91   **c)** $74.18

2. a) $228.59   **b)** $634.42   **c)** $325.58
d) $397.52   **e)** $906.90   **f)** $4615.68

3. a) $90.80   **b)** $228.32   **c)** $379.85
d) $159.76   **e)** $1006.55   **f)** $880.81

4. a) $685.77   **b)** $332.76
c) $64.50   **d)** $253.70

5. a) $998.19   **b)** $11 452.48
c) $693.84   **d)** $54.75

6. $634.42

7. $132.23

8. $144.83

9. $824.22

10. a) $75.38   **b)** $556.53
c) $18.49

11. a) $886.98   **b)** $216.23
c) $71.66   **d)** $436.15

12. $14.15

13. $130.00

14. $96.68

15. a) $89.77   **b)** $682.16   **c)** $80.81   **d)** $183.29

16. The regular deposit is $143.33.

17. $470.47

18. $40.98

19. $70.75

20. $125.53

21. a) $286.45   **b)** $137 496   **c)** $862 504

22. Option A because it requires Elizabeth to deposit less money over the 5 years.

23. $3660.84

4.5 Exercises, page 217

1. a) Investment ii)   **b)** Investment ii)
c) Investment i)   **d)** Investment i)
e) Investment ii)   **f)** Investment i)

2. a) Semi-annual deposits
b) Semi-annual deposits
c) Quarterly deposits
d) Monthly deposits
e) Annual deposits

3. Option B

4. Save now as she will earn more due to the interest accumulating during the first 5 years.

5. a) Option i) earns more money.
b) $5023.45

6. The amount more than doubles when the time is doubled.

7. The amount at maturity also doubles. In the formula for A, the R becomes $2R$, and this doubles the value of A.

Self-Check 4.3–4.5, page 219

1. a) $7153.29   **b)** $5218.54
    c) $9639.51   **d)** $10 625.56

2. a) $929.46   **b)** $2342.60
    c) $3666.70   **d)** $7215.02

3. a) $397.29   **b)** $530.08
    c) $58.98   **d)** $189.86
    e) $53.12   **f)** $164.47

4. a) $103.22
    b) $624.63
    c) Monthly option because Matt has to deposit less money

5. $141.86

6. $7605.36

4.6 Project, page 222

1. a) $4800.00   **b)** $337 229.24
    c) $122 628.82   **d)** $459 858.06

2. $47 466.17

3. a) $6840
    b) $492 838.71

4. a) $93 783.44
    b) $187 566.87
    c) Yes, because doubling the value of R in the formula doubles the value of A

5. a) $47 812.27; $518 031.89 at end of 25 years
    b) $111 561.97; $466 022.04 at end of 15 years
    c) $159 374.25; $256 673.82 at end of 5 years
    d) $91 576.50
    e) $1 332 304.25

Case Studies, page 224

Case 1
    $1 049 828.84; total contribution = $73 800
Case 2
    $411 883.77; total contribution = $75 600
Case 3
    $235 404.34; total contribution = $74 400
Case 4
    $133 149.24; total contribution = $78 000

Chapter 4 Review Exercises, page 225

1. a) $x = 1$ **b)** $x = 10$ **c)** $x = -7$
    d) $x = 1$ **e)** $x = 6$ **f)** $x = 0$

2. a) Geometric, common ratio is 2
    b) Not geometric
    c) Geometric, common ratio is $\frac{1}{2}$
    d) Not geometric
    e) Geometric, common ratio is 1.04
    f) Geometric, common ratio is $\frac{1}{2}$
    g) Geometric, common ratio is -3
    h) Not geometric

3. a) 9, 36, 144, 576   **b)** 5, -15, 45, -135
    c) 40, 64, 102.4, 163.84   **d)** $-\frac{3}{8}, -\frac{3}{4}, -\frac{3}{2}, -3$
    e) $-8, 4, -2, 1$

4. a) 9, 11, 13   not geometric
    b) 5, 10, 20   geometric, common ratio is 2
    c) 3, -6, 12   geometric, common ratio is -2
    d) 1, 7, 49   geometric, common ratio is 7
    e) 1, 16, 81   not geometric
    f) $\frac{1}{2}, \frac{5}{2}, \frac{25}{2}$ geometric, common ratio is 5

5. a) 3.5, 28, 56   **b)** 0.017, 0.17, 170
    c) 1.28, -6.4, 32   **d)** $\frac{1}{4}, \frac{1}{32}, \frac{1}{64}$

6. a) $t_n = 2(4)^{n-1}$, $t_{10} = 524\ 288$
    b) $t_n = 100\ 000(-1.2)^{n-1}$, $t_{10} = -515\ 978.0352$
    c) $t_n = 729(\frac{1}{3})^{n-1}$, $t_{10} = -0.0\overline{37}$
    d) $t_n = \frac{1}{96}(2)^{n-1}$, $t_{10} = \frac{16}{3}$
    e) $t_n = 3(1.1)^{n-1}$, $t_{10} \doteq 7.074$
    f) $t_n = 12\ 345(\frac{1}{10})^{n-1}$, $t_{10} = 0.000\ 012\ 345$

7. a) 12   **b)** 46   **c)** 10   **d)** 9

8. a) 16 380   **b)** 5 592 405   **c)** 132 860
    d) Approximately 168.70
    e) 33 554 430
    f) 111 111.1111

9. a) $t_n = 2^{n-1}$
    b) $S_n = 2^n - 1$, $S_8 = 255$

10. a) 0.5   **b)** 255.5

11. a) 2 505 397 587   **b)** 48 427 561
    c) Approximately 2561.20   **d)** Approximately 52.11

12. 65 532

13. a) 254   **b)** 3906.24
    c) 4372   **d)** 2047.75

14. $-132\ 860$

15. An annuity is a series of equal deposits made at equal time intervals.

16. a) $17 254.33   **b)** $4585.55   **c)** $2784.12
    d) $25 477.65   **e)** $6450.64

17. a) $141.39   **b)** $126.64   **c)** $485.91
    d) $61.57   **e)** $112.60   **f)** $67.51

18. $7666.20

19. a) Investment ii)   **b)** Investment ii)   **c)** Investment ii)

20. $46 487.02

21. $27 733.26

Chapter 4 Self-Test, page 229

1. 5, -10, 20, -40

2. a) 3, 6, 12   geometric, common ratio is 2
    b) 7, 9, 11   not geometric
    c) 1, 3, 9   geometric, common ratio is 3

3. 15 terms

4. a) $t_n = (-3)^{n-1}$ **b)** $S_n = \frac{(-3)^n - 1}{-4}$, $S_9 = 4921$

5. $S_9 \doteq 299.55$

6. a) $36 414.95   **b)** $33 687.32

7. a) $35.66   **b)** $368.92

8. $10 109.76

9. The monthly option is better as its value at maturity is greater.

Chapter 5 Annuities: The Cost of Credit

Necessary Skills
1 Review: Present Value
Exercises, page 232

1. a) $661.53   **b)** $438.15   **c)** $1066.91
    d) $297.89   **e)** $303.19   **f)** $935.92
    g) $842.83

2 Review: The Sum of a Geometric Series
Exercises, page 233

1. a) 333.33   **b)** 403.90   **c)** 249.51   **d)** 93.75

5.1 Exercises, page 238

1. a) 598.12   **b)** 2794.41   **c)** 1986.10

2. a) $12 118.94   **b)** $14 047.16   **c)** $4101.02
    d) $2924.20   **e)** $11 878.37   **f)** $65 613.48
    g) $10 757.28   **h)** $23 836.53

3. a) $4883.80   **b)** $42 575.06   **c)** $43 537.84
    d) $15 656.67   **e)** $67 863.11   **f)** $14 597.91
    g) $169 192.16   **h)** $21 389.95

4. $3287.10

5. $6757.41

6. $344 389.24

7. $13 429.15

8. $98 636.87

9. $347.96

10. $37 256.57

12. a) $24 815.02   **b)** $3984.98

13. $8341.51

14. Option A

15. a) Annuity A has the greatest present value because the payments are larger over a shorter period of time.
    b) A: $20 690.22; B: $18 014.69; C: $13 958.08

5.2 Exercises, page 244

1. a) $3442.66   **b)** $254.84
    c) $278.93   **d)** $343.14

2. a) $1576.14   **b)** $351.69   **c)** $368.25
    d) $132.86   **e)** $441.49   **f)** $133.58
    g) $456.85   **h)** $194.82

3. a) $847.79   **b)** $642.42   **c)** $361.52
    d) $117.60   **e)** $887.16   **f)** $226.39

4. $106.16

5. $1212.50

6. $881.98

7. a) $60.84   **b)** $190.24

8. $2870.32

9. a) $2309.75   **b)** $1547.22   **c)** $1128.25

10. Yes, Sandra's monthly withdrawal is twice Karl's because the present value of her investment is twice that of Karl's investment.

11. No. The withdrawal will not double. At 4%, the annual withdrawal is $2246.27. At 8%, the annual withdrawal is $2504.56.

12. At 3%, the interest is $558.64. At 6%, the interest is $1153.12. The interest earned more than doubles.

13. a) Annual: $5009.13; semi-annual: $2465.82; quarterly: $1223.13; monthly: $405.53
    b) Annual: $25 045.65; semi-annual: $24 658.20; quarterly: $24 462.60; monthly: $24 331.80
    c) Annual payments because they have the greatest amount

5.3 Exercises, page 248

1. a) $43.03   **b)** $63.60   **c)** $423.27
    d) $65.39   **e)** $154.39   **f)** $112.27
    g) $135.33   **h)** $106.62

2. $26 278.00

3. $892.86

4. $389.08

5. $2107.53

6. $3499.95

7. $8092.54

8. $25 872.57

9. $27 218.08

10. $106

11. a) $304   **b)** $274   **c)** $251
    d) $232   **e)** $216   **f)** $145

12. $0.97

13. $129.52

14. $172.44

15. $873.24

5.4 Exercises, page 252

1. a) $300.27, $301.62   **b)** $481.45, $2629.00
    c) $456.53, $3913.44   **d)** $1136.94, $273.88
    e) $79.96, $59.52   **f)** $953.81, $722.86
    g) $238.83, $821.28   **h)** $276.87, $644.88

2. a) $123   **b)** $900

3. a) $712.64   **b)** $4655.04

4. a) $217   **b)** $1513

5. $175.80

6. $9301

7. $846.37

8. a) $2270.10   **b)** $6325.44
  c) $3630.60   **d)** $2333.94
  e) $875.28   **f)** $6381.72

9. $3433.92

10. $271.44

11. a) $166.07   **b)** $3130.87   **c)** $854.81

12. Answers may vary. A credit rating is based on the number of loans taken out, how loans are repaid, credit card history, and so on. Credit files are available to lending companies.

Self-Check 5.1–5.4, page 255

1. a) $7469.60   **b)** $4039.65
  c) $21 445.67   **d)** $15 369.37

2. a) $32 386.46   **b)** $3613.54

3. a) $2117.82   **b)** $722.10
  c) $173.66   **d)** $193.93

4. a) $120.20   **b)** $769.60

5. No, the annual withdrawal will not double. At 3.5%, the withdrawal is $1501.35. At 7%, the withdrawal is $1678.37.

6. $181.75

7. a) $934.39   **b)** $4638.04

5.6 Investigating Early Investment in an RRSP, page 263

1. $1 405 979.77

2. $1 385 979.77

3. $11 631.09

4. $49 027.14

5. $762 308.07

6. $752 308.07

7. $6313.34

8. $24 513.57

9. $396 372.37

10. $386 372.37

11. $3242.42

12. $24 513.57

13. $156 638.90

14. $151 638.90

15. $1272.55

16. $12 256.79

Chapter 5 Review Exercises, page 270

1. a) $6107.93   **b)** $31 115.91   **c)** $19 376.28
  d) $22 190.74   **e)** $5673.03   **f)** $32 488.87
  g) $97 317.50   **h)** $17 234.40

2. $6633.16

3. $6698.65

4. a) $760.76   **b)** $454.77   **c)** $563.78
  d) $119.88   **e)** $617.76   **f)** $235.04
  g) $596.83   **h)** $121.37

5. $178 742.43

6. $615.03

7. No, at 5%, the withdrawal is $128.84. At 10%, the withdrawal is $148.21.

8. $280.52

9. $527.35

10. a) $5000   **b)** $689.17

11. a) $815.96   **b)** $638.25   **c)** $1261.44
  d) The payment that Gavin can afford to make per month

12. a) $227.52   **b)** $309.60   **c)** $396.60

13. Financing costs – Sara's: $21 850.56; Donna's: $23 729.76 Trudi should buy the boat at Sara's Marina because the boat costs less.

14. $12 231.60

15. $684.72

16. $713.10

Chapter 5 Self-Test, page 273

1. $53.52

2. $16 194.73

3. $2847.04

4. $5483.49

5. $24 851.21

6. Financing costs – For i), the amount is $3952.08. For ii), the amount is $4017.24. The first option is better because the amount is less.

7. $626.28

8. Answers may vary. Increase the payment, make a lump sum payment, and reduce the term of the loan.

Explore, Research, Report: Being an Informed Consumer

Explore, page 274

1. a) GST is a federal government tax and stores cannot waive it.
  b) $115
  c) $106.95
  d) No, the saving is $8.05, not the $7 of the GST.
  e) To make consumers think they are avoiding a government tax and they are getting a bargain

2. a) 1000 g

Size (g)	300	369	1000
Price per 100 g ($)	1.09	0.95	0.59
Price after coupon ($)	2.52	2.74	5.18
Price per 100 g after coupon ($)	0.84	0.74	0.52

b) After calculating the price per 100 g with a $1 coupon, the 1000 g packet is still the most economical.

3. a) $424.20   **b)** $2919.20
  c) i) $746.01
    ii) $3665.21
  d) i) $243.11; total paid = $2917.32
    ii) $223.43; total paid = $2681.16
    iii) $229.34; total paid = $2752.08

4. Total cost = $2643.85
  a) Total paid = $890.38
    Balance after 1 year = $2204.08
  b) $243.02 per month; total paid = $2916.24
  c) $132.63 per month; total paid = $3183.12

Chapter 6 Mortgages

Necessary Skills

1 Review: Using a Scientific Calculator to Evaluate Numerical Expressions

Exercises, page 284

1. a) 1.020   **b)** 1.482
  c) 17 987.472   **d)** 26 733.503

2 Review: Rational Exponents

Exercises, page 285

1. a) 8   **b)** 7776
  c) $\frac{1}{343}$ **d)** 0.960 030 721 5
  e) 1.015 240 7   **f)** 0.989 946 771 3

6.1 Exercises, page 289

1. a) $902.02   **b)** $1003.00   **c)** $839.37
  d) $1198.50   **e)** $1413.56   **f)** $1610.45
  g) $871.11   **h)** $1458.93

2. a) $270 606; $130 606
  b) $240 720; $100 720
  c) $302 173.20; $162 173.20
  d) $359 550; $159 550
  e) $424 068; $224 068
  f) $483 135; $283 135
  g) $156 799.80; $56 799.80
  h) $525 214.80; $275 214.80

3. Lenders could make more money because interest rates fluctuate.

4. The amortization period is the time in which the mortgage is paid off. The term is the period for which the interest rate is fixed.

5. a) i) $575.63   **ii)** $582.23   **iii)** $591.08
  b) To protect against future rate increases, and allow for long range planning

6. $1148.28

7. $836.90

8. Jai: $836.44; Genevieve: $1213.28
Halving the amortization period does not double the monthly payment.

9. a) $186 750   **b)** $1260.95

10. $1074.43

11. a) $135 843.15   **b)** $3000.00   **c)** $132 843.15

12. a)

Monthly payment	Total payments	Total interest paid	Interest saved
$1171.42	$140 570.40	$40 570.40	$75 306.60
$910.05	$163 809.00	$63 809.00	$52 068.00
$787.35	$188 964.00	$88 964.00	$26 913.00
$719.59	$215.877.00	$115 877.00	—

b) The monthly payment decreases.
c) The total interest paid increases.

13. $111.67

14. $1021.17

15. a) $1694.30   **b)** $1618.87   **c)** $117 732.72

16. $111 170.72

6.3 Exercises, page 298

1. a) $1762.31
  b)

Payment number	Monthly payment	Interest paid	Principal paid	Outstanding principal
0	—	—	—	$210 000.00
1	$1762.31	$1575.00	$187.31	$209 812.69
2	$1762.31	$1573.60	$188.71	$209 623.98
3	$1762.31	$1572.18	$190.13	$209 433.85
4	$1762.31	$1570.75	$191.56	$209 242.29
5	$1762.31	$1569.32	$192.99	$209 049.30
6	$1762.31	$1567.87	$194.44	$208 854.86

2. a) $1575.00   **b)** $190.13
  c) $9428.72   **d)** $208 854.86

3. a)

Payment number	Monthly payment	Interest paid	Principal paid	Outstanding principal
0	—	—	—	$150 000.00
1	$1231.42	$968.75	$262.67	$149 737.33
2	$1231.42	$967.05	$264.37	$149 472.96
3	$1231.42	$965.35	$266.07	$149 206.89
4	$1231.42	$963.63	$267.79	$148.939.10
5	$1231.42	$961.90	$269.52	$148 669.58
6	$1231.42	$960.16	$271.26	$148 398.32

b)

Payment number	Monthly payment	Interest paid	Principal paid	Outstanding principal
0	—	—	—	$90 000.00
1	$579.87	$450.00	$129.87	$89 870.13
2	$579.87	$449.35	$130.52	$89 739.61
3	$579.87	$448.70	$131.17	$89 608.44
4	$579.87	$448.04	$131.83	$89 476.61
5	$579.87	$447.38	$132.49	$89 344.12
6	$579.87	$446.72	$133.15	$89 210.97

c)

Payment number	Monthly payment	Interest paid	Principal paid	Outstanding principal
0	—	—	—	$275 000.00
1	$2143.82	$1982.29	$161.53	$274 838.47
2	$2143.82	$1981.13	$162.69	$274 675.78
3	$2143.82	$1979.95	$163.87	$274 511.91
4	$2143.82	$1978.77	$165.05	$274 346.86
5	$2143.82	$1977.58	$166.24	$274 180.62
6	$2143.82	$1976.39	$167.43	$274 013.19

d)

Payment number	Monthly payment	Interest paid	Principal paid	Outstanding principal
0	—	—	—	$300 000.00
1	$2579.50	$2325.00	$254.40	$299 745.50
2	$2579.50	$2323.03	$256.47	$299 489.03
3	$2579.50	$2321.04	$258.46	$299 230.57
4	$2579.50	$2319.04	$260.46	$298 970.11
5	$2579.50	$2317.02	$262.48	$298 707.63
6	$2579.50	$2314.98	$264.52	$298 443.11

e)

Payment number	Monthly payment	Interest paid	Principal paid	Outstanding principal
0	—	—	—	$129 000.00
1	$1177.59	$779.38	$398.21	$128 601.79
2	$1177.59	$776.97	$400.62	$128 201.17
3	$1177.59	$774.55	$403.04	$127 798.13
4	$1177.59	$772.11	$405.48	$127 392.65
5	$1177.59	$769.66	$407.93	$126 984.72
6	$1177.59	$767.20	$410.39	$126 574.33

4.

Payment number	Monthly payment	Interest paid	Principal paid	Outstanding principal
0	—	—	—	$240 000.00
1	$1973.14	$400.00	$1573.14	$238 426.86
2	$1973.14	$397.38	$1575.76	$236 851.10
3	$1973.14	$394.75	$1578.39	$235 272.71
4	$1973.14	$392.12	$1581.02	$233 691.69
5	$1973.14	$389.49	$1583.65	$232 108.04
6	$1973.14	$386.85	$1586.29	$230 521.75
7	$1973.14	$1680.89	$292.25	$230 229.50
8	$1973.14	$1678.76	$294.38	$229 935.12
9	$1973.14	$1676.61	$296.53	$229 638.59
10	$1973.14	$1674.45	$298.69	$229 339.90
11	$1973.14	$1672.27	$300.87	$229 039.03
12	$1973.14	$1670.08	$303.06	$228 735.97

5. $8476.31

Payment number	Monthly payment	Interest paid	Principal paid	Outstanding principal
0	—	—	—	$240 000.00
1	$1973.14	$1750.00	$223.14	$239 776.86
2	$1973.14	$1748.37	$224.77	$239 552.09
3	$1973.14	$1746.73	$226.41	$239 325.68
4	$1973.14	$1745.08	$228.06	$239 097.62
5	$1973.14	$1743.42	$229.72	$238 867.90
6	$1973.14	$1741.75	$231.39	$238 636.51
7	$1973.14	$1740.06	$233.08	$238 403.43
8	$1973.14	$1738.36	$234.78	$238 168.65
9	$1973.14	$1736.65	$236.49	$237 932.16
10	$1973.14	$1734.92	$238.22	$237 693.94
11	$1973.14	$1733.18	$239.96	$237 453.98
12	$1973.14	$1731.44	$241.70	$237 212.28

6. Making reduced payments reduces the amount of principal paid during the first 6 months. Hence, the customer pays more interest over the mortgage term.

7. a) $1403.10 **b)** $19 941.42 **c)** $84 186.00

8.

Payment number	Amount of payment ($)	Interest earned ($)	Increase in fund ($)	Balance of fund ($)
1	7083.75	—	7083.75	7 083.75
2	7083.75	115.11	7198.86	14 282.61
3	7083.75	232.09	7315.84	21 598.45
4	7083.75	350.97	7434.72	29 033.18
5	7083.75	471.79	7555.54	36 588.72
6	7083.75	594.57	7678.32	44 267.03
7	7083.75	719.34	7803.09	52 070.12
8	7083.75	846.14	7929.89	60 000.01

6.4 Exercises, page 303

1. a) 0.083 532 746   **b)** 0.117 105 530
c) 0.049 486 986   **d)** 0.112 337 830
e) 0.076 761 898   **f)** 0.093 172 598

2. a) 8.31%   **b)** 6.17%   **c)** 5.44%
d) 10.18%   **e)** 9.56%   **f)** 11.87%

3. Because a person pays less interest when interest is compounded semi-annually instead of monthly

4. a) $959.71   **b)** $1763.77   **c)** $1454.19
d) $1191.84   **e)** $1548.32   **f)** $815.63

5. a) $160 687.00   **b)** $163 029.60   **c)** $237 501.60
d) $107 014.00   **e)** $205 640.00   **f)** $352 427.00

6. $1646.00

7. $920.81

8. a) $662.69
b)

Payment number	Monthly payment ($)	Interest paid ($)	Principal paid ($)	Outstanding principal ($)
0	—	—	—	80 000.00
1	662.69	524.66	138.03	79 861.97
2	662.69	523.75	138.94	79 723.03
3	662.69	522.84	139.85	79 583.18
4	662.69	521.92	140.77	79 442.41
5	662.69	521.00	141.69	79 300.72
6	662.69	520.07	142.62	79 158.10

9. a) $296 785.00   **b)** $303 517.00

10. $6.16

11. a) $295 647.20   **b)** $286 777.78

Self-Check 6.1–6.4, page 305

1. a) $912.84   **b)** $2364.77

2. a) $182 547.00   **b)** $140 013.60

3. $1255.06

4. At 6.5% interest: $82 991.79
At 14.75% interest: $197 454.40
Difference in total interest paid: $114 462.61

5. a) $1130.85
b)

Payment number	Monthly payment ($)	Interest paid ($)	Principal paid ($)	Outstanding principal ($)
0	—	—	—	160 000.00
1	1130.85	933.33	197.52	159 802.48
2	1130.85	932.18	198.67	159 603.81
3	1130.85	931.02	199.83	159 403.98
4	1130.85	929.86	200.99	159 202.99
5	1130.85	928.68	202.17	159 000.82
6	1130.85	927.50	203.35	158 797.47

6. a) $933.33   **b)** $199.83
c) $158 797.47   **d)** $5582.57

7. a) 6.9%   **b)** 8.16%
c) 6.67%   **d)** 9.89%

8. a) $1297.46   **b)** $816.30

9. $5778.00

Chapter 6 Review Exercises, page 317

1. a) $756.53   **b)** $1395.64   **c)** $1983.12
d) $1987.72   **e)** $612.81   **f)** $2216.62

2. a) $124 371.00   **b)** $149 451.20   **c)** $375 982.80
d) $256 681.00   **e)** $205 300.00   **f)** $258 240.40

3. $5432.65

4. a) $1581.85   **b)** $1534.39   **c)** $7788.00
d) By increasing the monthly payment

5.

Payment number	Monthly payment	Interest paid	Principal paid	Outstanding principal
0	—	—	—	$187 000.00
1	$1505.77	$1324.58	$181.19	$186 818.81
2	$1505.77	$1323.30	$182.47	$186 636.34
3	$1505.77	$1322.01	$183.76	$186 452.58
4	$1505.77	$1320.71	$185.06	$186 267.52
5	$1505.77	$1319.39	$186.38	$186 081.14
6	$1505.77	$1318.07	$187.70	$185 893.44
7	$1505.77	$1316.75	$189.02	$185 704.42
8	$1505.77	$1315.41	$190.36	$185 514.06

6. a) $1324.58   **b)** $185.06
c) $1485.94   **d)** $10 560.22

7.

Payment number	Monthly payment	Interest paid	Principal paid	Outstanding principal
0	—	—	—	$264 000.00
1	$1906.50	$1592.78	$313.72	$263 686.28
2	$1906.50	$1590.89	$315.61	$263 370.67
3	$1906.50	$1588.98	$317.52	$263 053.15
4	$1906.50	$1587.07	$319.43	$262 733.72
5	$1906.50	$1585.14	$321.36	$262 412.36
6	$1906.50	$1583.20	$323.30	$262 089.06

8. a) $1590.89   **b)** $321.36
  c) $1910.94   **d)** $7944.86

9. a) 0.088 357 476   **b)** 0.076 761 898
  c) 0.093 172 598   **d)** 0.131 352 625
  e) 0.064 136 881   **f)** 0.133 719 026

10. a) 7.30%   **b)** 5.44%   **c)** 6.71%
  d) 10.52%   **e)** 8.49%   **f)** 9.25%

11. a) $1137.19   **b)** $1049.58   **c)** $1607.14
  d) $1550.67   **e)** $1922.97   **f)** $1263.02
  g) $2727.37

12. a) $176 574.00   **b)** $102 840.80   **c)** $180 694.00
  d) $364 100.00   **e)** $320 171.00

13. $1178.73

14. a) $1984.46   **b)** $595 338.00   **c)** $360 338.00
  d) 237.3   **e)** $505 867.02   **f)** $270 867.02
  g) $89 470.98

15. a) $1471.42
  b) $441 426.00; $256 426.00
  c) $367.86; 1023
  d) $376 320.78; $191 320.78
  e) $65 105.22

Chapter 6 Self-Test, page 321

1. a) $730.10   **b)** $1894.87

2. a) $197 633.00   **b)** $116 640.00

3. a) $1489.67
  b)

Payment number	Monthly payment	Interest paid	Principal paid	Outstanding principal
0	—	—	—	$185 000.00
1	$1489.67	$1310.42	$179.25	$184 820.75
2	$1489.67	$1309.15	$180.52	$184 640.23
3	$1489.67	$1307.87	$181.80	$184 458.43
4	$1489.67	$1306.58	$183.09	$184 275.34
5	$1489.67	$1305.28	$184.39	$184 090.95

4. 7.29%

5. a) $1366.16   **b)** $434.44

6. $1496.89

7. $63 414.50

8. Option B; $636.00 are saved.

9. The principal is paid off more quickly with weekly accelerated payments because four weekly accelerated payments are made every 28 days, while monthly payments are made every 30 or 31 days.

Chapter 7 Planning for the Future

Necessary Skills

1 Review: The Present Value of an Annuity

Exercises, page 324

  1. a) $670.03   **b)** $410.46

7.1 Exercises, page 332

1. Answers may vary.
  Advantages: longer warranty, choice of options and colours, never been driven
  Disadvantages: more taxes and fees to pay, overall cost will be more, uncertainty about whether the car is roadworthy as it has not been driven

2. a) GST = $893.55; PST = $1021.20
  b) GST = $1678.88; PST = $1918.72
  c) GST = $3057.53; PST = $3494.32
  d) GST = $2225.72; PST = $2543.68
  e) GST = $1368.01; PST = $1563.44
  f) GST = $2010.89; PST = $2298.16

3. a) $20 049.44; $22 549.44
  b) $26 105.09; $28 605.09
  c) $31 871.74; $34 371.74
  d) $20 666.53; $26 666.53
  e) $22 841.96; $27 841.96
  f) $25 017.38; $29 017.38

4. a) $18 736.13   **b)** $13 945.50   **c)** $8445.49
  d) $10 304.99   **e)** $10 152.57

5. a) $591.98   **b)** $519.39   **c)** $697.40
  d) $917.32   **e)** $310.91   **f)** $706.40

6. a) $2659.04   **b)** $2341.04   **c)** $8169.00
  d) $2928.68   **e)** $1197.76   **f)** $986.80

7. Approximately $18 400

8. a) If a car is in demand it may be easier to sell, so its value may depreciate slowly.
  b) The farther the car is driven, the greater the depreciation.
  c) Good maintenance reduces depreciation.

9. A car no longer manufactured may be in demand, so its resale value will increase.

10.

DEAL REVIEW			
MSRP	$32 804.00	Gas Fee	$20.00
Discount	$822.00	Lien Payout	0
Purchase Price	$31 982.00	Delivery Price	$38 201.55
Freight	$895.00	MFG Rebate	0
Tire/Air Tax	$100.00	Down Payment	$2500.00
Gas Tax	$75.00	Finance Fee	$54.00
Administration Fee	$85.00	Amount Financed	$35 755.55
Taxable Subtotal	$33 137.00	Interest Rate	4.9%
Trade-in Allowance	0	Loan Term	36 months
Taxable Total	$33 137.00	Monthly Payment	$1070.02
PST	$2650.96	Interest Due	$2765.17
GST	$2319.59	Balance Due	$38 520.72
Licence Fee	$74.00		

11.

DEAL REVIEW			
List Price	$22 489.00	Gas Fee	$20.00
Discount	$835.00	Lien Payout	0
Purchase Price	$21 654.00	Delivery Price	$15 146.35
Freight	0	MFG Rebate	0
Tire/Air Tax	0	Down Payment	0
Gas Tax	0	Finance Fee	$54.00
Administration Fee	$85.00	Amount Financed	$15 200.35
Taxable Subtotal	$21 739.00	Interest Rate	8.9%
Trade-in Allowance	$8650.00	Loan Term	48 months
Taxable Total	$13 089.00	Monthly Payment	$377.54
PST	$1047.12	Interest Due	$2921.57
GST	$916.23	Balance Due	$18 121.92
Licence Fee	$74.00		

12.

DEAL REVIEW			
MSRP	$45 607.00	Gas Fee	$20.00
Discount	$1500.00	Lien Payout	$7200.00
Purchase Price	$44 107.00	Delivery Price	$39 030.55
Freight	$1030.00	MFG Rebate	$3000.00
Tire/Air Tax	$100.00	Down Payment	0
Gas Tax	$75.00	Finance Fee	$54.00
Administration Fee	$85.00	Amount Financed	$36 084.55
Taxable Subtotal	$45 397.00	Interest Rate	5.9%
Trade-in Allowance	$17 800	Loan Term	48 months
Taxable Total	$27 597.00	Monthly Payment	$845.79
PST	$2207.76	Interest Due	$4513.37
GST	$1931.79	Balance Due	$40 597.92
Licence Fee	$74.00		

13. a)

DEAL REVIEW			
MSRP	$27 896.00	Gas Fee	$20.00
Discount	$1840.00	Lien Payout	0
Purchase Price	$26 056.00	Delivery Price	$31 260.15
Freight	$785.00	MFG Rebate	0
Tire/Air Tax	$100.00	Down Payment	0
Gas Tax	$75.00	Finance Fee	0
Administration Fee	$85.00	Amount Financed	0
Taxable Subtotal	$27 101.00	Interest Rate	0
Trade-in Allowance	0	Loan Term	0
Taxable Total	$27 101.00	Monthly Payment	0
PST	$2168.08	Interest Due	0
GST	$1897.07	Balance Due	0
Licence Fee	$74.00		

b) $755.84

14.

DEAL REVIEW			
List Price	$19 236.00	Gas Fee	$20.00
Discount	$875.00	Lien Payout	0
Purchase Price	$18 361.00	Delivery Price	$18 334.15
Freight	0	MFG Rebate	0
Tire/Air Tax	0	Down Payment	0
Gas Tax	0	Finance Fee	$54.00
Administration Fee	0	Amount Financed	$18 388.15
Taxable Subtotal	$18 361.00	Interest Rate	8.9%
Trade-in Allowance	$2500.00	Loan Term	36 months
Taxable Total	$15 861.00	Monthly Payment	$583.88
PST	$1268.88	Interest Due	$2631.53
GST	$1110.27	Balance Due	$21 019.68
Licence Fee	$74.00		

15. a) Through the bank because the total amount paid out will be less

b) Answers may vary. You might prefer the smaller payments available with financing for 60 months.

7.2 Exercises, page 341

1. Answers may vary. Length of the lease, distance allowance, and type of vehicle

2. a) $8893.35   **b)** $13 898.88   **c)** $14 941.74
d) $10 524.92   **e)** $9683.17   **f)** $9203.70

3. a) $47.46   **b)** $68.66   **c)** $26.12
d) $126.94   **e)** $170.37   **f)** $34.88

4. a) $646.82   **b)** $438.26   **c)** $520.67
d) $338.84   **e)** $866.83   **f)** $700.41

5. Answers may vary.

Advantages: having a new car every 3 or 4 years, lower monthly payments, and only paying for the time you use the car. Disadvantages: not owning the car, distance limit, and overall cost is usually greater.

6. a) $764.83   **b)** $411.92   **c)** $745.55
    d) $305.17   **e)** $612.36   **f)** $730.40

7. $501.71

8. $503.72

9. $781.32

10. $579.52

11. a)

LEASE QUOTE			
Term of Lease	36 months	Monthly Payment	$390.29
MSRP	$18 678.00	Interest Rate	4.9%
Gross Capital Cost	$18 000.00	1st Payment	$390.29
Trade-in Allowance	0	PST (down payment)	0
Down Payment	0	GST (down payment)	0
Total Capital Reduction	0	1st Year Fees	$130.00
Net Capital Cost	$18 000.00	Other Fees	$160.00
Residual Factor	0.41	PST on Upfront	$12.80
Residual Value	$7657.98	GST on Upfront	$11.20
Depreciation	$10 342.02	Security Deposit	$450.00
Base Payment	$339.38		
Monthly PST	$27.15		
Monthly GST	$23.76	Total Initial Payment	$1154.29

b) $14 364.44

12. a)

LEASE QUOTE			
Term of Lease	24 months	Monthly Payment	$440.57
MSRP	$29 405.00	Interest Rate	0.9%
Gross Capital Cost	$30 000.00	1st Payment	$440.57
Trade-in Allowance	0	PST (down payment)	$400.00
Down Payment	$5000.00	GST (down payment)	$350.00
Total Capital Reduction	$5000.00	1st Year Fees	$130.00
Net Capital Cost	$25 000.00	Other Fees	$160.00
Residual Factor	0.55	PST on Upfront	$12.80
Residual Value	$16 172.75	GST on Upfront	$11.20
Depreciation	$8827.25	Security Deposit	$475.00
Base Payment	$383.10		
Monthly PST	$30.65		
Monthly GST	$26.82	Total Initial Payment	$1979.57

b) $16 637.68

13. $31 494.24

14. a) $3600   **b)** $40 052.28

7.3 Exercises, page 348

1. a) 420 L   **b)** 3733.3 L   **c)** 4391.1 L
    d) 8527.2 L   **e)** 2492.0 L   **f)** 8826.2 L
    g) 1181.9 L   **h)** 20 584 L

2. a) $807.30   **b)** $146.12   **c)** $2985.18
    d) $3894.70   **e)** $6442.43   **f)** $7368.05

3. a) $62.54   **b)** $92.17   **c)** $116.85
    d) $102.04   **e)** $143.19   **f)** $215.60

4. Answers may vary. A driver's age, sex, years of driving, and accident record affect the cost.

5. $2036.23

6. $155.35

7. $696.94

8. $26.12

9. $313.43

10. $2872.80

11. $5665.22. The distance driven is distributed evenly throughout the year and the cost of fuel rises linearly.

12. $223.77

13. $264.66

14. $613.91

15. Greg should budget $577.51 per month. Since Greg plans to drive 40 000 km per year, the amount is high.

Self-Check 7.1–7.3, page 351

1. a) $14 006.27   **b)** $11 496.42

2. a) $854.34   **b)** $327.70

3. a) $2293.24   **b)** $2784.60

4. $587.68

5. a) 564 L   **b)** 3724.5 L

6. a) $684.00   **b)** $300.67

7.

DEAL REVIEW			
MSRP	$45 594.00	Gas Fee	$20.00
Discount	$1200.00	Lien Payout	$5137.42
Purchase Price	$44 394.00	Delivery Price	$44 497.02
Freight	$690.00	MFG Rebate	0
Tire/Air Tax	$100.00	Down Payment	0
Gas Tax	$75.00	Finance Fee	$54.00
Administration Fee	$85.00	Amount Financed	$44 551.02
Taxable Subtotal	$45 344.00	Interest Rate	4.9%
Trade-in Allowance	$11 200.00	Loan Term	48 months
Taxable Total	$34 144.00	Monthly Payment	$1023.96
PST	$2731.52	Interest Due	$4599.06
GST	$2390.08	Balance Due	$49 150.08
Licence Fee	$74.00		

8. $508.68

7.4 Investigating the Choice of a Vehicle, page 352

Case Study 1

a)

DEAL REVIEW			
List Price	$21 977.00	Gas Fee	$20.00
Discount	$500.00	Lien Payout	0
Purchase Price	$21 477.00	Delivery Price	$25 850.55
Freight	$660.00	MFG Rebate	0
Tire/Air Tax	$100.00	Down Payment	0
Gas Tax	$75.00	Finance Fee	$54.00
Administration Fee	$85.00	Amount Financed	$25 904.55
Taxable Subtotal	$22 397.00	Interest Rate	6.9%
Trade-in Allowance	0	Loan Term	48 months
Taxable Total	$22 397.00	Monthly Payment	$619.12
PST	$1791.76	Interest Due	$3813.21
GST	$1567.79	Balance Due	$29 717.76
Licence Fee	$74.00		

LEASE QUOTE			
Term of Lease	48 months	Monthly Payment	$452.62
MSRP	$21 977.00	Interest Rate	6.9%
Gross Capital Cost	$22 237.00	1st Payment	$452.62
Trade-in Allowance	0	PST (down payment)	0
Down Payment	0	GST (down payment)	0
Total Capital Reduction	0	1st Year Fees	$130.00
Net Capital Cost	$22 237.00	Other Fees	$160.00
Residual Factor	0.34	PST on Upfront	$12.80
Residual Value	$7472.18	GST on Upfront	$11.20
Depreciation	$14 764.82	Security Deposit	0
Base Payment	$393.58		
Monthly PST	$31.49		
Monthly GST	$27.55	Total Initial Payment	$766.62

b) $166.50

c) Total cost of lease = $22 039.76;
total cost to buy = $29 717.76

d) Answers may vary. Money available for monthly payments, distance he expects to drive, and whether having a new car every 3 or 4 years is important

Case Study 2

a)

DEAL REVIEW—NEW CAR			
MSRP	$24 572.00	Gas Fee	$20.00
Discount	$650.00	Lien Payout	0
Purchase Price	$23 922.00	Delivery Price	$28 691.05
Freight	$685.00	MFG Rebate	0
Tire/Air Tax	$100.00	Down Payment	0
Gas Tax	$75.00	Finance Fee	$54.00
Administration Fee	$85.00	Amount Financed	$28 745.05
Taxable Subtotal	$24 867.00	Interest Rate	4.9%
Trade-in Allowance	0	Loan Term	36 months
Taxable Total	$24 867.00	Monthly Payment	$860.22
PST	$1989.36	Interest Due	$2222.87
GST	$1740.69	Balance Due	$30 967.92
Licence Fee	$74.00		

DEAL REVIEW—USED CAR			
List Price	$14 950.00	Gas Fee	$20.00
Discount	0	Lien Payout	0
Purchase Price	$14 950.00	Delivery Price	$17 384.25
Freight	0	MFG Rebate	0
Tire/Air Tax	0	Down Payment	0
Gas Tax	0	Finance Fee	$54.00
Administration Fee	$85.00	Amount Financed	$17 438.25
Taxable Subtotal	$15 035.00	Interest Rate	9.9%
Trade-in Allowance	0	Loan Term	36 months
Taxable Total	$15 035.00	Monthly Payment	$561.86
PST	$1202.80	Interest Due	$2788.71
GST	$1052.45	Balance Due	$20 226.96
Licence Fee	$74.00		

   b) $298.36
   c) Total cost of new car = $30 967.92
   Total cost of used car = $20 226.96
   d) Answers may vary. Size of monthly payments, warranty, interest rate, and need or desire for a new car

7.5 Exercises, page 358

1. a) 20%   **b)** 42.5%   **c)** 25%
   d) 18.6%   **e)** 43.6%   **f)** 10.3%
   g) 23.7%   **h)** 250%

2. a) 11.5%   **b)** 88.5%

3. 22.6%

4. Answers may vary. Use the public library rather than buy books, use public transportation, wash rather than dry clean clothes, and entertain at home.

5. a) Housing and utilities: 32.5%
   Food and clothing: 17.5%
   Health and personal care: 2.5%
   Transportation: 30%
   Recreation and education: 7.5%
   Savings: 2.5%
   Miscellaneous: 7.5%
   b) i) Transportation
   ii) Food and clothing, Health and personal care, Savings, Miscellaneous
   iii) Housing and utilities, Recreation and education

6. 43.4%

7. a) $720 to $880   **b)** $533.33 to $693.33
   c) $320 to $373.33   **d)** $160 to $266.67

8. a) Total Spending: $2000
   Housing and utilities: 33%
   Food and clothing: 18%
   Health and personal care: 3%
   Transportation: 30%
   Recreation and education: 8%
   Savings: 3%
   Miscellaneous: 5%

   b) i) Transportation
   ii) Food and clothing, Savings, Miscellaneous
   iii) Housing and utilities, Health and personal care, Recreation and education

9. a) Housing and utilities: 26%
   Food and clothing: 21%
   Health and personal care: 3%
   Transportation: 29%
   Recreation and education: 9%
   Savings: 2%
   Miscellaneous: 10%
   b) i) Transportation, Recreation and education
   ii) Housing and utilities, Savings, Miscellaneous
   iii) Food and clothing, Health and personal care

10. a) Housing and utilities: 30%
   Food and clothing: 20%
   Health and personal care: 5%
   Transportation:13%
   Recreation and education: 4%
   Savings: 6%
   Miscellaneous: 21%
   b) i) Miscellaneous
   ii) Recreation and Education
   iii) Housing and Utilities, Food and Clothing, Health and personal care, Transportation, Savings
   c) Babysitting or daycare and child care supplies.

11. a) Housing and utilities: 0
   Food and clothing: 10%
   Health and personal care: 5%
   Transportation: 20%
   Recreation and education: 13%
   Savings: 46%
   Miscellaneous: 7%
   b) Because she lives at home
   c) Melissa uses public transportation and cabs for school, work, and recreation.
   d) She may be saving for future education or for a trip.
   e) Answers may vary. Melissa needs money for gas, maintenance, insurance, and car payments, so she might budget $300 for transportation, and make modest reductions in other budget categories.

Expense Category	Amount ($)
Housing and utilities	0
Food and clothing	50
Health and personal care	25
Transportation	300
Recreation and education	75
Savings	260
Miscellaneous	50

12. a) Housing and utilities: 33%
   Food and clothing: 22%
   Health and personal care: 4%
   Transportation: 19%
   Recreation and education: 3%
   Savings: 1%
   Miscellaneous: 17%

b) Answers may vary. The budget allows for the mortgage increase, with a decrease in miscellaneous expenses such as child care. Recreation and education also increase to allow for school related expenses.

Expense Category	Amount ($)
Housing and utilities	1400
Food and clothing	800
Health and personal care	150
Transportation	700
Recreation and education	125
Savings	50
Miscellaneous	375

13. Answers may vary.

a) Budget for first 2 months

Expense Category	Amount ($)
Housing and utilities	1250
Food and clothing	400
Health and personal care	75
Transportation	900
Recreation and education	50
Savings	1000
Miscellaneous	75

Money in all categories is reduced to allow for a $950 per month increase in savings. After 2 months, Pat and Steve will have $3000 in savings.

Budget when only Pat earns a salary

Expense Category	Amount ($)
Housing and utilities	1250
Food and clothing	350
Health and personal care	30
Transportation	900
Recreation and education	25
Savings	0
Miscellaneous	45

For the 4 months when Steve is not working, the $3000 in savings can be used to balance the budget.

b) Yes. Changes such as illness, job termination, or unexpected home maintenance may require budget flexibility.

Chapter 7 Review Exercises, page 368

1. a) $452.45   **b)** $1096.71
  c) $1429.92   **d)** $1391.72

2. a) $3148.60   **b)** $1246.04
  c) $5949.60   **d)** $8914.92

3. a) $4787.47   **b)** $16 853.24
  c) $14 993.00   **d)** $29 356.60

4. $10 906.49

5.

DEAL REVIEW			
MSRP	$38 998.00	Gas Fee	$20.00
Discount	$1250.00	Lien Payout	$4100.00
Purchase Price	$37 748.00	Delivery Price	$27 559.70
Freight	$860.00	MFG Rebate	$2500.00
Tire/Air Tax	$100.00	Down Payment	0
Gas Tax	$75.00	Finance Fee	$54.00
Administration Fee	$85.00	Amount Financed	$25 113.70
Taxable Subtotal	$38 868.00	Interest Rate	4.9%
Trade-in Allowance	$18 550.00	Loan Term	60 months
Taxable Total	$20 318.00	Monthly Payment	$472.78
PST	$1625.44	Interest Due	$3253.10
GST	$1422.26	Balance Due	$28 366.80
Licence Fee	$74.00		

6. a) Finance through the bank as the balance due is less.
   b) Smaller monthly payments may be preferable.

7.

DEAL REVIEW			
List Price	$17 543.00	Gas Fee	$20.00
Discount	$1090.00	Lien Payout	0
Purchase Price	$16 453.00	Delivery Price	$15 030.20
Freight	0	MFG Rebate	0
Tire/Air Tax	0	Down Payment	0
Gas Tax	0	Finance Fee	$54.00
Administration Fee	$85.00	Amount Financed	$15 084.20
Taxable Subtotal	$16 538.00	Interest Rate	8.9%
Trade-in Allowance	$3550.00	Loan Term	36 months
Taxable Total	$12 988.00	Monthly Payment	$478.97
PST	$1039.04	Interest Due	$2158.72
GST	$909.16	Balance Due	$17 242.92
Licence Fee	$74.00		

8. a) $590.76   **b)** $4571.48

9. $13 221.20

10. a) $12 195.95   **b)** $10 647.66
   c) $16 644.82   **d)** $10 576.32

11. a) $716.54   **b)** $383.77
   c) $480.87   **d)** $294.68

12. a) $86.82   **b)** $44.33
   c) $75.93   **d)** $99.25

13. a) $518.21   **b)** $373.33
   c) $540.13   **d)** $316.45

14. $13 757.25

15. a) 780 L   **b)** 4898.8 L
   c) 2764.3 L   **d)** 22 447.3 L

16. a) $998.64   **b)** $370.55
   c) $1007.35   **d)** $5279.11

17. $209.52

18. 630.5 L

19. $720.72

20. $304.37

21. 22.75%

22. a) $922.50 to $1127.50   **b)** $683.33 to $888.33
   c) $205 to $273.33   **d)** $102.50 to $170.83

23. a) $580.50 to $709.50   **b)** $129.00 to $215.00

24. a) Housing and utilities: 35%
    Food and clothing: 17.9%
    Health and personal care: 5%
    Transportation: 6.1%
    Recreation and education: 10%
    Savings: 21.4%
    Miscellaneous: 4.6%
  b) Overspending: Housing and utilities, Recreation and
    education, Savings
    Underspending: Food and clothing, Transportation,
    Miscellaneous
    Within guidelines: Health and personal care
  c) Josh may have low transportation costs because he can
    walk to work or he may not own a car. His clothing
    expenses may be low because a uniform is supplied at
    his work.

Chapter 7 Self-Test, page 373

1. $638.23

2. Answers may vary.
  a) Advantages: The total cost will be less and fees such as
    freight and tire/air tax do not have to be paid.
    Disadvantages: Warranty may not be as good and colour
    and options may not be chosen.
  b) Advantages: A new car every 3 or 4 years and lower
    payments
    Disadvantages: Not owning the car and a distance limit

3. Alexia should lease the truck because the monthly
  payments and total cost are less.

4. Answers may vary.

Expense Category	Amount ($)
Housing and utilities	540
Food and clothing	200
Health and personal care	50
Transportation	390
Recreation and education	260
Savings	30
Miscellaneous	30

Since Scott's education expenses increase, he can reduce his
expenses for other categories by not eating out, not buying
new clothing, and by spending less on recreation and
utilities such as his telephone.

Cumulative Review

page 384

1. $2212.50

2. a) 1   **b)** 10   **c)** 25   **d)** 145

3. a) $5n - 3$ **b)** 67   **c)** 28

4. −475

5. a) $960   **b)** $1126.39   **c)** $1175.63

6. a) 256   **b)** 400   **c)** 1 000 000
   d) 27 000 000   **e)** 1   **f)** 72

7. a) 625   **b)** 4   **c)** 3
   d) 3.14   **e)** 1.29   **f)** 0.88

8. a) $9835.66   **b)** $40 596.83

9. a) $836.39   **b)** $9378.83

10. 7 years

11. a) 3%   **b)** 8%

12. a) $5000(2)^n$ **b)** 81 920 000

13. a)

x	0	1	2	3	4
y	1	3	9	27	81

b)

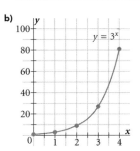

  c) 3.1
  d) x-intercept is 1; no y-intercept
  e) Domain: all x; range: $y \geq 0$

14. a) $29 000   **b)** 18%   **c)** $7229

15. a) 8   **b)** 4   **c)** 125

16. a) 4   **b)** 3   **c)** 2

17. a) $3(-4)^{n-1}$ **b)** −786 432

18. a) $3^n - 1$ **b)** 6560

19. a) Geometric, $a = 96$, $r = 0.5$
  b) Neither
  c) Arithmetic, $a = 48$, $d = -24$
  d) Neither
  e) Arithmetic, $a = 0.1$, $d = 0.1$
  f) Geometric, $a = 3$, $r = -5$

20. a) $45 549.13   **b)** $10 288.18

21. $145.49

22. $8193.97 for option 1; $6977.00 for option 2; option 1
  earns more because the interest has longer to compound.

23. $31 179.62

24. $380.18

25. a) $20 092.39   **b)** $4907.61

26. a) $401.68   **b)** $337.63

27. a) Sabrina pays $340.81; Sebastien pays $309.69.
    b) Sabrina pays $2269.16 in interest; Sebastien pays
       $1148.84.
    c) Sabrina pays $1120.32 more in interest.

28. Answers may vary.
    a) RRSP – Registered Retirement Savings Plan – no tax is
       paid on RRSP investments – a good way to save for
       retirement – early investments are best.
    b) GIC – Guaranteed Investment Certificate – a safe way to
       invest – interest rates are low – money is usually locked in.
    c) Debit card – money is withdrawn from an account
       instantly – can be used instead of cheques.
    d) Amortization period – the length of time over which a
       mortgage is repaid – usually 25 to 30 years – a longer
       term reduces monthly payments.

29. a) 7.39%   **b)** $1097.78   **c)** $179 334.00

30. a) $1834.41   **b)** $237 674.46   **c)** $151 194.79

31. After 7 years, $PV = $157 742.60$. New payments are
    $1351.71.

32. a) 8.35%   **b)** $184 621.49   **c)** $246 161.99

33. Housing: 42%, transportation: 9%

34. a) $15 424.00   **b)** $447.87

35. a) $7045.20   **b)** $12 316.80

administration fee: a fee charged to do the paper work in a transaction

amortization: the repayment of the principal and interest on a loan by a series of equal payments over a fixed period of time

amortization period: the length of time over which the principal and interest of a loan are repaid

amortization schedule: a table that shows in detail how a loan is repaid. It shows the payment number, the amount applied to interest, the amount applied to the principal, and the outstanding principal

amount of an investment: the value of the principal plus accumulated interest

annually: once a year

annuity: a series of equal payments or deposits made over equal periods of time

arithmetic sequence: a sequence in which the same number is added to each term to get the next term; for example, in the arithmetic sequence 1, 4, 7, 10, …, each term after the first is calculated by adding 3 to the previous term

arithmetic series: the indicated sum of the terms of an arithmetic sequence

asymptote: a line that a curve approaches but never reaches as one variable increases, decreases, or approaches a constant value

base: the factor repeated in a power; for example, in the power a^n, a is the base

bimonthly: twice a month

biweekly: every two weeks

bond: a contract between a lender and borrower that indicates the principal borrowed, the interest to be paid, the terms for payment of the interest, and the date by which time the principal will be repaid

budget: a plan outlining how money is to be spent

Canada Pension Plan (CPP): a pension plan administered by the government of Canada

Canada Savings Bond (CSB): a bond sold to the public by the government of Canada

commission: a fee or payment given to a salesperson, usually as a specified percent of the person's sales

common difference: the constant added to a term of an arithmetic sequence to give the next term; to calculate the common difference, subtract any term from the next term

common ratio: the constant that a term in a geometric sequence is multiplied by to give the next term; to calculate the common ratio, divide any term after the first by its preceding term

compound interest: a method of calculating interest in which the interest due is added to the principal and thereafter earns interest

compounding period: the time interval for which compound interest is calculated

conventional mortgage: a mortgage in which the principal is not greater than 75% of the value of the property

credit card: a card issued by a financial institution, retail store, or company that allows the holder to purchase an item now and pay for it later

debit card: a card issued by a financial institution that gives the holder electronic access to her or his accounts at the institution. Debit cards are frequently used for making purchases in which payment is made from existing funds in a bank account.

debt: money owed

decay factor: in exponential decay, a number between 0 and 1 that repeatedly multiplies the original amount

deposit: money placed in a bank account, or an initial payment toward a purchase

depreciation: the amount an item decreases in value over time

domain of a function: the set of all possible x-values (or valid input numbers)

down payment: a deposit or initial payment toward a purchase

driver's licence: a permit issued by the provincial government that allows the holder to drive a vehicle

earnings: money received as payment for work

equivalent rates: rates of interest with different compounding periods that for the same principal yield the same interest in a given period of time

exponent: a number raised as part of a power; for example, in the power a^n, n is the exponent

exponential decay: a situation in which the original amount is repeatedly multiplied by the decay factor, a number between 0 and 1. Exponential decay is modelled by the equation $y = Ab^x$ when $b > 0$ and $b < 1$.

exponential equation: an equation where the variable is an exponent

exponential function: a function with an equation of the form $y = Ab^x$, where A and b are constants ($b > 0$, $b \neq 1$), and x is any real number

exponential growth: a situation in which the original amount is repeatedly multiplied by the growth factor, a number greater than 1. Exponential growth is modelled by the equation $y = Ab^x$ when $b > 1$.

finance charge: the difference between the cash price and the sum of the payments made for an item

financing: an arrangement made to pay for an item over an extended period of time

fixed cost: a cost, such as rent or insurance, that remains constant over a given period of time

freight: the amount charged by a company, to the consumer, for shipment of an item from the manufacturer

fuel consumption: the rate at which a vehicle burns fuel, usually expressed in litres per 100 km or in miles per gallon

function: a rule that gives a single output number for every valid input number

gas tax: a tax charged on all new gasoline burning vehicles when they are sold

general term: an algebraic expression for the nth term in a sequence

geometric sequence: a sequence in which each term is multiplied by the same number to get the next term; for example, in the geometric sequence 1, 3, 9, 27, …, each term after the first is calculated by multiplying the preceding term by 3

geometric series: the indicated sum of the terms of a geometric sequence

Goods and Services Tax (GST): a federal tax charged on most goods and services in Canada

graph: a line or diagram that shows how one quantity depends on or changes with respect to another quantity

growth factor: in exponential growth, a number greater than 1 that repeatedly multiplies the original amount

Guaranteed Investment Certificate (GIC): a type of investment offered by a financial institution that usually gives a higher rate of interest than savings accounts. The investment is made for a fixed period of time and is not cashable until the end of the fixed period.

half-life: the time required for a radioactive sample to decay to one-half its original amount

income: the total money received from all sources by an individual during a specified period of time, usually one year

integer: the set of all positive and negative whole numbers, together with zero; that is, …, −3, −2, −1, 0, 1, 2, 3, …

interest: money earned or paid for the use of the money

interest rate: the amount charged to borrow money, usually given as a percent

investment: money deposited at a financial institution or used to buy securities or property with the expectation of future income or profit

irrational number: a number that cannot be written as a quotient of two integers; for example, $\sqrt{2}$ is an irrational number

lease: a contract to rent an item for a specified period of time, and for a specified amount of money

linear equation: an equation that represents a straight line

linear growth: a situation in which a positive number is repeatedly added to an original amount. Linear growth is modelled by a linear equation.

list price: the price of an item before any reduction or discount

lump sum payment: a single payment, other than a regular payment, used to reduce the outstanding principal on a loan

manufacturer's rebate: on a vehicle, money returned to the consumer by the manufacturer when the vehicle is purchased; commonly used to reduce inventories at the end of a model year

manufacturer's suggested retail price (MSRP): for a new vehicle, the "suggested" price set by the manufacturer, usually subject to negotiation

maturity date: the date on which an investment is due; for example, when the principal and interest on a GIC is paid to the investor

mortgage: a long-term loan on real estate that gives the person or firm providing the money a claim on the property if the loan is not repaid

mortgagee: the financial institution that holds a mortgage

mortgagor: the person or persons who borrow money to purchase real estate

mutual fund: an investment company that invests the pooled money of its members in a variety of securities

natural numbers: the set of positive whole numbers; that is, 1, 2, 3, 4, 5, …

percent: the number of parts per 100; the numerator of a fraction with denominator 100

power: an expression of the form a^n, where a is the base and n is the exponent

present value: the principal that must be invested today to obtain a given amount in the future

principal: the sum of money invested or borrowed

Provincial Sales Tax (PST): a provincial tax charged on most goods

quarterly: every three months

range of a function: the set of all possible y-values (or valid output numbers)

rational number: a number that can be expressed in the form $\frac{m}{n}$, where m and n are integers and $n \neq 0$

real number: any number that is either rational or irrational; that is, a number that can be expressed as a decimal

Registered Retirement Savings Plan (RRSP): a savings plan, for people who earn income, where funds contributed and interest earned are not taxed until the funds are withdrawn

regular annuity: an annuity in which the payment period is the same as the compounding period, and payment is made at the end of the payment period

residual value: the value of a vehicle at the end of a lease, usually pre-set by the leasing company at the start of the lease

savings account: a bank account whose primary purpose is to save money

semi-annually: twice a year

sequence: an ordered list of numbers

series: the indicated sum of the terms of a sequence

simple interest: interest calculated according to the formula $I = Prt$

stock: shares in a company

stock market: a central marketplace where stocks are bought and sold

term deposit: money placed in an interest bearing account for a predetermined period of time

tire/air tax: a government tax on a new vehicle to assist in the cost of disposing of old tires in an environmentally friendly manner

Toronto Stock Exchange (TSE): a marketplace in Toronto where stocks are bought and sold

trade-in: an item exchanged as partial payment for another item

treasury bill: an interest bearing certificate issued by the treasury department of the government, usually with a specified number of days for the term; for example, a 90-day treasury bill

variable costs: costs that do not occur at regular intervals

vehicle licence (plate): a permit issued by the provincial government that gives the holder permission to drive the licenced vehicle on the roads of that and other provinces

vehicle maintenance schedule: a list of regular maintenance that should be done on a vehicle as recommended by the manufacturer

weekly "accelerated" mortgage payment: a weekly mortgage payment that is calculated by dividing the monthly payment by 4

whole numbers: the non-negative integers; that is, the numbers 0, 1, 2, 3, …

INDEX

PHOTO CREDITS AND ACKNOWLEDGEMENTS

The publisher wishes to thank the following sources for photographs, illustrations, articles, and other materials used in this book. Care has been taken to determine and locate ownership of copyright material used in the text. We will gladly receive information enabling us to rectify any errors or omissions in credits.

PHOTOS

Cover Randy Wells/Stone; **Inside Front Page** Randy Wells/Stone; **Back Cover** Orion Press/Stone; **p. 2–3** (background), ©Gary Black/Masterfile; **p. 10** (centre), Dave Starrett; **p. 11** (centre right), Dick Hemingway; **p. 14** (bottom centre), Tony Mihok/Spetrum Stock; **p. 20** (top right), Nicholas DeVore/Stone; **p. 36** (centre left), Dick Hemingway; **p. 40** (centre right), Dick Hemingway; **p. 44** (top right), Dave Starrett; **p. 54–55** (background), Dave Starrett; **p. 61** (centre right), Dave Starrett; **p. 80** (centre right), Micael Jang/Stone; **p. 91** (bottom right), Canada Post; **p. 102** (top left), John Henley/The Stock Market/First Light Associated Photographers; **p. 103** (background), Luc Moulin/First Light; **p. 110–111** (background), ©Davy Crocket; **p. 122** (top right), Dave Starrett; **p. 126** (bottom right), Julian Baum/Science Photo Library/Photo Researchers; **p. 144** (centre right), David M. Phillips/Visuals Unlimited Inc.; **p. 152** (top right), ©Will McIntyre/Photo Researchers; **p. 156** (bottom left), ©Thomas Kitchen/First Light; **p. 158** (centre right), ©Johnny Johnson/Animals Animals; **p. 178–179** (background), Jon Feingersh/The Stock Market/First Light Associated Photographers; **p. 199** (centre right), ©Chuck Savage/The Stock Market/First Light Associated Photographers; **p. 208** (top centre), Artbase Inc; **p. 215** (top right), Dave Starrett; **p. 230–231** (background), Paul Eekhoff/Masterfile; **p. 234** (top right), Dave Starrett; **p. 246** (top right), Artbase Inc.; **p. 250** (top right), ©Tony Mihok/Spectrum Stock; **p. 253** (top right), ©David Stoecklein/First Light Associated Photographers; **p. 261** (centre right), Artbase Inc.; **p. 266** (bottom centre), ©Rick Strange/Index Stock; **p. 274** (top left), Dick Luria/FPG/Masterfile; **p. 274** (top left), Artbase Inc.; **p. 274** (bottom centre), Artbase Inc.; **p. 275** (top right), Bill Losh/FPG; **p. 282–283** (background), Artbase Inc.; **p. 286** (top centre), Artbase Inc.; **p. 296** (top right), ©R.W. Jones/First Light Associated Photographers; **p. 299** (centre right), Spectrum Stock; **p. 304** (top right), ©R.B. Studio/First Light; **p. 322–323** (centre right), Dave Starrett; **p. 329** (top right), Dave Starrett; **p. 339** (top right), Dave Starrett; **p. 348** (bottom right), Artbase Inc.; **p. 374** (top left), Dave Starrett; **p. 375** (top right), Artbase Inc.; **p. 375** (top left), Artbase Inc.; **p. 375** (bottom left), Artbase Inc.; **p. 375** (bottom right), Artbase Inc.

ILLUSTRATIONS

Greg Stevenson 160 (centre)
Margo Davis Leclair/Visual Sense 65 (centre left), 84 (centre left)

http://www.lone-star.net/literature/beowulf/beowulf.h

def leppord
- pour some sugar on me

www.jessem.com - router jig
jessem @ jessem.com   - mas t r plate

1- 866- 272-7492